The Library of Scandinavian Literature

EGIL'S SAGA

EGIL'S SAGA

TRANSLATED FROM THE OLD ICELANDIC
WITH INTRODUCTION AND NOTES BY
GWYN JONES

TWAYNE PUBLISHERS, INC., NEW YORK
&
THE AMERICAN-SCANDINAVIAN FOUNDATION

The Library of Scandinavian Literature
Erik J. Friis, *General Editor*

Volume 8
Egil's Saga

To My Wife

ACKNOWLEDGMENTS

Much of the work for this translation of *Egil's Saga* was done in Iceland during the summers of 1951 and 1952. I am grateful to the University of Iceland for inviting me to lecture there in the first of these years, and to my own College for enabling me to extend my visit. My second stay I owed to the generosity of the Leverhulme Trustees. My personal obligations are deep and many. But for the kindness of the then Rector of the Háskóli Íslands, Professor Alexander Jóhannesson, my stays would have been neither so profitable nor so pleasurable as they were. Professors Sigurður Nordal and Einar Ólafur Sveinsson were prodigal of time and learning and unstinting of their friendship. In this, as in other things, *Berr er hverr á bakinu, nema sér bróður eigi.* To Séra Léo Júlíússon and Mr. and Mrs. Eggert Einarsson I owe long periods of hospitality at Borg and Borgarnes (the ancient Digranes) and extensive travel in the *Egil's Saga* country. Mr. and Mrs. Hilmar Foss, Mr. Helgi Lárusson, and Mr. and Mrs. Einar Pjetursson, are other friends to whom my obligations are deep and many. Indeed, there is hardly an Icelandic placename in *Egil's Saga* which does not carry for me the memory of an Icelandic kindness.

My translation follows the text prepared by Professor Nordal for *Hið Íslenzka Fornritafélag,* and published in 1933; and I thank both Editor and Society for permitting me to benefit by their labors and enterprise. I am grateful to the Council of the British Academy for allowing me to use material from my Sir Israel Gollancz Memorial Lecture, "Egill Skallagrímsson in England," and to the Editor of the *Times Literary Supplement* for permission to quote and adapt some paragraphs first contributed to that journal. To Professor Stefán Einarsson of The Johns Hopkins University, for reading my manuscript before press; to Dr. Henry Goddard Leach for his personal interest, and to Mrs. Arpena Mesrobian for her editorial care, both exercised in the face of many difficulties; and to The American-Scandinavian Foundation and The Syracuse University Press for publishing my book, I offer thanks as warm-hearted as they may here appear brief. Finally, I am grateful to my colleagues of the Department of Geography and Anthropology at the University College of Wales for so successfully interpreting my ideas with respect to the illustrative maps.

The translation of poetry, like poetry itself, lies in Óðinn's gift, and for the verses of *Egil's Saga* I have deliberately sought no other help. Their faults are therefore all mine. So too are such errors of sense or style as may be found in the prose.

The Introduction and Notes have grown beyond my original intention, and in their expansion I have often reaped where others have sowed. By way of excuse I offer my long admiration and affection for my saga and a desire to please and serve the reader to whose suffrage I now resign my book.

University College of Wales,   Gwyn Jones
        Aberystwyth

CONTENTS

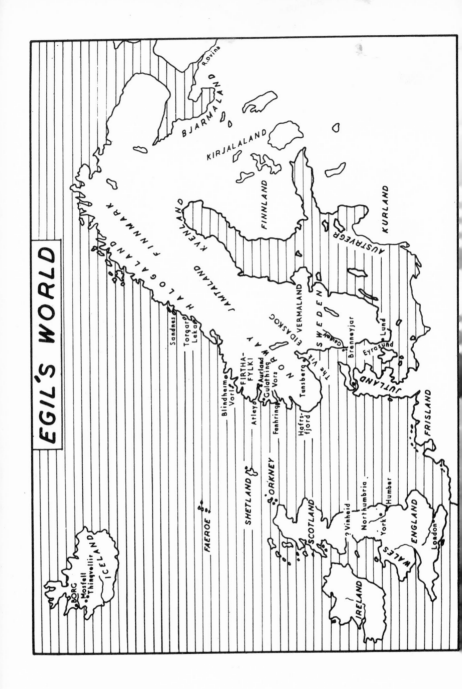

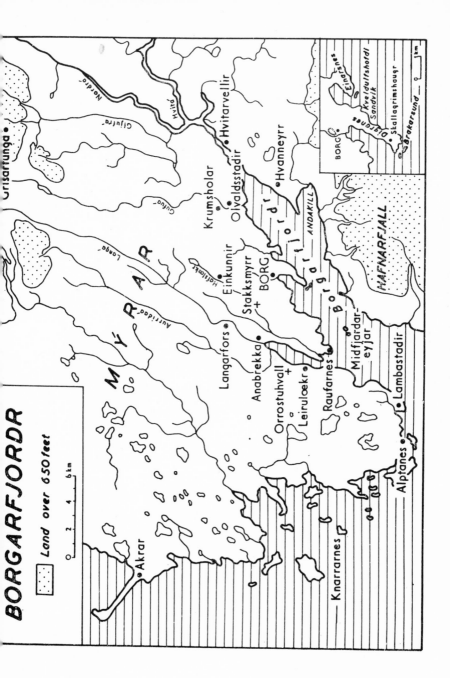

BORGARFJORDR

Land over 650 feet

0   2   4   6 km

Akrar

Knarrarnes

Alptanes • Lambastadir •

Orrostuhvall +
Leirulœkr •   Raufarnes •   Midfjardar-
                                eyjar

MÝ-RAR

Langarfors •
Anabrekka •

Stakksmyrr +
Einkunnir •   BORG •
Krumsholar •   Olvaldsstadir •   Hvanneyr •

Hvitarvellir •

ANDAKILL

B o r g a r f j o r d r

HAFNARFJALL

Hafslœkr
Langa
Aurlda
Gufua
Nordra
Gljufra
Hvita
Grisartunga •

Einarsnes
Kveldulfshofdi
Sandvik
Digranes
Skallagrimshaugr
Brakarsund

BORG •

0   1 km

INTRODUCTION

The Saga and Tradition

Egils Saga Skallagrímssonar is among the best, as it is among the most famous, of those prose narratives of medieval Iceland whose common title is the Sagas of Icelanders, *Íslendingasögur*. It recounts the history of four generations of the Mýramen, one of the great settlement families of Iceland, who took as their patrimony the rich grazing lands of Borgarfjörður, and from their home under the rock-bastion of Borg held patriarchal sway for centuries over friends and dependents, administered estates, dispensed justice, and set a deep and distinctive mark upon the history, culture and tradition of their new country. The period covered by the saga is from early in the second half of the ninth century to the end of the tenth, from the birth of Kveldúlf's sons to the death of his grandson Egil. Much of the action takes place in Norway, at the time of that country's unification under King Harald Fairhair; two notable sections tell of events in England, at Brunanburh and in the York of Eirík Bloodaxe; and it includes accounts of expeditions to Sweden, Denmark, Frisia and Shetland, and to the eastern waters of the Baltic, the so-called Austrvegr. It is thus not only a family saga, and the biography of a notable poet, but is also a foremost historical and viking saga. Nor is its literary quality unworthy of its historical importance. An abundance of oral and written tradition, in verse and prose, has been shaped by an artist into a powerful if unequal narrative, distinguished by a sense of history and an awareness of fate, by insight into events and by knowledge of the mainsprings of human action, whether flattering or unflattering to human nature. The prose throughout is excellent, at once forceful and succinct, mature and firm. The saga has been doubly fortunate, in the original author who composed it with such mastery of style and content, and in the scribe or reworker whose tact and judgment produced the Möðruvallabók version to which we must now trust in the absence of the archetypal manuscript.[1]

Egil's Saga is a work founded upon old tradition, and its author was concerned not to invent but to make the best use he could of the material at his disposal. This was of three kinds. First there was oral

---

[1] For a brief account of the MSS see p. 28.

tradition, the stories transmitted by word of mouth from generation to generation. Second there were written sources, "authorities," as we might call them. Third there were the poems and verses now incorporated in the saga or preserved in close association with it.

Oral Tradition

We may be sure that the poet Einar Jinglescale (see p. 218) was not the only man in Iceland who asked Egil about his adventures, and equally that he was not the only listener, willing or unwilling, to whom the grand old man of Borg delighted to discourse of his youth and manhood. Nor, as our saga so frequently indicates, would Egil be the only purveyor of information to posterity. The whole of Borgarfjörður must have speculated on the last resting place of Skallagrím's chest and cauldron; there were even schools of belief as to where Egil disposed of his money at Mosfell. It was "from old men's tales" (*af sögn gamalla manna*) that people concluded that the huge bones laid to their last rest "in the outer verge of the churchyard at Mosfell" were Egil's. The ball game in Hvítárvellir, Egil's mad-headed prank at the expense of Thórólf and his ship, the drowning of Bödvar and the masterly humoring of Egil by his wife and daughter which led to the composition of the elegy on his sons, all stories connected with the giving of placenames, those of the death of Brák and the killing of Lambi's thralls, for example, are obvious instances of oral tradition. Together with the verses these tales are the core of the saga. Among Egil's progeny were many poets and scholars, and conditions were particularly favorable for the preservation of stories about him; though we must recognize that since the events of the saga took place during the years *ca.* 860-1000, but were not recorded on vellum till 1220-25, all such oral traditions were open to change during so long a tenure of the memories and imaginations of the transmitters.

Written sources

The author of *Egil's Saga* would certainly have mastered these oral traditions before starting to write. Some things in the saga suggest that he had recourse to written sources too. The first of these is the historical and geographical description of Finnmark and Thórólf Kveldúlfsson's dealings with the Lapps, the Kvens and the Kirjáls. It is very unlikely that such close topographical information would be preserved in its present form along with oral stories about Thórólf. What is told here of these remote lands and far-off peoples is remarkably consonant with the description of the Hálogalanders and the Lapp-tribute given to Alfred the Great about 880-82 by the Hálogalander Óttar (Ohthere) and incorporated by the king in his translation of Orosius's *History of the World*.[2]

The account of Finnmark itself, reminiscent as it is of the first chapter of *Ynglinga Saga*, was probably taken from some twelfth-century work on geography. That the saga does not depend on oral tradition alone for events in Norway is self-evident. It would be un-natural if it did. There were several lives of Norwegian kings written in Iceland by the end of the twelfth century, and the saga declares plainly that at times it relies on such, for the campaigns of Harald Fairhair (p. 33, *eru þar langar frásagnir*) and Hákon the Good (p. 185, *svá sem sagt er í sögu hans*), for example. There are ver-bal correspondences between *Egil's Saga* and *Óláfs Saga Helga;* and no other saga of the Icelanders stands in such close relationship to *Heimskringla*, the Lives of the Norwegian Kings, as *Egil's Saga*. It is probable, indeed, that the saga was used in the compilation of *Heims-kringla;* certainly they show acquaintance with the same sources. And while the precise relationship of *Egil's Saga* and the record of the Ice-landic Settlement, *Landnámabók,* is hard to assess, it is tempting to assume some written source for the land-takings of Skallagrím, Grím Thórisson, and above all Ketil Hœng.

Brunanburh-Vínheiðr

No question concerning the historical sources and content of *Egil's Saga* has more interest for British readers than whether the battle of Vínheiðr can be identified with Athelstan's famous victory in 937 over the Scots and their confederacy at Brunanburh. One says "British" advisedly, for if we accept the identification then England, Wales, Scotland and Ireland, all made an actual or legendary contribution to the battle's griefs and triumphs.

What do we know of the battle of Brunanburh and its antecedent confederacy from trustworthy English and Irish sources? Briefly, this. Before the English King Edward died in 924 he had extended his

---

[2] See the note on p. 244.

dominion to the Humber and received the submission of King Rægnald (Rögnvald) of York, Ealdred of Northumbria, Constantine III
of Scotland, Donald or his successor Eugenius (Owen) of the Strathclyde Welsh, and the kings of the Norð-Wealas (the Welsh of
Wales). Rægnald of York died in 921 and was succeeded by Sihtric
(Sigtryggr) who had been king of Dublin. Athelstan succeeded his
father Edward as king of England in 924, confirmed Sihtric's authority at York (and Ealdred's for his part of Northumbria), and in 926
gave him his sister in marriage. In 927 Sihtric died and Guthfrith
(Guðröðr) his brother, who had ruled after him in Dublin, came to
York to act as regent there. But by this time Athelstan had decided to
rule all Northumbria through Ealdred and his brother Uhtred. Guthfrith was driven into Scotland and Anlaf Cwaran Sihtric's son (Óláfr
kváran Sigtryggsson) fled to Ireland. Guthfrith took refuge with Constantine in Scotland, but in face of Athelstan's threats Constantine and
Eugenius abandoned his cause. They acknowledged Athelstan's over-
lordship at Dacor in Cumberland, and meanwhile Guthfrith made an
unsuccessful attack on York before fleeing to Ireland. Athelstan now
destroyed the Danish fortress at York and thereafter once more
brought the Welsh kings to heel. Guthfrith died in 934 and was succeeded by his son Anlaf (Óláfr Guðröðarson). Back in England Athelstan in 934 led an army against the Scots and the Strathclyde Welsh,
probably to overawe them from starting hostilities themselves, but
when Anlaf Guthfrith's son invaded England in 937 Constantine
certainly, and Eugenius probably, made common cause with him.
Their reason was their desire to see Northumbria under some other
king than the martial Englishman.[3] The confederacy was shattered at

[3] (*a*) That Anlaf Cwaran was an ally who entered the Humber and overran York
is an addition of Florence of Worcester's. It seems unlikely that Anlaf would make
this great circuit of Scotland or England instead of landing on the west coast. *Egil's
Saga* admittedly reports that Óláf the Red defeated the two Anglophile earls set by
Athelstan over Northumbria.

(*b*) That the Welsh of Wales took part in the battle rests on the authority of
the Four Masters and of Gaimar (he speaks of *Combreis* and *Gawaleis*, but it is far
from certain that these two names distinguish the Welsh of Strathclyde and the
Welsh of Wales). *Egil's Saga* says that the Welsh kings Hringer and Aðils (*sic*)
deserted Athelstan and fought for Óláf the Red of Scotland. It is safer to deny than
to accept both these additions to the historical record. The best account of Brunanburh (and Vínheiðr) is Alistair Campbell, *The Battle of Brunanburh*, London,
1938, which prints all the evidence and is severely scholarly in its tone and
conclusions.

the battle of Brunanburh; Anlaf Guthfrith's son returned to Dublin with the Norse survivors; Constantine ruled a few years longer and then entered a monastery; there is no further mention of Eugenius. The poem, *The Battle of Brunanburh*, which occurs in the Anglo-Saxon Chronicle *sub anno* 937, informs us further that Athelstan and his brother Edmund with an army of West-Saxons and Mercians fought a great battle at Brunanburh against Constantine and his Scots and Anlaf and his Norse sailors (*scipflotan*). After a furious but not overlong encounter the enemy fled; there was a hot pursuit and a great slaughter of Scots and Norsemen; five young kings, seven of Anlaf's earls, and Constantine's own son fell on the field.

The description in *Egil's Saga* of a great battle between Athelstan and the Scots is tantalizingly like and unlike the historical account of the battle of Brunanburh. At Vínheiðr Athelstan with an army of English and Norsemen crushes a Scottish invasion led by Óláf (O. E. Anlaf) the Red, and supported by the Welsh earls Hring and Adils. Athelstan's Norsemen are led by Thórólf Skallagrímsson and his brother Egil. The battle lasted for two days till the enemy was routed. King Óláf of Scotland was slain and the Welsh earls with him, while among Athelstan's men it is the loss of Thórólf which most interests the saga's author. But despite these and other differences, and they are serious, there can be no reasonable doubt that Brunanburh and Vínheiðr are the same battle. No other engagement so great and decisive was fought by Athelstan against an invading force composed partly of Scots and with a leader named Óláf. No other battle of the period so lent itself to the purposes of historical, pseudo-historical, and legendary tradition. And finally the difficulties of accepting the Brunanburh-Vínheiðr equation are nothing to the difficulties raised by its rejection.

Four challenging features of the account of the battle in *Egil's Saga* are: the confusion and impropriety of personal names; the description of the *locus actionis*; the name Vínheiðr; and the part played by the brothers Thórólf and Egil in the battle.

The confusion of names and persons is extreme. Constantine, Óláfr Guðröðarson, and Óláfr kváran Sigtryggsson have become one man, Óláfr Rauði. Álfgeir and Goðrekr are either inventions or wrong names for Ealdred and Uhtred. No conceivable ingenuity can make

Hringr and Aðils appear suitable names for Welsh kings. It is as certain as such things can be that they are taken from the common stock of Northern heroic names, that they are here attached to legendary figures in a battle whose description is enriched with such traditional features as the challenge to a set field, the respite till the battle, the three requests to make peace and the three-day journeys of the envoys, the strongholds and the open place.[4] Nor can we place any reliance on our saga's description of the battlefield or from it determine where the battle took place. Every suggestion so far advanced for a site has been at best unproved, at worst discredited. The saga's description of the *locus actionis* is curiously circumstantial, its account of the battle suspiciously high-flown, but both are a tribute to the corruptions rather than the stability of oral tradition. Per Wieselgren and Knut Liestøl, in many respects following Neilson,[5] have seen in both an example of the reliability of Icelandic tradition; Nordal, however, has his doubts; and Hollander and Campbell lead us to a correct conclusion. "The saga remains, accordingly, unsupported in practically all its details, and, in view of its frequent gross errors and confusions, cannot be used as a source for the history of the war of Æthelstan and Anlaf. If we abandon it, and abandon it we must, all hope of localizing Brunanburh is lost."[6]

Can any safe conclusions be drawn from the name Vínheiðr? We would approach the problem with more confidence if we knew the site of Brunanburh and the meaning of the name. The various MSS of the Anglo-Saxon Chronicle spell this name sometimes with a single *n*, sometimes with a double, Brunanburh, Brunnanburh. The form with one *n* appears to mean either "Bruna's stronghold" or "the stronghold by the river Bruna." The form with *nn* would appear to mean "the stronghold by the stream." Even if we could decide which form and meaning is correct, we should still be unable to find any unforced correspondence between Brunanburh-Brunnanburh and Vínheiðr. But it happens that Simeon of Durham, writing some one hundred

---

[4] See in particular Lee M. Hollander, "The Battle on the Vin-heath and the Battle of the Huns," *Journal of English and Germanic Philology*, XXXII, 33 ff., which draws attention to the parallels between the account in *Egil's Saga* of Vínheiðr and those of the battle in *Hervarar Saga ok Heiðreks Konungs*.

[5] G. Neilson, "Brunanburh and Burnswork," *Scottish Historical Review*, VII, 37 ff.

[6] Alistair Campbell, *The Battle of Brunanburh*, London, 1938, p. 80.

and fifty years after the battle, places it *apud Weondune, quod alio nomine Etbrunnanwerc vel Brunnanbyrig appelatur.*[7] Elsewhere he uses the form Wendune,[8] and on the relationship between Wendune-Weondune and Vínheiðr much speculation has been spent. There is no difficulty over regarding *dun, dune* as equivalent in meaning to *heiðr,* but it is not so easy to equate *Weon, Wen* with *Vín, Vin.* Even if we set aside Campbell's suggestion that, "Owing to the great similarity of *n* and *r* in O. E. MSS, it is most likely that *Weondun, Wendun* are forms due to a scribal error in the source of Simeon of Durham, and that the original form was *Weordun.* A northern chronicler would be most likely to place the battle at some place by the river Wear (O. E. Wēor)"[9]—even then it does not follow that the first element of the English names is a river name. Ekwall in his *Oxford Dictionary of English Placenames* (p. 483) thinks it an O. E. adjective *weoh,* "holy." But even if it is a river name, there remains the question why an English stream should in *Egil's Saga* be called by the name of the famous Russian river Dvina (*Vína*), and an English wood by the name of the Russian forest, *Vínuskógr?* Campbell's is the most satisfactory answer: that Thórólf's earlier great battle by the Dvina on Eirík's Bjarmaland expedition was confused with this second great battle, and so "a typical description of a battlefield in Bjarmaland has been grafted on to the Norse traditional account of Brunanburh."[10] However, whether we accept Weondun, Wendun and Vínheiðr as a deliberate equation on the part of the author of *Egil's Saga,* whether we regard their resemblances as coincidental but valid, or whether we charge all to the vagaries of tradition, the general identification of the battles of Brunanburh and Vínheiðr must still be accepted.

The brothers' part in the battle is undoubtedly much exaggerated. Not unnaturally the (highly fictitious) events of the two-day encounter are seen in an Icelandic and even a family perspective, so that the glory of the event is first Thórólf's and then Egil's. It is Campbell's bold suggestion that Thórólf had been killed twelve years earlier by the Dvina, that Brunanburh was Egil's battle, and that

[7] *Historia Ecclesiæ Dunelmensis,* ed. Arnold, I, 76.

[8] *Historia Regum,* ed. Arnold, II, 93.

[9] Campbell, *op. cit.,* p. 62, n 2.

[10] Campbell, *op. cit.,* pp. 73-74; and see particularly n. 1.

tradition confused these two famous battles of the sons of Skallagrím.[11]
But though we hear little of Thórólf Skallagrímsson outside of *Egil's
Saga*, and some of that is derivative, the same, *mutatis mutandi*, can
be said of others in the saga too, including Arinbjörn Hersir.[12] And
against Campbell's theory that after the Bjarmaland expedition in 925
Thórólf seems never to act independently, but is a mere traveling
companion of Egil, and is thus easily provided with a career, may be
set the arguments that in fact he does figure in the saga independently
of Egil (in the episode of the axe, King Eirík's gift, and surely in his
marriage), and that the tribute to Thórólf in *Sonatorrek* suggests a
long and arduous sharing of battles together. But Campbell's suggestion that Thórólf must have been older than most editors of *Egil's
Saga* have allowed is a reasonable and tempting one.

It remains still to comment on the possible progress of English
traditions to Iceland and the decisive importance of the battle of Vínheiðr for the chronology of *Egil's Saga*. If in England itself there was
so much subsequent confusion about Brunanburh, its events and personalities, it is not surprising if the confusion was greater in Iceland,
six hundred miles away. If we grant that Egil took part in the battle
and told of it at home, then direct Icelandic oral tradition may have
contributed to this part of the saga's narrative. On the other hand English traditions and historical works were certainly carried to Iceland
during the twelfth century, a period when the Icelanders were so
zealously studying the newly-discovered riches of European learning
and literature. The School at Oddi was particularly well placed to receive information both from England, through its direct contacts with
Lincoln, and from Scotland, through its close connections with the
Orkneys.[13] This would be of particular significance if we believe that
the author of *Egil's Saga* was educated at Oddi.

    [11] Campbell, *op. cit.*, p. 74. Axel Olrik (*Viking Civilization*, 1930, p. 186) thinks
Egil's share in Brunanburh "quite unhistorical, but it is a romance which the saga
teller—or the saga tellers—invented in order to provide an explanation for Egil's
youthful verses written about the time of Thórólf's death." But see the same work,
p. 162.
    [12] In the *Landnámabók* of Sturla Thórðarson he is said to have fallen in *Vindland*.
Is this an error from Vínheiðr-England? Thórólf's fall in England, in the service of
King Athelstan, is noted in Hauk Valdisarson's *Íslendingadrápa*, v. 9. The poem is
of the second half of the twelfth century.
    [13] Halldór Hermansson, *Sæmund Sigfússon and the Oddaverjar*, Islandica XXII;
Einar Ól. Sveinsson, *Sagnaritun Oddaverja*, Reykjavík, 1937.

One of the main difficulties in identifying Vínheiðr with Brunanburh was the apparent irreconcilability of the chronology of *Egil's
Saga* as first established by Gudbrand Vigfusson in his *Um Tímatal í
Íslendinga Sögum* (Copenhagen, 1855) with the fixed date of the
battle of Brunanburh, 937. Vigfusson set Vínheiðr in the year 927,
Finnur Jónsson in the year 925. However, some thirty years after his
first and fundamental study Vigfusson most brilliantly challenged his
own universally accepted conclusions,[14] while in 1921 Halvdan Koht
demonstrated convincingly that the accepted dating of those main
events in Norwegian history which had been used to determine the
chronology of the sagas was sometimes from ten to thirty years too
early.[15] In 1927 Per Wieselgren recharted the chronology of *Egil's
Saga* in so masterly a fashion that subsequent editors and commenta-
tors have found little or no need for alteration. The chronology to be
found on page 30 of the Introduction is taken from Nordal's edition,
pp. lii-liii, but agrees in almost every respect with that worked out by
Wieselgren in *Författarskapet till Eigla*. The only comments needed
are the obvious ones that Wieselgren's chronology brings Brunanburh
and Vínheiðr into line, and that his all-important date, *ca.* 885, for the
battle of Hafrsfjörður accords far better than the old date, 872, with
the coordinated demands of Norwegian, Icelandic, and English
history.

The Poems and Verses

Neither the oral traditions nor the written authorities used by the
author of *Egil's Saga* are now extant. There remain the poems and
single verses. If genuine these vouch for the truth, or rather the faithfulness to tradition, of the saga; whether genuine or not they teach us
a good deal about its composition. It follows that the most important
question we can ask about the sources of *Egil's Saga* concerns the
authenticity of the verses.

Their number is considerable, as becomes a skald's saga: sixty verses
and three long poems. The three poems, *Höfuðlausn, Sonatorrek,* and
Arinbjarnarkviða, are universally accepted as Egil's and need no
avouchment. Of the verses all save eight are attributed by the saga-

[14] In *Corpus Poeticum Boreale*, II, 487-500.
[15] *Innhogg og Utsyn í Norsk Historie*, Kristiania, 1921.

man to Egil, and the bulk of this writing does seem homogeneous, the work of one man, as tradition has insisted. It seems unlikely that a later poet, with an original or imitative gift, could have added substantially to the Egil canon, unless his work is so exactly like Egil's that it is now past hope to separate them. In the great majority of these verses there is nothing to conflict with what we expect in the way of substance and thought, vocabulary and expression, from a tenth-century poet. Yet there have been many attempts to sort them into sound and unsound, the work of Egil and that of imitators and false pretenders. Perhaps the best approach to the problem is to recognize along with Sigurður Nordal that there can be "genuine" verses of two kinds. First are those verses whose authenticity has never been convincingly questioned and need not be questioned now.[16] Second comes a group of verses which we cannot believe were composed in the precise circumstances to which they are ascribed by the sagaman, but which there is no good reason for denying to Egil even so. These are such verses as Egil would *wish to have composed* on a given occasion and which it is reasonable to think he composed at leisure after the event. The two stylistically typical verses said to be the work of the three-year-old Egil are a case in point, and so are some of the single verses composed during the adventure at York. At some subsequent time he "wrote them into" his story—if "wrote" is the correct word.

Between them these two kinds of "genuine" verses account for most of the poetry attributed to Egil. The verses least likely to be authentic are those bound up with doubtful prose material. Suspicion inevitably attaches to some of the Vínheiðr verses (especially Nos. 16, 18, and 21), and the set of verses associated with Egil's extraordinary encounter with Ljót the Pale plainly invites us to be wary.

In general there is close correspondence between the stuff of the saga and its verses. The notable exception is Egil's visit to York and the poems connected with it, more especially *Höfuðlausn*. Chapters 59-61 tell us that it was what its name implies, a "Head-ransom," a poem composed by Egil at York in one night in honor of King Eirík, and composed with one end in view, that the king would spare his

---

16 In general Nos. 7-11, 19, 20, 22-24, 26, 28-32, 34-36, 43, 50-60, have been exempt from or undamaged by criticism.

life in return for it. But though we should accept this as being in general the truth, there are substantial reasons for not accepting the saga's account in detai.. The first twelve verses of *Arinbjarnarkviða* tell of the same episode, but without resolving its difficulties. The saga says that one year after Egil left Norway for Iceland, King Eirík was driven overseas by Hákon, Athelstan's foster son. The English King Athelstan set Eirík to rule over Northumbria, and Eirík dwelt at York. But Gunnhild still bore her old grudge to Egil and wrought a spell that he might not rest in peace in Iceland till she should look on him again. The spell succeeded, Egil was drawn forth from Iceland, and intended to come and visit King Athelstan in England. The saga's conflict with history and chronology need not for the moment detain us. Athelstan had died *ca.* 940, his successor and half brother Edmund died in 946, and by 948 a third brother Eadred ruled England. One stresses the year 948, because Egil could not have revisited England before the autumn of that year. Eirík was not driven from Norway by Hákon till 947, and did not become king of Northumbria till 948. His first spell of rule there lasted less than a year, nor was that under the ægis of the English king, but by the unstable favor of the Northumbrians themselves, who replaced him by Óláf kváran to placate Eadred in 948, then took him back in 952 for another two years before driving him out again in 954. The uncertainty of Eirík's tenure may explain his unwillingness to offend Arinbjörn on the occasion of Egil's visit, and it certainly adds sting and point to Gunhild's words: "King Eirík need no longer deceive himself how all kings are today grown his lords and masters" (see p. 160). But serious as these discrepancies are for our view of the historicity of *Egil's Saga* at this point (and the saga stays wrong about the kings of England down to Chapter 67), they count hardly more than Gunnhild's spell against the authenticity of *Höfuðlausn* and the conditions of its composition. But the sagaman has made a more troubling mistake of fact. He is badly astray in his geography, and this compels him to invent nonsensical reasons for Egil's seeking out Eirík at York. Let us assume for the sake of argument that Egil has set sail for England to see England's king (or for any other reason) and is shipwrecked at the mouth of the Humber, near Spurn Head. Here to his surprise he learns that Eirík Bloodaxe and Gunnhild are in England and have Northumbria in their charge, and that Eirík is "a short way off up in the town of York," and Arinbjörn with him. "Escape seemed to him hopeless": he must travel so far a way to get out of Eirík's realm; and further, he would be easily recognized by any who might see him. But York is at least fifty miles away from Spurn Head; all he had to do to get out of Eirík's realm was to cross the Humber, even if we assume Eirík's uncertain grasp to reach so far; and we cannot believe that any save the king's personal retainers would recognize Egil or know anything of his offenses against their master. The wrongheadedness of all this has been many times discussed and need not be discussed again. For we are confronted with a major contradiction: that Egil, who has been brought near his deadliest enemy by accident and realizes in what peril he stands, then takes considerable pains *not* to avoid that enemy's presence. Is there an explanation? Sigurður Nordal thinks the saga's narrative shows such contradictions as might proceed from the use of two sources. Egil's shipwreck is taken from one of these, that he sought Eirík of his own will may be from the other. The two poems, *Arinbjarnarkviða* and *Höfuðlausn,* and verse 33 support the notion that he visited York because he wished to. Nor would the errors of geography and the consequent need for untenable reasons for the visit be apparent to listeners at home in Iceland. Presumably they would accept them as they accepted the freedoms taken by the sagaman in his account of the Vermaland expedition.

If we seek a reason why Egil should go to York of his own will, the saga helps us little. Its emphasis is on Egil's offenses against Eirík and the mortal peril of his position. Egil had killed many of Eirík's men, beginning with Bárd in Atley, and he had defied the king in a most flagrant manner; on leaving Norway he did him the deadly insult and injury of raising the *niðstöng* against him and his queen; and least forgivable of all, he slew his young son Rögnvald.[17] Thórólf Kveldúlfsson's offenses against Harald Fairhair were less grievous

---

[17] Nordal suggests that tradition had exaggerated Egil's offences. Rögnvald Eiríksson is unknown to history apart from what is said of him in Egil's Saga and one not very convincing reference in Flateyjarbók I, 49. Snorri does not record his name in Heimskringla. Had he then found reason to disbelieve in Rögnvald's existence between writing Egil's Saga and Heimskringla? (ES, xxiii-iv). On the other hand the killing of Rögnvald and its consequences have been most carefully integrated into Egil's Saga (including verse 31).

by far than Egil's against Eirík; nor was there anything in Eirík's character or record to suggest that he would be merciful to Egil. It has been urged that Egil visited England in order to see again the friend of his heart Arinbjörn. Once Arinbjörn had thrown in his lot with Eirík and shared his exile from Norway, then Egil must either resign himself never again to see him or must seek a reconciliation with Eirík. Further, there was no certainty in 948 that Eirík would not regain the kingdom of Norway, and Ásgerd's estates would be once more in his power. And, even while Eirík was in exile, Egil could not know when in the course of his travels he would be blown face to face with him.[18] All these are possibilities, but at best they are weak reasons for Egil's thrusting the head he prized so highly into the wolf's mouth or baring his neck to the stroke of Eirík's bloody axe.

The saga's own explanation is, of course, perfect of its kind. If Gunnhild's spell could draw Egil forth from Iceland, it could addle his wits at the mouth of the Humber and in swallow-likeness interfere with his composition of the *drápa*. If the spell were itself a fact it would cover all the other facts.

Almost as much has been written about *Höfuðlausn* itself as about Egil's visit to York. It has been regarded as a *drápa* written in praise not of Eirík but of Athelstan, or as the reworking of an earlier poem —though these are both unlikely theories; as having been written with the poet's tongue in his cheek; and as a poem written earlier and held in readiness for a projected visit to Eirík. Scholars as notable as Finnur Jónsson and Per Wieselgren have seen in its general hyperbole and lack of minute particulars, and its hollow, conventional praise of the king's unspecified campaigns and unillustrated generosity, an exercise in irony at Eirík's expense. But it is hard to believe that Egil would have composed an ironical poem about an enemy without the irony being more apparent. If it is objected that he composed it while in that enemy's power and dared not be more explicit, the answer seems to be that it is then unthinkable he should deal in irony at all. The "emptiness" of the poem, its rhetorical ring and lack of supporting detail, are more credibly explained by its being the work of one night and by Egil's unwillingness even in sore straits to dole out more praise

[18] Nordal, *ES*, xxiii, thinks that verse 36 supports the notion that Egil did not wish to have Eirík's wrath and power hanging over him. But I have always thought that the verse refers specifically to Eirík's power at York and Arinbjörn's help there.

than he must. There is no reason whatever for thinking it beyond Egil's powers to put together a twenty-verse *drápa* in so short a time; modern Icelanders have not found it difficult to repeat the feat, and *runhenda* is a much easier meter to compose in than *dróttkvæðr háttr*. Patently *Höfuðlausn* is a poem much inferior to *Sonatorrek* and · *Arinbjarnarkviða*, and may properly be regarded as a triumph of technique under difficulties. The theory that the poem was composed before Egil left Iceland depends upon the antecedent theory that Egil sought Eirík of his own will. The phrases in *Höfuðlausn* invoked to support the theory (they are to be found more especially in the first two and a half verses) are equally consistent with Arinbjörn's plan to convince King Eirík that Egil did come freely into his presence.

Unquestionably *Höfuðlausn* impressed its royal hearer in the tenth century more than it seems to have impressed its critics of the nineteenth and twentieth. In return for its twenty verses Eirík gave Egil his head, let his enemy go in peace, despite his many and ample grievances. If we ask why, we are not likely to answer that it was for the poem's content, its empty praise and glitter. But when we consider the form of the poem a possible explanation assaults the eye and strikes upon the ear. It is composed in end-rime verse, and with certain insignificant exceptions it is the first poem so to be composed by any Norse skald. In court meter, *dróttkvæðr háttr*, rime and assonance are to be found only within the line, the lines themselves being linked by alliteration. It is Sigurður Nordal's opinion[19] that the riming lines of *Höfuðlausn* burst like a thunderclap upon his audience at York. Like Alexander before him,

> With ravished ears
> The monarch hears,
> Assumes the god,
> Affects to nod,
> And [hopes] to shake the spheres.

In its ring and rime Eirík heard the promise of his immortality, and spared the artifex of his renown.

Whatever the truth of this, whether the effect of this new rimed sonority was so overwhelming, and whether its chimes rang Egil forth

---

[19] *La Poésie Islandaise: Un Millénaire*, Reykjavík, 1948.

to safety, to Egil must be given the glory of introducing a new kind of poetry to the North. The origin of end-rime in poetry is relevant to our present inquiry only in so far as we must seek a model for Egil's *runhenda* meter. Finnur Jónsson thought no model need be sought, and that it was an invention of the Mýramen. Neckel thought that Egil had learned this meter in England; and Heusler was of much the same opinion, that Egil had heard rimed poetry in the west and had adapted it to his needs. Nordal thinks that Egil during his stay at Athelstan's court would have been impressed by the rimes of Latin and English poetry. G. Turville-Petre considers that Egil was not likely to be influenced by Old English poetry in rime, scanty as that was, but by the rimed Latin hymns he would hear in church after he had been primesigned in England. It seems certain that Old English end-rimed verse was itself written on the model of these Latin hymns, whose rime and perhaps meter have been shown by Stéfan Einarsson to derive in turn from Irish-Latin hymns.[20] The Old English poem to which *Höfuðlausn* shows the closest metrical similarity is the so-called *Riming Poem,* though other end-rimed poems may possibly have been written but lost.[21] Although the *Riming Poem* is substantially older than *Höfuðlausn* (it is probably of the eighth century), it cannot of course be regarded as its model. Its sigificance consists in its evidence that end-rime poems were known in England, where Egil had spent some time; and that end-rime in Old English poetry preceded end-rime in Icelandic or Norse poetry.

Egil, it is worth remarking, made no further use of end-rime. It had served him well for a metrical tour-de-force, but was utterly inadequate for his heartfelt masterpieces, *Sonatorrek* and *Arinbjarnarkviða,* in later years. For these he employed *kviðuháttr,* a meter known in Scandinavia since the eighth century.

[20] F. Jónsson, *Litt. Hist.,* I, 408; G. Neckel, *Beiträge zur Eddaforschung,* p. 368 ff.; A. Heusler, *Deutsche Versgeschichte,* I, 291 ff.; S. Nordal, *ES,* xx, *La Poésie Islandaise,* p. 4; G. Turville-Petre, *The Heroic Age of Scandinavia,* p. 170; *Origins of Icelandic Literature,* 1953, pp. 41-2; Stéfan Einarsson, "The Origin of Egill Skallagrímsson's Runhenda," *Scandinavica et Fenno-Ugrica, Studier Tillnägnade Björn Collinder den 22 Juli 1954; A History of Icelandic Literature,* 1957, p. 49.

[21] For the *Riming Poem,* see Krapp and Dobbie, *The Exeter Book,* 1936, and the references there given, pp. xlvii-xlix.

Date and Authorship

The direct evidence for the date and authorship of *Egil's Saga* is so slight that inquiry is most profitably pursued in the wide context of when and how the Icelandic sagas came into being in the form in which we know them. To begin with, the long-accepted estimate of the sagas as strict historical records has been abandoned by the scholars of Iceland; however much history a given saga may contain, it is now judged safest to regard them as historical novels about Egil, Grettir, or whoever the hero may be. Nor is it any longer believed that the best sagas came first in point of time, because they would thus be the closest to oral tradition. Rather, the art of saga-writing shows, like so much mundane achievement, a rude beginning, a swift mastery by one dominant mind, a time of triumph, and a sure decline. The older view, current almost universally till after 1920, and of which Finnur Jónsson may be taken as the most distinguished and influential protagonist, was that the best of the sagas were written in the period 1170-1200; but we know now with certainty that the thirteenth century, not the twelfth, was the great age of saga. Further, the "oral" theory of the origin of the sagas has been substantially modified. Since Björn M. Ólsen's celebrated lectures at Reykjavík in 1912-17 (published posthumously in *Safn*, 1937-39) and the publication of Nordal's book on Snorri Sturluson in 1920, we have come (sometimes unwillingly) to recognize that the Icelandic family saga is not a mere transcription of an oral tale or tales, but a work of deliberate literary composition, and that we must ascribe a saga in its present form to an author, and not to a scribe. In Ólsen's words, "The more closely we read our sagas and conduct research into them, the clearer it becomes that they are works of art, that an artist's quill inscribed them on vellum, and that behind him was no unified oral tradition enshrining a completely shaped saga, but only a mass of separate oral tales which the author must collect and from which he selected the material to make his own integrated whole."[22] Finally it may be noted that the sagas are much less uniform in style and com-

[22] *Safn*, VI, 5, 11.

position than many have supposed, and that "schools" of saga-writing are to be sometimes tentatively and sometimes clearly discerned.

When and how did the process start? In the *Libellus Islandorum* of Ari the Learned, and presumably in his lost *Liber* (ca. 1122-33), the emphasis is on historical truth; and Ari, according to Snorri Sturluson, was the first Icelander to write scholarly works in the native language. By the time of *Viglundar Saga* and similar productions of the fourteenth century the historical element has disappeared. Between these extremes there can be traced a development of Icelandic narrative writing having its origin in historical scholarship but soon compelled to take notice of an audience's desire for entertainment as well as instruction, for fiction as well as truth. At first slowly, and then with some rapidity, the creative artist gains on the historian, till at length artistry and history are in equipoise in *Egil's Saga*; in *Njála* some fifty years later the untrammeled artist achieves his greatest triumph, though his narrative rests on the bedrock of historical and antiquarian scholarship; by the time of the latest recension of *Grettis Saga*, about 1310-20, the author is treating his material even more freely, and the bone of history is less discernible under the tissue of romance and wondrous tradition; and finally, in *Viglundar Saga*, history has died into an absurd pretense of historical coloring.

Once we discern this main line of progression and discard the mechanical theory that sagas were nothing but oral tradition written out by scribes and copyists, we are enabled to trace how written sagas served as sources for or influences upon later writers, to assess their use of native, foreign and religious material, to notice how they reflect the changing taste of authors and audience, and to account for variations of style and tone among many authors of differing quality and ambition.

Three schools of writing played a part in the development of the historical and the family sagas. The first in point of time was the Southern school located at Oddi and Haukadal, with which were associated the glorious names of Sæmund and Ari. This was an aristocratic school, scholarly in its interests, and productive of formal histories, genealogies, annals, and summaries of biographical fact which were later to be used extensively by writers of sagas. It is possible too that books on poetics were written in the Southern school. By way of

contrast there was a more romantically minded Northern school associated with the Benedictine monastery which was founded at Thingeyrar in 1133. It was here that Abbot Karl completed his life of King
Sverri in a style freer and more entertaining than that of Ari; and it
was here that the monks Odd Snorrason (fl. 1190) and Gunnlaug
Leifsson (d. 1218) wrote with zest their Latin lives of King Óláf
Tryggvason which were translated into Icelandic and used as source-
books by Snorri Sturluson among other historians. With the turn of
the century the Northern school begins to influence the Southern,
but what is more significant for our present purpose is the emergence
of a third school of historical and family saga writing in Borgarfjörður, with Snorri Sturluson as its most distinguished representative.
The characteristics of the schools at Oddi and Thingeyrar were now
united in the person of a writer of genius. He took the legendary
sagas of the two Óláfs associated with Thingeyrar, and applied to them
the canons of criticism and scholarship he had learned during his
fostering at Oddi. The measure of his achievement in Óláfs Saga
Tryggvasonar and Óláfs Saga Helga is too well known to need stress-
ing. Egil's Saga is a main product of this Borgarfjörður school. The
question at once arises: Could any but Snorri Sturluson be its writer?

It is certain that Egil's Saga was written by a man closely acquainted
with Borgarfjörður; and it would seem impossible to argue a case for
its being written anywhere outside of Thverárthing. Its author, we
feel, had a native's knowledge of Borg and its environs. His fidelity
to the landscape, his precise topography, are borne in with absolute
conviction upon any one who wanders through Borgarfjörður with
the saga in mind. Even if we disregard the circumstantial account of
Skallagrím's landtaking, as perhaps based on early written sources,
we must be convinced by the chapters (80-84) which describe Thorstein Egilsson's dealings with Steinar Sjónason. How Thorstein
walked up on to the rock at Borg and looked about him and saw where
Grani grazed his beasts on Stakksmýr; Egil riding up to the varthing
along Gljúfrá; Íri's warning to Thorstein about Steinar's ambush;
Thorstein's visit to Álftanes and all that befell on his outward and
home journeys: these and other things have been recorded by a man
with every stream and bog and rock and hill clear before his eye. And
it is significant that when Skallagrím sinks his chest and cauldron in

Krumskelda there is no need for our author to describe the place, for it would be well known to the Mýramen; but when Egil hides his silver, Athelstan's gift, away at Mosfell, he supplies his readers with an accurate picture of the ground.

In *Egil's Saga* the working up of oral and written sources has been done with so individual a skill that even supporters of the theory of an oral development of the sagas have felt here the impact not of a compiler, recorder or copyist, but of a conscious and creative artist or author. Attempts to identify him have led uniformly in the one direction. The most recent and decisive presentation of a case which has always been strong in probabilities but weak in clinching evidence is that offered by Sigurður Nordal, partly in the Fornrit *Egil's Saga* in 1933, and partly in his commemorative essay on Snorri Sturluson in *Skírnir*, 1941.[23] A brief preliminary account of Snorri's life will help the English reader to assess its value.

Snorri was born of a leading family in the Vestfirðir in 1179, the son of Sturla of Hvamm and his wife Guðny Böðvarsdóttir, a descendant on her father's side of the Mýramen. He was brought up south in Oddi by the great Jón Loftsson, and it was there that he obtained his training in history and poetry, in law and Icelandic politics. About the year 1200 he returned to Borgarfjörður upon his marriage to Herdis Bersadóttir of Borg, and this marriage made him a rich and powerful man. For several years he lived at Borg itself, on that very soil where Skallagrím and Egil too had lived, and when in 1205 he removed to Reykholt and built his famous dwelling there, he was in line to become the most influential man in that part of Iceland.[24] But along with his energy and foresight in acquiring and developing estates went a passionate interest in every aspect of the older Icelandic culture. He early attracted notice as a skilful if uninspired poet, and by 1215 was a sufficiently notable lawyer to be elected *lögsögumaðr* or Lawspeaker of the Althing. From 1218 to 1220 he was in Norway, for most of the time with Jarl Skúli and King Hákon Hákonarson,

[23] *Snorri Sturluson*: "Nokkurar hugleiðingar á 700 ártið hans." *Skínir*, 1941, pp. 5-33.

[24] Later tradition was to suggest that Egil still kept a close eye on the Mýramen's business. On this occasion he appeared in a dream before his descendant Egil Halldórsson and expressed his displeasure that "our kinsman Snorri" was thinking to leave the ancestral home for Reykholt. *Sturlunga Saga, II*, 30-31.

and returned to Iceland the king's liegeman and with a commission
to promote his fellow-countrymen's peaceful submission to Norway.
From 1222 till 1231 he was again *lögsögumaðr* in Iceland, and worked
hard to increase his wealth and strengthen his position at home by a
series of marriage and family alliances. From this same period came
his known literary works, the *Prose Edda* (completed in 1223) and
Heimskringla, the Lives of the Norse Kings (completed not much
later than 1230). Meantime he was doing little or nothing to imple-
ment his diplomatic promise to the Norwegian king, and by about
1233 he had ceased to be the most powerful man in Iceland. It is
generally held that his intelligence, ambition and acquisitiveness much
exceeded his courage and desire for action, and his immense contribution to history and literature during this decade and a half may be
regarded by different observers as cause, symptom, or effect of his
aversion from military action at once grandiose and sustained. He was
driven from Reykholt by his kinsmen Sighvat and Sturla in 1236,
and was under a cloud when he left for Norway in the following year.
The shattering defeat of Sturlung hopes and the deaths of Sighvat
and Sturla at Örlyggsstaðir in 1238 made him anxious to return to
Iceland, and he did so, in defiance of the king's command. Once more
he went to live at Reykholt with Halveig his second wife, but after
some bitter quarrels with his family over moneys and estates he was
slain there with the king's approval on September 23, 1241.

The relevance of this biography for Snorri's authorship of *Egil's
Saga* lies in (a) his sixteen years' training in scholarship and letters
at the Southern school of Oddi, (b) his long-continued supremacy,
both political and cultural, over Borgarfjörður, (c) his literary career
and achievement, more especially after 1220, and (d) his unrivalled
opportunities to know men and affairs at home and abroad as well
as he knew books.

Reference has already been made to the emergence of the third
Icelandic school of historical and saga writing, in Borgarfjörður, early
in the thirteenth century. What was the state of saga writing during
the next twenty years? The oldest of the family sagas is thought to be
Heiðarvíga Saga, written at Thingeyrar shortly ofter 1200. *Fóst-
brœðra Saga* is certainly an early saga, from the Vestfirðir, and was
written down about 1210. *Bjarnar Saga Hítdœlakappa* shows no sign

of being influenced by Snorri's work, but may well have been influenced by Thingeyrar, and there is good reason to place it in the period 1215-20. *Kormáks Saga* was written in Miðfjörður in the north of Iceland rather earlier than 1220, and *Hallfreður Saga* about 1220. From the Southern school there is no known family saga before the middle of the thirteenth century; and from Borgarfjörður nothing before *Egil's Saga*. It would seem then that shortly before the year 1220 the art of saga-writing awaited a stimulus from some outstanding mind. It is a safe assumption that the kings' sagas of Snorri played a large part in perfecting saga art after 1230; and it is evident that *Egil's Saga* and these historical writings represent one and the same stage in the development of Icelandic prose narrative. The more tempting then to think that Snorri made use of all he had learned from his intensive study of Icelandic historical works before 1220 to produce a saga far superior to the poorly constructed and blundering narratives which were all that were known to the writers of family sagas at that time. We know of no other writer either of histories or family sagas who could have achieved this; still more emphatically no writer existed in Borgarfjörður, was conversant with the whole area and especially with the environs of Borg, had a chieftain's and a historian's upbringing, and possessed those highly individual (and unparalleled) literary qualities to which we must now turn our attention, save Snorri Sturluson himself.

If we except the stylistic, as a thing not to be proved in the context of a translation, what are the most striking qualities of Snorri the author, as he displays them in *Heimskringla*?[25]

> Among such qualities are his sure judgment of sources, his powers of characterization, his sure taste, his personal style, and his control of the arrangement and treatment of his subject matter. We can even find his equal in any one of these qualities, although there is no other saga-writer who possesses them all together in the same balance and proportion. Yet there is one quality which he did not inherit from his predecessors, and which his successors have not learned from him to any noticeable extent. This is his pragmatism: the need and the ability to sift the causes and results of events and not to give up till they have

[25] For the stylistic arguments for and against Snorri's authorship of *Egil's Saga*, see Nordal's Introduction, pp. lxxi-lxxxviii (and especially lxxvi ff.). The student will find on pp. lxxxiii-v a textual comparison of the θ fragment (ca. 1250) and the relevant passages of the shortened Möðruvallabók text. See the note on MSS, p. 28.

been understood and interpreted. In illustration of this it is sufficient to mention the debates of the Upland kings when they join forces with Saint Óláf and, later, when they revolt against him; or how a case is made out for Óláf's opponents before the battle of Stiklastaðir and how the supports melted away when his sanctity was so swiftly praised by some of his opponents; or the comparison between Óláf and Harald Hardráði, or the explanation why Harald could not maintain his rule in Denmark although he had defeated Sveinn Úlfsson in every battle. All this points to one thing, that Snorri, his outstanding intellect apart, had gained from his many-sided experience as a chieftain the wide vision of the arbitrator and that impartiality of judgment which does not allow the feelings to over-ride the reason. In addition, I believe that he had learned a great deal from foreign, classical historians, especially from Sallust who had taken Thucydides as his model.

If we now turn to *Egla*, it is perfectly clear how as saga literature it is distinct from all other family sagas. The first of its qualities is the author's ability to relate foreign events; for example, the causes and results of the battle of Vínheiðr and the efforts to unite Norway. The second is his ability to depict kings and their way of thinking, especially Harald Fairhair, Eirík Bloodaxe, Gunnhild, and Hákon the Good. The third is the author's skill in illuminating both sides of a question, so that we understand equally well the slander of the sons of Hildiríd and its effect on King Harald, the pride of the king and the haughtiness and rebellion of Thórólf Kveldúlfsson, . . . the quarrel of Arinbjörn Hersir and Queen Gunnhild over Egil at York, without our being able to decide which has the better case, . . . Egil depicted showing force against Önund Sjóni and Steinar, but his decision explained in historical perspective. At the same time we can see how the history of Iceland develops under the author's general view of history, and how the subject is sketched in with the same sure touch found in Snorri's *Heimskringla*. In other Icelandic sagas the descriptions of events outside Iceland are generally unconvincing and sometimes childish, and never go beyond what directly concerns the Icelandic characters of the saga. Even in such notable works as *Eyrbyggja*, *Hrafnkatla* and *Njála*, there are passages which the author of *Egil's Saga* would have written differently and with a better understanding of what he was doing: for example, the struggle of Snorri Godi for control of the Dales, the developing power of Hrafnkel at Hrefnkelsstaðir, and the slander of Mörd Valgardsson.[26]

[26] Sigurður Nordal, *Snorri Sturluson*, 1941, p. 27. I have quoted the passage in R. G. Thomas's translation, *Studia Islandica*, Part I, in *Modern Language Quarterly*, XI, 3, 288-89.

To these general and weighty considerations many "trifles light as air" might be added to confirm the drift of critical opinion. The likeliest time for Snorri to have written *Egil's Saga* was early in his literary career, during the years 1220-25. And who shall say that it is a saga unworthy of the genius which gave us the prose Edda and *Heimskringla,* a genius nurtured in Oddi and Borgarfjörður more than in courts abroad, and not least where the fast white waters of Hvítá mix with the sea near Borg?

Aspects of the Saga

More than any other saga *Egil's Saga* is an historian's saga. Many other sagas tell of Norway in the days of Harald Fairhair, but no other sagaman has shown the inevitability of Harald's success, and the futility of even a splendid resistance. To the modern student Norway seems ripe for political change in the second half of the ninth century; the Middle Ages were pressing on the old Germanic Heroic Age, and Society needed a reordering. Snorri saw and expressed this clearer than any of his countrymen; but it was always his way to stress and indeed exaggerate the role of the individual; in *Heimskringla* and *Egil's Saga* he sees political and economic movements in terms of personalities. The bitter struggle between the concepts of kingship and feudalism on the one hand and regionalism and petty if patriarchal lordship on the other, he expresses in *Egil's Saga* as a struggle between Harald Fairhair and such kinglets and proud lordlings as Audbjörn and Sölvi Klofi for the one part and Thórólf Kveldúlfsson for the other. Kveldúlf is past his prime, he appears to recognize the inevitable without wishing to play any part for or against it; but Thórólf takes his stand on the king's side, becomes his right-hand man, and at last grows so rich and powerful that Harald sees in him a rival in the north, and thereafter removes him. Our sympathies may be all with Thórólf, but Harald has reason on his side. The slanders of the sons of Hildiríd, all lies on the surface, rest on a foundation of truth: Thórólf is too strong to live in the same land as the king. The apparent and the real causes of Harald's decisive action are concurrently brought home to the reader.

The pattern thus strongly established persists throughout the saga.

Old Kveldúlf is driven into open enmity against the Norwegian royal
line; his son Skallagrím, sunk in his family loyalties, fierce and stiff-
necked, refuses service and reconciliation with the tyrant; they take
vengeance and flee to the new land west over the ocean,

> Where sheltering from a tyrant's lawless pride,
> A Northern folk, on the world's utmost verge,
> Found out the heavenly Muses' contests sweet,
> Life self-sustained, and holy freedom's laws.[27]

But history repeats itself in the next generation. For a time a second
Thórólf, Skallagrím's son, finds favor with Eirík Haraldsson and for-
bearance from Harald himself, but his brother Egil is fated to give
offense in Norway and kill the king's men. As a result the favor of
Gunnhild, Eirík's queen, is withdrawn from Thórólf, she plans to
have both brothers slain, and like their father and grandfather before
them they flee the land. Thórólf is killed in England but Egil's quarrel with Eirík and Gunnhild persists most murderously till the climax
of their meeting at York in 948. Finally, even Eirík's successor in Norway, King Hákon the Good, was ill-disposed towards Egil and spared
him only for his fosterer Athelstan's sake.

This long-continued strife between Kveldúlf's descendants and the
kings of Norway gives weight, coherence, and strength to the story-
telling. There is more at stake, and always a mightier background to
the immediate action, than is customary in the sagas. The five outstanding sections of *Egil's Saga* are the dealings of Thórólf Kveldúlfsson and King Harald, the account of Egil's boyhood in chapter 40,
Egil's visit to York, the account of Egil's skaldship in Chapter 78, and
the concluding description of his old age and death. (One may be
tempted to extend the list with such things as Skallagrím's settlement,
Egil at Athelstan's court, and Egil's last words with his father, diamond cut diamond, but sometime one must make an end). Of the five
triumphant sections mentioned above only one, the account of Egil's
boyhood, draws not at all on the family feud with Harald and his
sons. Two are entirely taken up with it; *Arinbjarnarkviða* pays long
and close attention to the episode at York; and that old, blind, stum-
bling Egil, driven from the fireside by a sharp-tongued woman-

---

[27] From an unpublished rendering by Charles Kingsley of Robert Lowe's epigram,
Χᾶιρε χαὶ ἐν νεΦέλαισι, in Sir Edmund Head's *Viga-Glum's Saga*, 1866, p. v.

servant, would be at once less pathetic and less terrible but for his constant reminiscence of royal acquaintance, the mantle of magnificence that still drapes the bowed craggy shoulders of this one-time friend and foe of mighty kings. When Arinbjörn tells Gunnhild: "No one will call Eirík a bigger man though he should kill a farmer's son from abroad," he is speaking for a purpose; in fact this was a farmer's son who had rubbed shoulders with princes and louted to none of them. His saga, for all its homely detail, is an aristocratic saga, a high tale of haughty men.

In one way Kveldúlf and his descendants are committed to a losing cause. They cannot in the nature of things match the power of kings. Their future lies in Iceland: Norway has rejected them. The saga contains two remarkable portraits of royal persons, not merely kings or queens, but two who understand what it was to be konungmaðr, a king not merely by title but in every fibre of the being. The first of these is Harald Fairhair. He is drawn differently from the Harald of Heimskringla, is at once less strong and less admirable than the just, generous and wise king Snorri depicts there. In Egil's Saga Harald is a suspicious and moody monarch, greedy and resentful, easily led by evil counselors, a poor judge of men, and acting by fits and starts. Yet, strangely enough, we are made to feel all the time that he is the same king as the Harald of Heimskringla. There is an inner power in Harald which reconciles his apparent inconsistencies: something of himself is withheld from us today as it was from his informants and counselors a millennium ago; we are never fully in his heart. Perhaps, we think, he is all along making use of the Háreks and Hrœreks, the Sigtryggs and Hallvards, the Bárds and Thórólfs, in accordance with long-laid and farsighted plans of his own; he treats them well or ill as they seem good or bad for his royal ambitions; and when he strikes his blows fall like the thunderbolt, swift, unwardable, unsparing. The second person in Egil's Saga who has completely grasped the idea of royalty is Eirík's queen, Gunnhild. She appears in many of the Íslendingasögur, middle-aged or ageing, amorous of the handsome young Icelanders who visited her court, cruel, treacherous, and a sorceress. The Historia Norwegiæ declares that she was the daughter of Gorm the Old, and sister to Harald Bluetooth, both famous kings of Denmark, and everything points to this being true; but according

to Icelandic tradition she was the daughter of Özur Tóti, a neighbor of
the Lapps (a people notorious for their sorcery), and Eirík won her
to wife on his expedition to Bjarmaland in 925. Her devotion to her
husband's career, and the careers of her many sons after his day, made
her in contemporary eyes the evil genius of them all, and of Norway
too. Why should they not be such kings as Harald Fairhair had been,
or Gorm himself? And so time and time again we see Gunnhild
bracing her husband to harsh but decisive deeds, decrying his scruples,
begging him to assert the royal prerogative, strike down his enemies,
destroy the sons of Skallagrím, and show himself to the world both
king and *konungmaðr*.[28] The scene at York would be incomparably
poorer had Snorri been content to represent it as a clash of wills between Eirík and Egil, with Gunnhild as a minatory and Arinbjörn as
a mediative chorus. The real clash there is between Arinbjörn and
Gunnhild, between the lordly retainer (if not a king-maker, a king-
sustainer) and the protagonist of absolutism. But her weapon breaks
in her hand; Eirík is an under-dog among kings; fate has cast him for
no better part. All that is left for her is loyalty to his person and her
own ideal. And unless with Snorri we recognize this loyalty, so mag-
nificently twofold, Gunnhild's story is stripped of its true significance.

Yet among all the characters of the saga, Harald and Gunnhild, the
two Thórólfs and the sons of Hildiríd, Skallagrím, Thorstein the
White and Steinar Sjónason, the noble, steadfast, and deeply understanding Arinbjörn, it is Egil himself who is the most impressive crea-
tion, at once a mass of contrarieties and an individual so unique that
we know him to his heart's core. And this though he has not been
fully explored by his author. He acts as man and speaks as poet, and
what is told of him and by him brings him right home to our bosoms.
"In his life and character, as in his person, he seems to unite extremes
which make him a type of the age in which he lived. Steadfast in love
and hate, cool and passionate to madness, crafty and reckless, grasping
and generous, he passes through a checkered life as poet and pirate,
chief and champion, the henchman of Athelstan and the hereditary
foe of Eirík, now an honored guest at court, now a helpless prisoner,
now a mighty lord, in such fashion as fits the typical Northman of

our tradition."[29] These are the broad outlines, the heavy strokes to be illustrated from the saga's account of Egil's exploits, clashes and journeys. We can see the man closer than this, often unattractive but always fascinating, the great grim baldhead at Athelstan's court, black-visaged, slamming his sword half in, half out, of its scabbard, his grotesque eyebrows twitching—and who knows what dire thoughts in his clouded mind? This oppressive phantom at the feast, who has just clasped bracelets of gold about his slain brother's arms, and is to be won to mirth only by the king's calculated gift of a gold ring: this is one of the unforgettable pictures of Egil in his prime. Or the same vast head sunk under the rim of a cloak, the shoulders bowed, the torso drooping forward, because he is in love, save the mark, and is afraid to tell of it. The same Egil after the drowning of his son Bödvar, dragging himself off like a wounded animal, and like an animal willing himself to die. Or the giant crumbled in age, groping his way along the wall and falling, and the farm women jeering at him. And most wonderful of all, the blind and deaf old viking ordered like a dog from the fireside by a servant, a woman-servant too, still with a demon of destruction and mischief in him, a little gross now that desire and performance are dead, and at the end of his days by his last slayings closing the circle that began with the killing of Grím Heggsson by a lad of six at the ball game on Hvítárvellir.

It is in his poems and verses that Egil is most himself. Certain quirks of character, his wry humor and jesting pleasure in his ugliness, are best displayed here. And nowhere else is his nobility of soul so apparent. Here too he shows himself a good hater, exultant in many a ferocious moment; and here above all he reveals the deep, tender, passionate side of his nature. It is revealed in his warm and unchanging regard for his friend Arinbjörn, his almost mortal sadness after his sons, his throbbing affection for his parents and brother. In the body of the saga it is easy to overlook these things. When his wife Ásgerd died, Egil gave up his farm and went to live south at Mosfell with Grím and Thórdís, "for he loved Thórdís his stepdaughter above all people who then drew breath on earth"; and in his last years it was his greatest joy to be talking with her. These are delicate and poignant

[29] G. Vigfusson, *Sturlunga Saga*, Oxford, 1878, I, xlviii. See too, Axel Olrik, *Viking Civilization*, 161-65 and 183-87.

strokes, in true saga style, but they are not over-incised. In the poems
the emphasis is heavier, the terms more sustained, the love and
friendship, grief and loyalty, more naked and moving. And it is from
Sonatorrek that we learn how Egil, like Jacob in the place called
Peniel, has wrestled with his God and would not let him go except he
blessed him; for Mímir's friend, the Wolf's hard foe, has given him
"all wrongs' amendment," his poet's art, and its grave yet triumphant
outpouring in the greatest elegy sung in the Northlands. It is a happy
stroke of fortune that the life and writings of this most individual and
versatile of skalds have been preserved with such a wealth of detail and
with so much art in the second greatest of sagas.

The Manuscripts

Egil's Saga must have been popular with readers at all times, and in
the number of its early manuscripts is outdone only by *Njála*. It is
preserved in three main MSS: Möðruvallabók, AM 132 fol. (1320-
50); Wolfenbüttelbók (*ca.* 1350), now with considerable lacunæ,
copied by Ásgeir Jónsson for Árni Magnússon in the 17th century;
and Ketilsbók, AM 453 4to, copied twice by Ketil Jörundarson, d. 1670
(the second copy, AM 462 4to, contains ten leaves by another hand)
from an original not certainly identified, and important as the sole
preserver of *Sonatorrek*. In addition ten fragments of various vellums,
in size ranging from one to eight leaves, have been bound together in
AM 162 A, fol.; while the beginning of the saga has been preserved in
the fourteenth century Perg. 4to nr. 7 in Stockholm. Of the fragments in AM 162 A, fol. four are older than any of the main MSS.
The four leaves of θ (theta), *ca.* 1250, go back to within some thirty
years of the saga's composition, and may well be the oldest surviving
Icelandic MS (reproduction in Jón Helgason, *Handritaspjall*, Reykjavík, 1958, facing page 33). This, the oldest fragment, has preserved a text undoubtedly closer to the original saga than Möðruvallabók, which in its relevant passages shows a consistent shortening
or contraction of the text. Möðruvallabók lacks only two leaves of
Egil's Saga (though it records merely the first verse of *Sonatorrek*
and nothing of *Höfuðlausn*), and has been used as the basis of all
the printed editions of the saga. In recent editions the two missing

leaves have been supplied from fragments δ (delta) *ca.* 1300, and *θ*. But recently Jón Helgason in his *Athuganir um Nokkur Handrit Egils Sögu* (*Nordæla, Afmæliskveðja til Sigurðar Nordals,* Reykjavík, 1956, pp. 110-48) has made a striking plea for a reconsideration of the value of various paper MSS of the seventeenth century which may well affect future editors of the saga.

Egil's Saga was first printed at Hrappsey in 1782, and then with a Latin translation at Copenhagen in 1809. In 1856 the saga was edited at Reykjavík by Jón Thorkelsson, with an admirable commentary on the verses. Of Finnur Jónsson's two notable editions the first was published at Copenhagen, 1886-88, with apparatus and commentary, the second in the Altnordische Saga-Bibliothek, 1894 (2nd revised edition 1924). Sigurður Nordal's edition was prepared for Hið Íslenzka Fornritafélag, Reykjavík, 1933, with an introduction of great significance for saga studies. The saga has been twice translated into English, by W. C. Green in 1893, and by E. R. Eddison in 1930.

Chronology

EGIL'S SAGA

I

There was a man named Úlf, the son of Bjálfi and that Hallbera who was daughter of Úlf Unafraid and sister to Hallbjörn Halftroll in Hrafnista, the father of Ketil Hœng. Úlf was a man so big and strong that there was nobody to match him; his early manhood he spent viking and raiding. Associated with him was the man known as Berdla-Kári, a noteworthy man, outstanding for his strength and daring: he was a berserk.[1] He and Úlf held their purse in common and there was close friendship between them. When they left off raiding Kári, now a very rich man, returned to his home in Berdla. He had three children, a son named Eyvind Lambi, and a second Ölvir Hnúfa, while his daughter's name was Salbjörg—the loveliest of women and a great and noble lady. Úlf married Salbjörg, and then he too went to settle down at home. Úlf was rich in both land and personal goods; he took the rank of a landed man,[2] such as his forefathers had held, and became a great lord.

The tale runs that Úlf was a great husbandman. It was his practice to rise early in the day and make the rounds of men's tasks, or where the smiths were at work, and attend likewise to his stock and tilled lands; again, between whiles he would consult with any who had need of his advice, and in every case could offer good counsel, for he had a deep insight into things. But every day as evening drew near he grew so sullen that few could hold speech with him. He was drowsy of an evening, so that people maintained he would be a great shape-changer or werwolf. He was known as Kveldúlf.

Kveldúlf and his wife had two sons, the elder named Thórólf and the younger Grím, who when they grew up were both big, strong men, just like their father. Thórólf was the handsomest and most accomplished of men. He took after his mother's people, was amiable and generous, and extremely active and enterprising in every way.

Everyone liked him. But Grím was black and ugly, the image of his father both in looks and temper. He too grew up to be a great husbandman, was skilled in wood and iron, and developed into the greatest smith. Often during the winter he would be out after the herring with his net-fishing boat, and many a housecarle along with him.

When Thórólf was twenty years old he prepared to go raiding. Kveldúlf provided him with a longship. Berdla-Kári's sons, Eyvind and Ölvir, decided to go with him, together with a big company of their own and a second longship; they went viking that summer, won themselves wealth, and had much booty to share out. It was many a summer they spent viking, but the winters they spent home with their fathers. Thórólf brought home many costly treasures and bestowed them on his parents: those were happy days for a man's fame and fortune. Kveldúlf was now far advanced in age, but his sons were in their prime.

2

At that time the king over Firthafylki was named Audbjörn. There was an earl of his called Hróald, and this earl's son was named Thórir. Atli the Slender was an earl then too and lived at Gaular; his children were Hallstein, Hólmstein, Herstein, and Sólveig the Fair. It happened one autumn that there were a lot of people at Gaular for the autumn sacrifice, and it was then that Ölvir Hnúfa set eyes on Sólveig and fell head over heels in love with her. Later he asked for her hand, but the earl held that there was a disparity of rank and was unwilling to give her. Ölvir afterwards made many love songs about her. So greatly was Ölvir set on Sólveig that he gave over his campaigning, and then there were campaigning Thórólf and Eyvind Lambi.

3

Harald the son of Hálfdan the Black had taken the inheritance after his father east in Vík. He had sworn this oath, not to have his hair cut or combed till he should be sole king over Norway (he was nicknamed

Harald Shock-head.)[1] He next made war on those kings who lived nearest to hand and subdued them, and there are long stories about this. Later he won possession of the Uplands; and from there proceeded north into Thrándheim, and had many a battle there before becoming sole master of the entire Thrándlaw.

Next he decided to proceed north into Naumudal against the brothers Herlaug and Hrollaug, who at this time were kings over Naumudal. When the brothers heard tell of his coming, Herlaug went with eleven men into the funeral mound which they had been three years a-building. The mound was then closed upon them. But King Hrollaug tumbled himself out of the kingdom and took the rank of an earl, and afterwards submitted to King Harald and surrendered his realm. In this way King Harald won possession of the Naumdœla-fylki and Hálogaland, and set men there in charge of his kingdom.

Next King Harald made ready out of Thrándheim with a fleet, and went south to Mœr and fought there against King Húnthjóf, and won the victory. Húnthjóf fell there, whereupon King Harald won possession of Nordmœr and Raumsdal. But Húnthjóf's son Sölvi Klofi had escaped, and made his way to Sunnmœr to King Arnvid to ask him for help, saying thus: "Though this trouble has for the present overtaken us, it will not be long before the selfsame trouble comes home to you, for I believe King Harald will march this way the minute he has enslaved and subjugated to his heart's content everybody in Nordmœr and Raumsdal. You will have the same hard choice as we had, to defend your wealth and freedom and throw into the struggle every man whose help you can hope for. It is against this tyranny and injustice that I offer myself and my following. But by way of alternative you must be prepared to swallow such counsel as the Naumdalers did, entering into servitude of your own free will and becoming Harald's thralls. To my father it seemed glory to die a king in honor, rather than become another king's underling in his old age. I think it will look that way to you too and those others who show a high port and would be gallant fellows."

By such persuasion as this the king's resolve was hardened to collect an army and defend his land. He and Sölvi now leagued themselves together and sent word to King Audbjörn, who ruled over Firthafylki, that he should come and help them. And when the ambassadors

reached King Audbjörn and brought him this message, he talked it
over with his friends, and everyone advised him to collect an army
and go join with Mœr, even as he was sent word. King Audbjörn had
the war-arrow dispatched and sent a summons to war the length and
breadth of his kingdom. He sent messengers to the great lords to
summon them before him; but when the king's messengers reached
Kveldúlf and told him their errand, how the king wanted Kveldúlf
to appear before him with all his housecarles, he made this answer: "The king will consider it my bounden duty that I should
march out with him if he must defend his land and is harried in
Firthafylki, but I cannot think it any part of my bond to proceed north
into Mœr and fight there to defend their lands. To cut a long story
short then: when you meet your king you can tell him that Kveldúlf will remain at home through all this rush to arms, that he will
not collect an army, and will not sally out from home to fight against
Harald Shock-head; for I think that he has an ample load of luck,
while our king has not a fistful."

The messengers returned to the king and told him the result of
their mission. But Kveldulf stayed where he was, in his own home.

4

King Audbjörn proceeded north to Mœr with that army which was
in his service, and there met with King Arnvid and Sölvi Klofi, and
all in all they had a big force of men. King Harald too had moved out of
the north with his army, and their encounter took place on the inner side
of Sólskel. There was a big battle there and a great slaughter in either
host. In Harald's host there fell two earls, Ásgaut and Ásbjörn, and two
sons of Earl Hákon of Hladir, Grjótgard and Herlaug, and a number of
other leading men; and in the host of Mœr King Arnvid and King
Audbjörn. But Sölvi Klofi made his escape by flight, to become in
course of time a noted viking; and such great and frequent hurt did
he inflict on King Harald's kingdom that he gained the nickname
Sölvi Cleaver.

After this King Harald subdued Sunnmœr. Now Vémund, the
brother of King Audbjörn, still held Firthafylki and made himself its

king. This was late in the autumn, and King Harald was advised not to proceed south about Stad during the autumn, so he now set Earl Rögnvald over the two Mœrs and Raumsdal, and turned back north to Thrándheim, keeping a strong body of men about him.

This same autumn the sons of Atli attacked Ölvir Hnúfa at his home, and planned to kill him. They had so strong a force that Ölvir could offer no real defense and made his escape by flight. He then went north to Mœr where he fell in with King Harald and became his man. He accompanied the king north to Thrándheim during the autumn and came into the greatest favor with the king and remained with him for a long time afterwards and became his poet.

This same winter Earl Rögnvald took the inner road across Eidsjó south to the Firths; he had King Vémund's movements spied upon, and arrived by night at the place called Naustdal, where Vémund was feasting. Earl Rögnvald seized their house and burned the king indoors with ninety men. After that Berdla-Kári came to Earl Rögnvald with a fully-manned longship, and the two of them headed north for Mœr. Rögnvald seized whatever ships King Vémund had possessed, and all the movable goods he could lay hands on. Berdla-Kári then went north to Thrándheim to meet King Harald and became his man.

The following spring King Harald proceeded south along the land with a fleet and subdued the Firths and Fjalir, setting his own men in command there. He set Earl Hróald over Firthafylki.

Once he had established possession of these territories which were newly come into his power, King Harald paid close attention to the landed men and leading farmers, and all those from whom he suspected some rebellion might be looked for. He made everybody do one thing or the other: either become his retainers or quit the country, or, for a third choice, suffer hardship or forfeit their lives; while some were maimed hand or foot. King Harald seized possession in every district of all odal rights[1] and the whole land, settled and unsettled, and equally the sea and the waters, and all husbandmen should become his tenants, and those too who worked in the forests, and salt-men, and all hunters by sea and land—all these were now made subject to him. But many a man fled the land from this servitude, and it was now that many desert places were settled far and wide, both east in Jamtaland and Helsingjaland and in the Western lands, the Hebrides

and Dublin district, Ireland, and Normandy in France, Caithness in
Scotland, the Orkneys and Shetland, and the Faeroes. And it was now
that Iceland was discovered.[2]

5

King Harald encamped with his army in the Firths. He sent messengers round the land there to find those men who had not appeared
before him, and with whom it seemed to him he had business. The
king's messengers visited Kveldúlf and received a good welcome at
his hands. They delivered their message, declaring that the king
wanted Kveldúlf to appear before him.

"He has heard tell," they informed him, "how you are a notable
man and come of a good family. You will have the chance of great
honors at his hand. The king is anxious to have on his side all who he
hears are outstanding for strength and daring."

Kveldúlf answered by saying he was now old, so that he was unfit
to be at sea in warships. "For the time being I will stay at home and
leave off serving kings."

"Then let your son go to the king," urged the messengers. "He is a
big, gallant fellow. The king will make you a landed man, Grím, if
you are willing to serve him."

"I will not be made a landed man in my father's lifetime," said
Grím, "for he shall be my master so long as he lives."

The messengers left, and when they reached the king they told him
everything Kveldúlf had delivered himself of to them. The king took
offense at this, and had something to say of it, reckoning these must
be men of high stomach, and what could they be thinking of?

Ölvir Hnúfa was standing nearby and asked the king not to be
angry. "I will go and see Kveldúlf myself. He will be willing to appear before you once he knows you consider it important."

Later Ölvir went to see Kveldúlf and told him how the king was
angry, and that nothing would do but that one or other of them,
father or son, should go to see him; he said that they would get great
honor from the king if they were prepared to serve him, telling them at
length (as was true enough) that the king treated his retainers well,
with wealth and honor alike.

Kveldúlf said it was his foreboding, "That we father and sons will have no luck with this king, and I am not going to see him. But if Thórólf returns home this summer he will be easily won into going, and so become the king's retainer. Tell the king this: that I will be his friend, and that I will keep on friendly terms with him all who obey my word. Also I will hold the same in rule and stewardship at his hand as I have already held of a former king, if the king would have it so. And later on we shall see how the king and I get along together."

Later Ölvir returned to the king and told him that Kveldúlf would send him one of his sons, adding that he was the fitter of the two for this who just then happened not to be at home. The king let it rest there. That summer he proceeded into Sogn, but as autumn drew on prepared to go north to Thrándheim.

6

Thórólf Kveldúlfsson and Eyvind Lambi returned home from their viking cruise in the autumn, and Thórólf went to his father's. Father and son fell to talking together, and Thórólf asked what was the business of those men Harald had sent to them. Kveldúlf said that the king had sent instructions that Kveldúlf or one or other of his sons should become his retainer.

"How did you answer?" Thórólf asked him.

"I said what I thought, that I would never pay homage to King Harald. And so would you two do, had I my way. I believe it will be found that the king will prove fatal to us in the long run."

"Then it will turn out very different from what I expect," replied Thórólf. "For I believe it my destiny to win the greatest advancement from him. I have fully made up my mind to appear before him and become his man. I have learned for certain that his bodyguard is manned with the best men only. It seems to me a most desirable thing to enter their ranks, if they will have me. They stand in better state, those men, than anyone else in Norway. The report I hear of the king is that he is generous with gifts of money to his followers, and no less swift to advance them and give command to those he thinks fit for it. But what I am told about all those who want to cold-shoulder him and not give him friendly service is that they all become nobodies, some of them forced to flee the country and some becoming his renters. I find it strange, Father, in a man as shrewd and ambitious as you, that you would not accept with gratitude that handsome offer the king made you. But if you thought yourself a prophet in this, how misfortune must come upon us from the king, and he will choose to be our enemy, then why did you not march to battle against him with the king whose liegeman you already were? For it seems to me quite shameful, to be neither friend of his nor foe."

"It turned out," said Kveldúlf, "just as I expected, that they would go no conquering road who fought with Harald Shock-head north in Mœr. In just the same way it will be found true that Harald will prove a great affliction to my family. Still, Thórólf, you will want to rule your own affairs. I am not afraid, though you are enrolled among Harald's bodyguard, that you will not prove up to the mark and a match for the best of them in every trial. But take care not to go beyond your measure or fight with men stronger than yourself. Not that you are the man readily to back down before anyone!"

And when Thórólf made ready to leave, Kveldúlf led him down to his ship, and embraced him, and wished him good luck, praying that they might meet again safe and sound.

7

There was a man living in Hálogaland by the name of Björgólf. His home was at Torgar. He was a landed man, powerful and rich, and half a mountain-giant in strength, size, and ancestry too. He had a son called Brynjólf, who was the same kind of man as his father. By now Björgólf was an old man, and his wife dead, so he had handed over all his affairs to his son, and found him a wife too—he was married to Helga, Ketil Hœng's daughter from Hrafnista. They had a son named Bárd who from his earliest days was tall and handsome, and grew into a man of parts. It happened one autumn that a crowded banquet was held there, and these two, Björgólf and his son, were the most notable men at the feast. As was customary, lots were cast for drinking-partners over the evening. Also attending this banquet was a man named Högni, who had a home in Leka. He was very rich and personable, a wise man of modest birth who had done very well for himself. He had an extremely good-looking daughter whose name was Hildiríd. It fell to her lot to sit by Björgólf; they were talking together a good deal that evening, and the girl's beauty impressed him deeply. A little later the banquet came to an end, but that same autumn old Björgólf set off from home, taking a skúta¹ which he owned and thirty men aboard her. His journey took him to Leka, where twenty of them went up to the house and ten kept an eye on the ship. As they reached the farm Högni came out to meet him and gave him a good welcome, inviting him to stay there with his followers. He accepted, and they went inside the living-room. Once they had removed their outdoor clothes and put on their over-mantles, Högni had a tub full of beer carried in, from which Hildiríd, the farmer's daughter, served ale to the guests.

Björgólf called farmer Högni to him. "My business here," he said, "is that I want your daughter to come back home with me. So I will improvise a wedding for her here and now."

Högni saw no other choice before him but to let everything go as Björgólf would have it. Björgólf bought her with an ounce of gold, and they went into the one bed together. Hildiríd accompanied Björgólf home to Torgar, where Brynjólf took a poor view of the whole transaction. Björgólf and Hildiríd had two sons, one named Hárek, and the other Hrœrek. In time Björgólf died, and as soon as he was carried from the house Brynjólf forced Hildiríd to go away with her sons. So she went to Leka to her father's, and that is where Hildiríd's sons were brought up. They were good-looking men, small of stature and blest with plenty of sense, just like their mother's people. They were known as Hildiríd's sons, after their mother. Brynjólf had little use for them and allowed them no share in their father's estate; but Hildiríd was sole heiress to Högni, and she and her sons took the inheritance after him, and from then on lived in Leka and had abundance of riches. They were much of an age, Bárd Brynjólfsson and the sons of Hildiríd. That father and son, Björgólf and Brynjólf, had long been entrusted with the Lappland-journey and with collecting the Lapp-tribute.

North in Hálogaland there is a fjord called Vefsnir. A fine big
island lies in the fjord there, called Álöst. On it stands a farm called
Sandnes, where lived a man by the name of Sigurd. He was the rich-
est person there in the North, a landed man of great wisdom and foresight. His daughter, whose name was Sigríd, was reckoned to be the
best match in Hálogaland. She was his only child and stood to inherit
after Sigurd her father.

Bárd Brynjólfsson made a journey from home; he had a skúta with
thirty men aboard her, and traveled north to Álöst, and so to Sigurd
at Sandnes. Bárd set out his business and asked for Sigríd in marriage; his suit had a good and promising answer, and it ended with
the girl becoming betrothed to him. The wedding should take place
the following summer, when Bárd was to come up north for it.

8

That summer King Harald had sent messages to the great men who
were living in Hálogaland, summoning before him any who had not
already been to see him. Brynjólf decided to make the journey, and
his son Bárd with him. They journeyed south to Thrándheim that
same autumn and met the king there. He gave them a most gracious
welcome. Brynjólf now became the king's landed man, the king providing him with large revenues in addition to those he had owned
before. He confirmed him too in the Lappland-journey, the king's
stewardship on the mountains, and the Lapp-trade. Later Brynjólf departed for home, but Bárd stayed on and became a member of the
king's bodyguard.

Of all his retinue the king honored his poets most. Their place was
the second high-seat. Innermost of them sat Audun Ill-skald, who was
the oldest of them and had been poet to Hálfdan the Black, King
Harald's father. Next sat Thorbjörn Hornklofi, and next came Ölvir
Hnúfa, and the place next to him was filled by Bárd. He was called
Bárd the White there, or Bárd the Strong, and he was held in high
regard by them all. Between him and Ölvir Hnúfa there was close
comradeship.

That same autumn Thórólf Kveldúlfsson and Eyvind Lambi, Berdla-

Kári's son, came to King Harald and got a good welcome. With them they brought a well-manned twenty-oared snekkja¹ which they had owned earlier when out on viking cruises. Room was found for them in the guest-hall together with their company. When they had waited till they judged it time to go and see the king, Berdla-Kári and Ölvir Hnúfa went along with them. They greeted the king, and then Ölvir Hnúfa announced that Kveldúlf's son had come there, "Whom I told you in the summer Kveldúlf would send to you. Every one of his promises to you will be kept in full. You can now see sure signs that he wants to be wholeheartedly your friend, in that he has sent his son here into your service, and such a fine man as you can see for yourself. It is the petition of Kveldúlf and of us all that you receive Thórólf with honor and make him a great man with you."

The king answered his plea graciously, promising that he would do so—"if Thórólf proves himself as good a man to me as in looks he is every inch the soldier."

After this Thórólf became the king's own man and entered the community of his bodyguard, whereas Berdla-Kári and Eyvind Lambi his son traveled south with the ship which Thórólf fetched north. Kári returned home so, and Eyvind along with him, but Thórólf remained with the king, who directed him to sit between Ölvir Hnúfa and Bárd, and the greatest friendship developed between them all. It was the general opinion of Thórólf and Bárd that they were equal for good looks and stature, and in strength and all feats of skill. Thórólf remained there now in high favor with the king, and Bárd along with him.

But when winter passed away and summer had come Bárd asked leave of the king to go and attend to this wedding which had been promised him last summer. And when the king knew that Bárd had business so urgent he gave him leave to go home. Once he had won leave, he asked Thórólf to go up north with him, telling him—as was true—that he would be able to meet many noble kinsmen of his there whom he would not have seen or been acquainted with before. Thórólf found this after his own heart, so they obtained the king's leave, put themselves in readiness thereafter with a good ship and ship's company, and made off as soon as they were set. As soon as they reached Torgar they sent messengers to Sigurd to have him informed

how Bárd was now desirous of proceeding with the marriage they
had contracted between them last summer. Sigurd said he wished to
stand by everything they had then discussed; they reached a decision
about the marriage-gathering, and Bárd and his people were to come
north there to Sandnes. And when the day arrived, Brynjólf and
Bárd set off, taking a lot of great men with them, kinsmen of theirs
and relations by marriage. It happened as Bárd had said, that Thórólf met a number of his relations there with whom he had no acquaintance before. They kept on until they reached Sandnes, where
there was a magnificent feast, and once the feast came to an end
Bárd returned home with his wife, to remain there for the summer,
and Thórólf with him. But in the autumn they traveled south to the
king and stayed with him a second winter.

That winter Brynjólf died. So when Bárd heard how the inheritance there had fallen vacant for him, he asked leave to go home, and
the king granted it. But before they parted Bárd became a landed
man, such as his father had been, and held at the king's hand all such
revenues as Brynjólf had held. Bárd returned home and soon became
a great chieftain, though the sons of Hildiríd got no more of the
inheritance now than before. Bárd had a son by his wife who was
named Grím. Thórólf, however, remained with the king and was
held in high esteem there.

9

King Harald called out a great levy and mustered a fleet, and gathering to himself a force from wide throughout the land, he left Thrándheim and sailed to the south country. He had learnt how a great host
had been drawn together all over Agdir and Rogaland and Hördaland, assembled from far and wide, both down from the country and
from Vík in the east, and how a lot of great men had come together
there, intending to defend the land against King Harald. King Harald held from the north with his own forces. Himself he had a big
ship manned by his bodyguard. In the stem were Thórólf Kveldúlfsson and Bárd the White, together with the sons of Berdla-Kári,
Ölvir Hnúfa and Eyvind Lambi; but in the bows were the king's

twelve berserks. Their encounter took place south in Rogaland, at Hafrsfjörd. This was the biggest battle King Harald had ever taken part in, and there was a great slaughter in each host. The king laid his ship in the van, and it was there that the fighting was hardest; but the end of it was that King Harald won the victory and King Thórir Haklang from Agdir fell, while Kjötvi the Rich took to flight, with all of his host who could stand, save those who submitted after the battle.

When the roll-call was taken of King Harald's host, many had fallen and many were badly wounded. Thórólf was wounded badly, and Bárd still worse, and no one was without wounds on the king's ship forward of the sail, except those whom iron would not bite on (those were all berserks). Then the king had his men's wounds bound up; he thanked men for their valor, and gave out gifts, bestowing most praise where it seemed to him most deserved; he promised them to increase their honors, naming to this end his ships' captains, and next to them his stemkeepers and other forecastlemen. This was the last battle King Harald had in Norway. From now on he found none to stand against him, and seized possession thereafter of the whole country.

Those of his men whose luck it was to live the king had tended, and to the dead he paid such rites as were then the custom.

Both Thórólf and Bárd were laid up with their wounds. Thórólf's wounds began to heal, but Bárd's came to look mortal. Then he had the king called to him and said these words to him: "Should it happen that I die of these wounds, then I would ask this of you, that you let me have the disposal of my inheritance." And when the king had agreed to this, he went on: "I want my friend and kinsman Thórólf to take all my inheritance, my land and my movables too. And I want to give him my wife, and my son to bring up, for I believe him the very best of men for this purpose."

He confirmed this bequest, as the law then stood, by permission of the king. Later Bárd died, his rites were paid him, and his death was much lamented. But Thórólf recovered from his wounds and served with the king that summer, having won outstanding fame.

In the autumn the king proceeded north to Thrándheim. Then Thórólf asked leave to travel north to Hálogaland to see those bequests realized which he had received during the summer from his kinsman Bárd. The king gave him leave for this, providing him with messengers and tokens so that Thórólf might take over everything Bárd had bestowed on him, and proclaiming too that this bequest had been made with the king's approval, and that he would have it so. The king next made Thórólf a landed man and presented him with all the revenues which Bárd had held before, and granted him the Lappland-journey on just such terms as Bárd had held it earlier. The king gave Thórólf a fine longship with all her gear, and helped further his journey from there as well as he knew how. Afterwards Thórólf set off on his journey, and the king and he parted the best of friends.

When Thórólf arrived north in Torgar there was a glad welcome for him. He gave them the news of Bárd's death, and this besides, how Bárd had bestowed lands and movables on him in succession to himself, as well as the wife he had had before. He then showed them the king's message and tokens. When Sigríd heard this news she felt she had suffered a great loss in her husband; but Thórólf was already well-known to her, she realized that he was a man of the first distinction, and the proposed match a rare one. So, since it was the king's command, she saw fit, and her friends with her, to pledge herself to Thórólf, if this was not against her father's will. With that Thórólf took into his hands the whole management there, and the king's stewardship as well.

Thórólf next prepared for a journey from home; he had a longship with almost sixty men aboard her; and, as soon as he was ready, stood north along the land. One day he made Álöst at Sandnes in the evening, and put his ship into harbor. When they had rigged awnings and put all to rights Thórólf walked up to the house with twenty men. Sigurd gave him a warm welcome and invited him to stay there, for they were well-known to each other already, ever since the time Sigurd and Bárd had become relatives by marriage. Thórólf and his men entered the hall and were entertained there. Sigurd sat down to talk with Thórólf and asked him the news. Thórólf told of the battle which had taken place that summer in the south country, and of the fall of many a man whom Sigurd had known well. Thórólf added that Bárd his son-in-law had died of the wounds he received in bat-

tle—which both of them thought the most grievous loss. Then Thórólf told Sigurd how much of a private agreement there had been
between him and Bárd before he died, and so advanced the king's
directive, how he wanted this to hold good, and he displayed the
tokens too. Next Thórólf opened his marriage-proposal to Sigurd,
asking for the hand of Sigríd his daughter. Sigurd welcomed this
proposal, declaring that many things favored it: first, that the king
would have it so, and also that Bárd had urged it, and further, that
Thórólf was known to him, and he felt that his daughter was being
given into good hands. This was an easy suit to plead with Sigurd.
The betrothal took place, and the wedding was fixed for Torgar in
the autumn.

Thórólf and his comrades then returned home and prepared a great
feast there and invited a large crowd of men to it. A lot of Thórólf's
noble kinsfolk were present. Sigurd too made ready from the north,
and had a big longship and a choice body of men. There was a considerable gathering at that feast. It was quickly apparent that Thórólf
was a free-handed man and one to be reckoned with. He kept a big
body of men about him, and soon this grew very costly and made great
demand on his supplies. But it was a good year, that, and it was not
difficult to procure what was needed.

That same winter Sigurd died at Sandnes and Thórólf took the
entire inheritance after him, which was very great wealth indeed.
The sons of Hildiríd went to see Thórólf and raised that claim they
considered they had to the property their father Björgólf had owned.

Thórólf made this answer: "I knew enough of Brynjólf, and still
more of Bárd, that they were men sufficiently generous to have shared
with you as much of Björgólf's inheritance as they knew to be right
and proper. I was standing nearby when you raised this same demand
with Bárd, and it sounded to me as though he saw no justice in it,
for he called you base-gotten."

Hárek said they were prepared to bring witness that their mother
was bought with dower. "Yet it was true that at first we did not press
this question with our brother Brynjólf. Besides, that was a case of
sharing with one's own near kin. From Bárd, though, we looked for
a full restitution; even so, our dealings were not of long duration. But
now the inheritance has fallen to men unrelated to us, and we cannot

lie entirely supine under our loss. But maybe this time again there
will be the same disparity of strength as before, so that we are to get
no fair play from you in the matter, if you are not even willing to hear
what witness we have to bring forward that we are odal-born men."

"I am the less inclined to believe you born to inherit," Thórólf
answered curtly, "in that I am told how the mother of the pair of you
was carried off by force and brought home a captive."

And with that they broke off this discussion.

IO

During the winter Thórólf made his journey up into the mountains,
taking with him a biggish troop of not less than ninety men. Earlier
it had been the practice of the stewards to take thirty men, and sometimes even fewer. He also took a lot of merchandise with him. Soon
he had arranged a meeting with the Lapps, collected tribute from
them, and held a market with them. All went off softly and friendly
between them, though the Lapps were not without some misgivings.

Thórólf traveled widely throughout the Mark. When he pressed
east towards the mountains he learned how the Kylfings had moved
in from the east and were traveling there on the Lapp-trade, and in
some places robbing. Thórólf set the Lapps to spy out the Kylfings'
movements, while he himself came following on behind to attack
them. He came across thirty men in a single lair and killed them all,
so that not one got away, and later he came across fifteen or twenty
together. In all they killed almost a hundred men, seizing countless
wealth there, and with so much for their trouble made their way back
in the spring. Thórólf now returned to Sandnes and stayed there
a long while. In the spring he had a big longship built, with a dragon
head, fitted her out with the best, and took her with him down from
the north.

Thórólf swept in much of the catch that was then in Hálogaland.
He had his men on the herring banks and for the cod-fishing also.
There was plenty of sealing too, and egg-collecting: all these things
he had brought home to him. He never had fewer than a hundred
freemen at home. He was an open-handed and generous man, quick

to make friends with all men of distinction who were living near him. He became a lordly man and paid great attention to the quality and appearance of his ships and weapons.

I I

That summer King Harald made a progress into Hálogaland, and feasts were arranged in readiness for him, not only where his own houses happened to be, but the landed men and leading farmers did as much too. Thórólf arranged a feast in readiness for the king, sparing no expense over it, and it was all arranged as to when the king should arrive. Thórólf invited a multitude of guests and had the best possible pick of men present. The king had almost three hundred men when he came to the feast, but Thórólf had five hundred. He had a big granary which stood there put in readiness, furnishing it with benches and holding the drinking there, because there was not one room in the house so big that the whole assembly could be fitted inside. There were shields too fastened all round the inner walls of the building.

The king sat in the high-seat. But when all were in their places, both near to him and further away, the king looked round him and reddened, without saying a word, and men could tell that he was angry. The feast was a splendid one, and everything provided was of the best. The king was rather sulky, but stayed there the three nights that had been arranged. The day the king was to depart Thórólf went before him to ask that they should walk down to the shore. The king did so. There, floating offshore, lay the dragon-ship which Thórólf had had built, with her awnings and full gear. Thórólf presented the ship to the king, asking him to believe—as was indeed his reason—that he had so great a body of men present only that it might be an honor to the king, and not for emulation's sake against him. The king welcomed Thórólf's words, and grew friendly now and cheerful. Many added tactful words, saying, as was simple truth, that the entertainment was most honorable and the parting gift the finest conceivable, and that such men were a great asset to the king. So they parted after all on very good terms.

The king proceeded north into Hálogaland as he had planned, but made back south in the course of the summer, still attending feasts wherever they had been arranged for him.

12

Hildiríd's sons went to meet the king and invited him home to a three nights' entertainment. The king accepted their offer, stipulating when he would come along. When the day came the king arrived together with his retinue; there were not many there to meet him, yet the feast went off as well as could be: the king was in the best of spirits. Hárek struck into talk with the king, and the burden of his talk was this, that he made inquiry about those of the king's journeys which had taken place that summer. The king had an answer for everything he inquired after, reckoning that everyone had made him most welcome, and each pretty much according to his means.

"What a big difference there must have been then," said Hárek. "And the most crowded feast of all would be the one at Torgar?"

The king said that was so.

"Still, that was only to be expected," Hárek went on, "for the most formidable preparations were made for that feast, and the vastest good luck came your way, King, when it so turned out that you did not run into peril of your life. It happened, as was only to be expected, that you were most wise and fortunate in that you had misgivings that all was not well the minute you saw that great body of men which had been assembled there. Now I was told that you kept your whole retinue constantly under arms, or had trusty watch maintained both day and night."

The king gave him a stare. "Why should you be saying such things, Hárek?" he asked. "And what have you to tell me about all this?"

"King," he replied," have I leave to speak what I please?"

"Speak you," said the king.

"Then I believe, King," said Hárek, "if you heard what everyone is saying when men speak their innermost thoughts at home, about what servitude you seem to lay on everybody, it would not seem well to you. For to tell you the truth, King, the common people lack nothing to rise against you except courage and a leader. And it is not surprising," he continued, "in such a man as Thórólf, that he considers himself superior to all. He lacks neither strength nor fine presence; he has his bodyguard about him too, just like a king; and has a mort of money, even if he had only what he is entitled to; but what is more, he makes as free with other people's property as his own, while you too have granted him huge revenues. And now everything was set that he should make you no wholesome return for it; for to tell you the truth, once it was known that you were making your way north into Hálogaland with no bigger following than those three hundred men you had, then it was their plan here to assemble an army and kill you, King, with all your following; and Thórólf was leader in these plans, because he had been invited to become king over Háleygafylki and Naumdœlafylki. So in and out he went of every fjord, and round all the islands, drawing together every man and weapon he could get, and it was no secret that that army should be directed against King Harald in battle. But it is true, King, that though you had rather the lesser force when you met them, yet terror touched the hearts of those bumpkins once they saw your sailing. So then a new plan was adopted, to go and meet you in a friendly way and invite you to a feast, though it was the intention, if you grew drunk and lay sleeping, to make an attack upon you with fire and sword; and if I heard rightly, this by way of proof, that you were conducted into a granary, because Thórólf had no wish to burn down his own living-quarters, all new and richly furnished as they were. And this again was the proof, that every building was crammed with weapons and armor. Then, when they could get nowhere with their wicked plots against you, they fell back on what now seemed their best resource—to cut adrift these machinations. I reckon they all have wit enough to keep these devices hidden, because few of them, I fancy, know themselves clear of blame should the truth come to light. Now it is my advice, King, that you take Thórólf in hand, and let him serve in your bodyguard, and carry your standard, and be in your ship's stem. For this he is the best fitted of any man alive. But if it is your wish that he stay a landed man, then provide him with revenues south in the Firths, where all his family is to be found. You can then see to it that he does not puff himself up too big. But hand over the stewardship here in Hálogaland to men who are not over-ambitious, but will serve you faithfully—men who have their family-roots here, and whose kinsmen have discharged just such duties here before. My brother and I will hold ourselves ready and willing for anything you care to use us for. Our father held the king's stewardship here for a long time, and it prospered in his hands. It will be a problem for you, King, putting men in charge here, for you will come visiting but seldom in these parts yourself. There is small scope in the land here for you to move about with your retinue, and it will never happen again that you will be traveling this way with a small following, because there are so many here not to be trusted."

The king grew very angry at these reports, yet spoke softly, as he would always do when he heard news which was of great moment. He then inquired whether Thórólf was at home in Torgar. Hárek said there was no possibility of this. "Thórólf is clever enough to know better than to stand exposed to your royal power, King: for he could expect that they would not all be so close of speech, King, that you would not grow acquainted with this news. He went north to Álöst the moment he heard you were on your way from the north."

The king made little comment on these matters in anyone's hearing, but it was obvious he would put firm trust in these stories which were told him. Later the king continued on his way. The sons of Hildiríd saw him off honorably with gifts, and he promised them his friendship. The brothers invented business for themselves in Naumudal and made such a circuit round the king that they fell in with him every now and again, and he had a ready ear for their talk at all times.

13

There was a man named Yelling-Thorgils, a retainer of Thórólf's, whom he held in highest regard of all his housecarles. He had served with Thórólf when he was out viking, and in those days was his forecastle-man and standard-bearer. Thorgils had been at Hafrsfjörd in King Harald's host, where he was master of Thórólf's ship, the same one he used when viking. Thorgils was a man of great bodily strength and very daring. After the battle the king had presented him with friendly gifts and promised him his favor. Thorgils was manager of the house at Torgar whenever Thórólf was not at home; at all such times he took charge there.

Now when Thórólf left home for Álöst, he had sorted out all the Lapp-tribute which he had brought off the mountains and which belonged to the king, putting it in Thorgils's charge and instructing him to convey it to the king, should he himself not arrive home before the king left the north for the south. Thorgils made ready a fine big ship of lading belonging to Thórólf, carried the tribute on board, and had almost a score of men with him. He sailed south in the king's wake and caught up with him in Naumudal. When Thorgils had audience of the king he gave him Thórólf's greetings and explained that his mission there was with the Lapp-tribute which Thórólf was sending him. The king glowered at him without making any reply, and it was obvious that he was very angry. So Thorgils went away for the time being, hoping to find a more auspicious day to talk with him. He came to see Ölvir Hnúfa and told him everything that had happened, then asked whether he had any idea what was the matter.

"That I don't know," Ölvir replied. "On the other hand I have noticed this, that the king falls silent whenever Thórólf is mentioned, ever since we were in Leka; and from that I suspect he is being slandered. I know this much of the sons of Hildiríd, that they are continually in private session with the king, and it is easy to discover from their words that they are no friends of Thórólf's. However, I shall soon know the truth of it from the king himself."

Later Ölvir walked in before the king, saying: "Your friend Yelling-Thorgils has arrived with the tribute which comes out of Finnmark and is your property; and the tribute is far bigger than it has ever been before, and the wares much better. He is greatly concerned as to his return. Be so good, king, as to come and see for yourself, for no one can ever have set eyes on gray wares[1] of such high quality."

The king made no reply but went all the same to where the ship was lying. Thorgils at once brought out his wares and displayed them to the king. And when the king saw it was true that the tribute was

much bigger and better than it had ever been before, his brow light-
ened a little, and Thorgils could now have a word or two with him. He
presented to the king some beaver skins which Thórólf had sent him,
and other valuables besides which he had obtained in the mountains.
At this the king brightened and asked what was the news about his
and Thórólf's travels, whereupon Thorgils gave him an exact account of it all.

"It is a great pity," said the king then, "that Thórólf will not be
true to me or should want to kill me."

At this many who were nearby made answer, and all the one way,
maintaining it would be the slander of base fellows if such had been
reported to the king, and that Thórólf would be found completely
innocent. So now it came about that the king confessed he would
rather like to believe them. He was now affable in all his talk with
Thorgils, and they parted on excellent terms.

But when Thorgils met Thórólf he told him the whole story of
what had happened.

14

That winter Thórólf proceeded once more to the Mark, taking close
on a hundred men with him. This time again he proceeded as the
winter before, holding a market for the Lapps and traveling wide
throughout the Mark. But when he pressed far east and his movements were heard tell of there, Kvens came to him, saying they had
been sent to find him, and that Faravid king of Kvenland had done
this. They said that the Kirjáls were raiding in his land, and that he
sent a request that Thórólf should come to his aid. This message
followed: that Thórólf should have equal shares with the king, and
each of his men even as three Kvens. Now it was the law among the
Kvens that their king should take a one-third share as compared with
his following, and, over and above that, all beaver skins and sables
and martens as his special lot. Thórólf put this to his followers, and
gave them the choice whether they should go or not. The majority
chose to risk it, since so great a booty lay at stake, and it was decided
that they would travel east with the messengers.

Finnmark[1] is extremely broad. To the west lies the sea, and from the sea there extend great firths, and likewise to the north and the whole way east; but southwards lies Norway, and the Mark fills nearly the whole interior to the south, even as Hálogaland the coast-line. Eastward from Naumudal lies Jamtaland, and then Helsing-jaland and then Kvenland, then Finnland, then Kirjálaland. But Finnmark stretches north over all these territories, and up in the Mark there are fell-settlements far and wide, some in the valleys and some alongside the lakes. In Finnmark are to be found extremely big lakes, and alongside these lakes big forests, but high mountains extend the whole length of the Mark, which are called Kilir, the Keels.

Once Thórólf arrived east in Kvenland and met with King Faravid, they made ready for their march and had three hundred men, with the Norwegians making a fourth. They took the upper road through Finnmark and on the mountains came upon these same Kirjáls who had earlier been raiding the Kvens. As soon as these learned of their enemy they mustered their forces and marched against them; this time again they expected victory as before. But when battle was joined the Norwegians went forward strongly. Further, they had tougher shields than the Kvens. Then it turned to a slaughter in the Kirjáls' army; many fell and some took to flight. King Faravid and Thórólf won wealth past counting there and returned to Kvenland, but later Thórólf and his following set off to the Mark. King Faravid and he parted in friendship.

Thórólf came down off the mountains into Vefsnir, and in the first place went home to Sandnes, to stay there a while; but in the spring he and his following left the north for Torgar. When he arrived there he was told how Hildiríd's sons had spent the winter in Thránd-heim with King Harald, and, what was more, that they would not give over slandering Thórólf to the king.

Thórólf was closely informed as to the substance of their slander, and this was his answer: "The king will not believe it, even though such lies are uttered before him, for there is no substance in the charge that I want to betray him; for he has done handsomely by me in a great many things, and never a grain of ill. Why, far from wanting to do him an injury, even if I had the chance, I would much rather be his landed man than be called king, while there lived that fellow-countryman of mine who if he chose could make me his slave."

15

Hildiríd's sons had spent that winter with King Harald, together with various retainers and neighbors of theirs. The brothers were often talking with the king and had always the same tale to tell of Thórólf.

"Were you well pleased, King," asked Hárek, "with the Lapp-tribute which Thórólf sent you?"

"Very well indeed," said the king.

"Then you would have been delighted," said Hárek, "had you received the whole of what belonged to you, which was far from being the case. That other portion which Thórólf kept back for himself was far and away the bigger. He sent you three beaver skins as a gift, yes, but I know for certain that he held back thirty of them rightly belonging to you, and I understand it was the same story with everything else too. It is simple truth, King, that if you hand over the stewardship to us brothers we will bring you greater wealth."

Anything they said against Thórólf, their companions testified to it with them, and as a result the king was as angry as could be.

16

In the summer Thórólf traveled south to Thrándheim to see King Harald, taking with him the whole of the tribute and much wealth besides, as well as ninety men who were all well accoutered. When he came to the king, room was made for them in the guesthall and they were entertained admirably. Later in the day Ölvir Hnúfa went to see Thórólf his kinsman, and they talked things over. Ölvir reported that Thórólf had been gravely slandered and that the king was lending his ear to such tales.

Thórólf asked Ölvir to state a case for him to the king. "For I shall be blunt with him," he said, "if he will sooner believe these slandering blackguards than the truth and loyalty he can prove on me."

The next day Ölvir came to see Thórólf and told him he had discussed his case with the king. "But I have no more idea now than before," he said, "what he has in mind."

"Then I must approach him myself," said Thórólf.

He did so. He appeared before the king as he sat at table, and greeted him the moment he came inside. The king acknowledged his greeting and said to serve Thórólf drink. Thórólf said he had the tribute there which belonged to the king and was come from Finnmark. "And I have still further things as remembrancers, King, which I must transfer to you. For I know that what I have done by way of pleasing you is more to my credit than all else I have done."

The king replied that he had nothing but good to expect from Thórólf. "For indeed," he added, "I deserve nothing else. Yet on the whole men are speaking two ways about how far you are concerned to please me."

"I am not honestly reported," countered Thórólf, "if any say that I have shown bad faith to you, King. I believe those who have run to you with tales of that sort will prove less your friends than I. And another thing is only too clear, that they want to be fixed enemies of mine. Well, it is likely they will get more than they bargain for if we come to fight it out between us."

With that Thórólf took himself off, but the following day he paid over the tribute while the king was standing by. When the whole of it had been paid over Thórólf brought out some beaver skins and sables, saying he wished to present them to the king. Many of the bystanders said that was handsomely done and deserving of friendship, whereat the king retorted that in this transaction Thórólf had already cut himself his own award.

Thórólf answered that he had done all he knew to please the king, and in good faith too. "However, if he is dissatisfied, there is nothing I can do about it. All the while I lived with him in his following, the king knew my style. I find it strange if he now reckons me a different man than he found me then."

"Thórólf," retorted the king, "while you lived with me you be-

haved yourself properly. I still maintain that the best thing to do is
for you to re-enter my bodyguard. Take up my standard and the
captaincy of my other bodyguard men—then no one will slander you
if I keep watch night and day how you behave yourself."

Thórólf looked to his right hand and his left, where his housecarles were standing. "I shall be loth to abandon this following of
mine. It is for you, King, to decide about these titles I hold and your
revenues, but I shall not abandon my followers while my means last
out, even though I must manage on my own account. Yet it is rather
my prayer and wish, King, that you come and visit me in my home
and hear the words of men you trust, what witness they bear me in
this affair. Then act as you find the truth of it."

The king answered by saying that he would not accept Thórólf's
hospitality a second time, so Thórólf took his leave and later prepared
for his journey home. And when he had taken himself off, the king
made over to Hildiríd's sons the stewardships in Hálogaland which
Thórólf had held before, and the Lappland-journey too. The king
seized possession of the house at Torgar and all the properties which
Brynjólf had owned, and gave it all, lock, stock and barrel, into the
keeping of Hildiríd's sons. The king dispatched messengers with
tokens to see Thórólf and inform him of these arrangements he had
made; at which Thórólf took such ships as he had and carried into
them all the movable property he could travel with, and took all his
men with him, both freemen and thralls, and afterwards went north
to his house at Sandnes, where he kept no fewer men and no lesser
style than before.

17

So now Hildiríd's sons took over the stewardship in Hálogaland. No
one spoke out against this, because of the king's power, but to many
who were kinsmen or friends of Thórólf's the change went much
against the grain. They went on to the mountains that winter, taking
thirty men with them. The Lapps held these stewards much less in
awe than when Thórólf made the journey, so the tribute which the
Lapps should yield was paid over in every respect worse.

That same winter Thórólf went up on to the mountains with a hundred men; he at once proceeded east to Kvenland and met King Faravid. They laid their heads together and decided to go on to the mountains like the winter before; they had four hundred men, and made a descent on Kirjálaland, where they attacked those settlements which seemed to them manageable for their strength of men. They raided there, winning immense wealth, and then as winter wore on went back up to the Mark. Thórólf returned home in the spring. He now had men at the cod-fishing in Vágar, and some at the herring-fishing, and hunted about for all kinds of provision for his home.

Thórólf owned a big ship. She had been built for ocean-going, was fitted out as handsomely as could be, and was richly colored down to the water-line. She carried a sail striped with blue and red bands, and the entire ship's gear was of the choicest. Thórólf had this ship put in readiness and found housecarles of his to go with her, had dried fish and hides and white wares[1] carried on board. He had a lot of gray wares too to keep them company, and further skin-wares which he had carried off the mountain—and all this came to immense wealth. He had Yelling-Thorgils hold west to England with this ship, to buy him such clothes and other provisions as he needed. They held south along the land and afterwards to the open sea and came their ways to England, where they had a good market, loaded the ship with wheat and honey, wine and clothes, then held for home in the autumn. They had a following wind and made Hördaland.

That same autumn Hildiríd's sons set off with the tribute and brought it to the king. As they paid it over, the king was standing there in person, looking on. "Is all the tribute you gathered in Finnmark now paid over?" he asked.

"It is so, indeed," they replied.

"Two things then," said the king. "The tribute paid is far smaller and poorer than when Thórólf collected it, yet you reckoned that he was dishonest in his stewardship."

"It is as well, King," Hárek replied, "that you have considered how great a tribute usually comes from Finnmark, for then you will realize how much you stand to lose if Thórólf is to void the entire Lapp-tribute for you. We were thirty of us together in the Mark this winter, as has been your stewards' practice up to now. Then, later,

along came Thórólf with a hundred men. We got news of him, how
he was planning to kill us brothers and every man of our company;
and the reason he offered, King, was that you had transferred to us
the stewardship he wanted to have himself. We could see that our
best chance was to keep out of his path and save our lives, and for
that reason we proceeded only a short way past the settlements on to
the mountains; whereas Thórólf traveled the entire Mark with an
army of men, and had the whole of the trade. It was to him the Lapps
paid tribute, for he had sworn that your stewards should not come
on to the Mark. He is planning to become king over the North there,
over the Mark and Hálogaland too, and it is a puzzle how you let him
have his own way. And clear evidence of the wealth Thórólf confiscated from Finnmark will be found in this circumstance, that the
biggest ship in Hálogaland was fitted out at Sandnes this spring, and
Thórólf claimed that he owned the entire cargo which was aboard
her. I believe she was pretty well loaded with gray wares, and I
believe more beaver and sable might be found on her than anything
that Thórólf conveyed to you. Yelling-Thorgils has gone with her. I
gather that he has sailed west to England, but if you want to know
the truth of it, then keep a look-out for Thorgils's voyage when he
journeys back east, for I believe that no merchant ship of our time has
carried anything to equal it. I judge it simple truth to say that every
penny on board her was yours, King."

His comrades swore to the truth of everything Hárek said, and in
this particular matter no one had the knowledge to refute them.

18

There were two brothers with King Harald by the name of Sigtrygg
Smartfarer and Hallvard Hardfarer—men from Vík. Their mother's
family belonged to Vestfold, and they were kinsmen of a sort to King
Harald. Their father had had family on both sides of the Gautelf. He
had a home in Hísing and was a very rich man, but by now they had
succeeded to their paternal inheritance. They were four brothers. Of
the others one was named Thórd and one Thorgeir, but these were
younger and lived home and looked after the farm. Sigtrygg and Hall-

vard had all the king's errands, both at home and abroad, and had
gone many journeys which were highly dangerous, both for the killing of men and to confiscate wealth from men the king wanted to
have attacked in their homes. They kept a big troop about them. They
were not over-beloved of folk in general, but the king held them in
high esteem, and certainly they were the best of men for travel on foot
or by ski, and at sea-voyages too they were brisker than other men.
They were gallant big men, and of shrewd judgment in most things.
They were in residence with the king when these events were taking
place.

In the autumn the king went feasting throughout Hördaland. Then
one day he had the brothers Sigtrygg and Hallvard summoned before
him, and when they came in told them that they must be off with
their troop and keep a look-out for the ship in which Yelling-Thorgils
was sailing. "He took her west to England this summer. Bring me that
ship and everything in her except the men. Let them go their ways in
peace, unless they want to defend the ship."

The brothers were ready enough for this, and each of them took
his longship; they set off afterwards to find Thorgils and his men and
heard tell how he had arrived back from the west and was sailing
north along the land. They pursued them northwards and caught up
with them in Furusund; they recognized the ship immediately, laid a
second ship on her seaward side, while some of them made their way
ashore and out on to the ship by the gangways. Thorgils and his
crew had no thought of danger and were keeping no watch. They had
no inkling of what was happening before a crowd of fully-armed men
had boarded them, and they were all seized and afterwards led ashore
unarmed, and had only their workaday clothes about them. Hallvard
and his men slid out the gangways, slipped the cables and hauled the
ship out, then altered course and sailed south till they reached the
king, and fetched him the ship and everything that was in her. And
when the cargo was carried from the ship, the king could see what
immense wealth it was, and that what Hárek had told him was no lie.

Thorgils and his shipmates got themselves transport and set off now
to find Kveldúlf and his son Grím; they let them know that theirs had
not been a smooth passage, but they received none the worse welcome
for that.

Kveldúlf said the proof was now at hand of what he had maintained earlier, how Thórólf would not forever find good fortune in
King Harald's friendship. "But this money-loss which Thórólf has
now suffered would strike me as of little importance if nothing worse
comes to pass later. I am troubled now as before that Thórólf will not
really know how to recognize his own strength, in face of such overwhelming force as he must contend with." And he told Thorgils to tell
Thórólf this: "It is my advice," said he, "that he should leave the
country, for maybe he will do better for himself if he seeks service with
the English king, or the Danish king, or the king of the Swedes."

Next he provided Thorgils with an oared ship, together with all her
gear, awnings too and provisions and everything they needed for their
journey. They set off thereafter and made no stay till they reached
Thórólf up north and told him what had happened.

Thórólf took his injury well, reckoning he would not go short of
money. "It is good to lay up money with a king."

Later Thórólf bought meal and salt and what other things he
needed for his troop's maintenance. His housecarles, he said, would
not make so brave a show as he had planned yet awhile. Thórólf sold
his estates, and some he mortgaged, but he kept to his full style as
before. Also he kept no smaller retinue than the winters before. On the
whole, indeed, he had rather more men. Likewise with feasts and
invitations to his friends: he spent more lavishly on all these than
before. He remained at home the whole winter.

19

When spring came and the snow and ice loosed, Thórólf had a big
longship of his launched and fitted out, then manned her with his
housecarles, more than a hundred men in all. They were the handsomest company and very well armed. Once he had a following wind
Thórólf held south along the land with his ship, but as soon as he
arrived south around Byrda they took the outer passage outside all the
islands, sometimes so far out that the sea seemed half way up the
mountains, set course so south off the land, and had no news of men
till they came east into Vík, where they learned that King Harald too

was in the Vík, meaning to proceed that summer to the Uplands. The people of the place knew nothing of Thórólf's movements. He had a good wind and held south for Denmark, and from there to the Baltic, where he raided for the summer, but found it an unprofitable season.

In the autumn he held back from the east to Denmark at the time when the Eyr fleet goes its several ways. As usual, there had been a great many ships that summer from Norway. Thórólf let the whole assembly sail ahead and let nothing be known of his presence. Then one day he sailed in the evening to Mostrarsund. In the harbor in front of him was a big cargo ship newly arrived from Eyr. Her master was named Thórir Thruma. Thórir was a collector of dues for King Harald, and had charge of his house at Thruma. This was a big house where the king stayed for long stretches whenever he was in the Vík. Great provision was needed for the house, and that was why Thórir had gone to Eyr, to buy a cargo of malt and wheat and honey, on which he had spent a lot of money belonging to the king. They attacked the ship, giving Thórir and his men the choice of defending themselves, but because they lacked strength for a defense against such force as Thórólf had, they gave in. Thórólf seized the ship with all her cargo, but Thórir he set ashore on the island. Then Thórólf held with both ships northwards along the land.

When they arrived off the Elf, they lay up there and waited for nightfall. As soon as it was dark they rowed the longship up into the river and made for the farm owned by Sigtrygg and Hallvard. They got there before day and threw a ring of men round it, then roared their warcry, and at that those who were inside awoke and jumped up hot-foot for their weapons. Thorgeir instantly took to his heels out of the sleeping chamber. There was a high wooden fence round the house. Thorgeir jumped for this fence and gripped with his hand high up on a fence-stake and so swung himself out of the yard. Standing near was Yelling-Thorgils, who swept after Thorgeir with his sword and caught him on the hand, severing it against the fence-stake. Then Thorgeir ran off to the forest, but his brother Thórd was killed there with more than twenty men. Next they plundered all the goods there and burnt the house, and afterwards went back down the river to the sea.

They now had a following wind and sailed north into the Vík.

Once again they fell in with a big merchant-ship which the Vík-dwellers owned, loaded with malt and meal. Thórólf and his men attacked the ship, but those on board her judged they had no means of defense and gave in. They went up on shore weaponless, but Thórólf and his men seized the ship with her freight, then bore on their way. Thórólf now had three ships as he sailed from the east through the Fold; he sailed the usual route to Lídandisnes, proceeding with dispatch, yet putting off landing parties wherever they came and holding cattle-slaughters on shore. But when they bore north from Lídandisnes they went more by way of the outer passage; though wherever they came close to land they robbed.

Once Thórólf arrived north off the Firths he turned in off his course and went to see Kveldúlf, his father. Their welcome was a warm one. Thórólf told his father what adventures had befallen on his travels that summer. He made only a short stay there, and Kveldúlf and his son Grím saw him down to his ship. Before they parted they talked together.

"Thórólf," said Kveldúlf, "things have turned out not far different from what I told you when you set off for Harald's court, that it would so turn out that there would be no luck in it either for you or for us your kinsmen. You are now following the plan I most warned you against, when you go pitting yourself against King Harald. And though you carry your full freight of courage and skill, you have not the luck to hold your own with him—something which has never come the way of any other man here in the land, though in the old days he had great force and following of men. I have a feeling that this will prove our last meeting together. It would seem natural because of our ages that you should live the longer of us two, but I believe it will work out otherwise."

Thereafter Thórólf boarded his ship and held away on his course. It is not reported that anything happened worth telling of on his voyage before he reached Sandnes and had all the plunder he had fetched home carried to the house and his ships laid up. There was no lack of means now to feed his people over the winter. Thórólf remained home the whole time, and had no smaller following of men than the winters before.

20

There was a rich, powerful man named Yngvar. He had been a landed man of the kings of old, but ever since Harald came to power Yngvar stayed home and gave the king no service. Yngvar was a married man and had a daughter whose name was Bera. His home was in the Firths. Bera was his only child and stood to inherit after him. Grím Kveldúlfsson asked for Bera's hand in marriage, and the match was made. Grím married Bera the winter following that summer they and Thórólf parted. Grím was now twenty-five years old and bald-headed, and ever afterwards he was called Skallagrím, Bald-Grím. He had the management of the whole household, his father's and his own, and of all its provisioning; even so, Kveldúlf was a hale and hearty man. They had a lot of freemen with them and many men who had grown up at home there and were much the same age as Skallagrím. Of these many were remarkable for their strength, for Kveldúlf and his sons chose strong men as their retainers, then broke them to their own temper.

Skallagrím was the image of his father in size and strength, and in looks and temper too.

21

King Harald was in the Vík at the time Thórólf was out raiding; that autumn he proceeded to the Uplands, and from there north to Thrándheim, and spent the winter there with a big body of men about him. Sigtrygg and Hallvard were there with the king at the time, and had heard tell how Thórólf had treated their quarters in Hísing, and what slaughter and robbery he had wrought there. Often they reminded the king of it, and of this too, how Thórólf had robbed the king and his thanes and gone harrying there within the land. The brothers begged leave of the king that they should set off with the force which usually accompanied them, and attack Thórólf at his home.

The king made them this answer: "You will be thinking you have good cause to make away with Thórólf, but I cannot help thinking that you come far short in luck for this deed. Thórólf and you are not a match, though you consider yourselves brave men and handy."

The brothers reckoned this would soon be tested if the king gave permission, maintaining that they had often taken a greater chance with men on whom they had less to avenge, and for the most part it had been victory that came their way.

When spring had come men made ready for their travels. It happened again that (as was related earlier) Hallvard and his brother persisted in their request to the king.

He agreed to give them leave to take Thórólf's life. "And I know you will bring me his head when you return, and many a treasure besides. And yet it is some men's guess," added the king, "that if sail speeds you north, both sail and oar will speed you south again."

At this they made ready as fast as they could, using two ships and a hundred and eighty men; and, as soon as they were set, took the north-east wind out along the fjord. But that is a head-wind for travelers north along the land.

22

King Harald, who was in residence at Hladir when Hallvard set off with his brother, instantly bestirred himself with all such speed as he could and went aboard ship. They rowed in along the fjord past Skarnssund, and so past Beitsjó in to Eldueid, where he left the ship behind, traveled north over the neck of land to Naumudal, and there requisitioned the longships which the farmers owned and got aboard with his company. He had his bodyguard and almost three hundred men in five or six ships, all of them big ones. They met with a fresh head wind but rowed night and day as hard as they could go. The night-time was then light for traveling.

They reached Sandnes late in the day after sunset, and saw floating there in front of the house a big longship under awnings. They recognized the ship as Thórólf's. He had had her fitted out, for he intended to leave the country, and by now had had the ale brewed for his parting feast. The king ordered every man he had out of the ships and had his standard raised. It was only a short distance up to the house, and Thórólf's watchmen were seated indoors at the drinking and had not gone on watch, so there was not a soul outside. The whole company was seated indoors at the drinking. The king had a ring of men thrown round the hall. They raised their warcry and a war-blast was sounded on the king's trumpet. And when Thórólf and his men heard that they rushed to arms, for each man's armor hung over his place. The king had them shout to the hall and tell the women and boys and old men, the thralls and the bondmen, to get outside.

At that Sigríd, the housewife, came out, and with her the women who were inside and those others who had permission to leave. Sigríd asked whether the sons of Berdla-Kári would be present. They both stepped forward, asking what she wanted of them.

"Take me to the king," she said, and they did so. And when she came before the king she asked: "Is it any use, Lord, to seek for terms between you and Thórólf?"

"If Thórólf will give himself up," replied the king, "and throw himself on my mercy, he shall save life and limb. But his men must stand the punishment their offenses deserve."

With that Ölvir Hnúfa walked over to the hall and had Thórólf summoned to speak with him. He told him the offer the king had made.

"I'll not take a forced atonement from the king," Thórólf answered. "Tell him to let us come out. And then let events take their course."

Ölvir went to the king and told him what Thórólf was asking for himself.

"Set fire to the hall," [1] ordered the king. "I have no intention of fighting blow for blow with him and so throwing away my men's lives. I know Thórólf will work great slaughter on us if we must attack him out in the open, when we consider how he will not be overcome all that quickly indoors, even though he has a smaller force than we."

Fire was now carried to the hall, and it caught quickly, for the timber was dry, the woodwork tarred, and the roof thatched with birchbark. Thórólf told his men to break down the boarding which stood between the hall and the entrance-hall, and that was seen to quickly. Then when they got at the beams, as many men as could lay hand on it seized a single beam and dashed the one end so hard into the angle that the log-ends burst open on the outside and the walls sprang apart, so that there was a big passage outwards. Thórólf was the first out, and then Yelling-Thorgils, and then the rest of them, one after the other. There was hard fighting there, and for a while it happened that the hall protected the backs of Thórólf and his men: but when this began to burn the fire drove out at them. It was now that many of their company fell. Then Thórólf ran forward, cutting right and left, driving on to where the king's standard was. Now Yelling-Thorgils fell. And when Thórólf reached the shield-wall he thrust his sword through the man who carried the standard.

"Now," cried Thórólf, "I came three feet short!"

Both sword and spear stood in him, but it was the king himself dealt him his deathblow, and Thórólf pitched forward at the king's feet. Then the king called out and said to stop killing any more men. This was done. The king next told his followers to get down to the ships.

"Now take your kinsman Thórólf," he ordered Ölvir and his brother, "and pay him his rites with honor, and so with the others who have fallen here, and give them burial; and those men who are expected to live, have their wounds bound up. But no one shall go robbing here, for this is all my property."

Afterwards the king went down to the ships, and most of his troop with him. Once they had got aboard men started bandaging their wounds. The king moved about the ship, studying men's wounds. He saw where a man was bandaging a glancing wound, and the king reckoned Thórólf had not dealt that one. "His weapons bit quite another way. There are few, I fancy, who bandage the wounds he dealt. There is great loss in such men."

First thing in the morning the king hoisted sail and bore south as fast as he could. In the course of the day the king's men met with many rowing-boats in every island strait, and that gathering had intended to go and join Thórólf, for he had his informants as far south as Naumudal and wide throughout the islands. They had come to know how Hallvard and his brother were on their way from the south with a great force and were planning to attack Thórólf. Hallvard and his men had a head wind the whole time, and had hung about in various havens till news had traveled by the inland road and Thórólf's informants had come to know of it, and this rush to arms had taken place for that reason.

The king sailed with a fresh fair wind till he reached Naumudal, where he left the ships behind and traveled the overland road to Thrándheim. There he took the ships which he had left behind earlier, and held away for Hladir with his company. This news spread quickly and reached Hallvard and his men in the place where they were hove to. So now they made their way back to the king, and theirs was thought rather a fools' errand.

The brothers Ölvir Hnúfa and Eyvind Lambi stayed on for a while at Sandnes. They had the slain attended to who had fallen there. Thórólf's body they saw to after the old fashion, even as was then the practice to see to the bodies of notable men, and they erected memory-stones after him. The sick men they had tended, and they brought the household to order too, in company with Sigríd. All the animals had survived, but the household fittings and table furniture and men's clothes had for the most part been burnt indoors. Once the brothers were ready they left the north and came to find King Harald where he was staying in Thrándheim and remained with him for a time. They were close mouthed and had little to say to anybody.

It happened one day that the brothers walked in before the king. "We want, we brothers," said Ölvir, "to ask leave of you, King, that you let us make ready for home. For such things have taken place here that we are in no mood to share drink and bench with the men who bore arms against Thórólf our kinsman."

The King looked at him and answered rather curtly. "I shall not give you leave for that. You must stay here with me."

The brothers took themselves off and went back to their seats. The following day the king was seated in open hall and had Ölvir and his brother called before him.

"You shall now be informed," announced the king, "as to that matter you raised with me yesterday and your request to go home. You have been here with me a good while and have shown yourselves fine men. You have done splendid service always, and I have been satisfied with you in every respect. Now, Eyvind, I want you to go north to Hálogaland. I will give you in marriage Sigríd of Sandnes, the woman

who was Thórólf's wife. I will also give you all the wealth Thórólf
had. In addition you shall have my friendship—if you know how to
keep it. But Ölvir must stay with me. Him I will not let go, because of
his many accomplishments."

The brothers thanked the king for the honor he did them, saying
they would accept it eagerly. Eyvind then made ready for his journey,
and got himself a good ship to meet his needs. The king provided
him with tokens for this business. Eyvind had a good voyage and came
up north to Álöst, to Sandnes, where Sigríd gave them a good welcome. Afterwards Eyvind set out the king's tokens and his errand to
Sigríd, and advanced his proposal, saying it was the king's directive
that Eyvind should succeed in this suit. Sigríd could see only the one
choice before her, things being what they were: to let the king have
his way, and the affair so proceeded that Eyvind married Sigríd. He
then took over the house at Sandnes and all the wealth which had
been Thórólf's. Eyvind was a most notable man. Their children were
Fid Skjálgi, the father of Eyvind Skaldspiller, and Geirlaug whom
Sighvat the Red married. Fid Skjálgi married Gunnhild, the daughter
of Earl Hálfdan. Her mother's name was Ingibjörg, daughter of King
Harald Fairhair. Eyvind Lambi remained a friend of the king's as
long as they both lived.

23

There was a man named Ketil Hœng, son of Thorkel the Naumdalers'
Earl and that Hrafnhild who was the daughter of Ketil Hœng from
Hrafnista. He was a man both noble and distinguished. He had been
a close friend of Thórólf Kveldúlfsson, and a blood-relation of his.
He was in that sally when the army assembled in Hálogaland, when
men were aiming to help Thórólf, as was written earlier. But when
King Harald left the north and men came to know that Thórólf's life
was taken, they then dissolved their gathering. Hœng had sixty men
with him and headed for Torgar, where Hildiríd's sons were in residence with a small following. As soon as Hœng arrived at their farm
he made an assault upon them. Hildiríd's sons fell, with most of the
men who were present there, and Hœng and his men seized all the

wealth they could lay their hands on. After that Hœng took two of the biggest ships of lading he could get hold of, and had carried out to them all the wealth he possessed and might get away with. He took his wife and children with him, as well as all the men who had been with him on that deed. In charge of the second ship was a man by the name of Baug, Hœng's foster brother and a rich man of good family. And when they were ready and had a following wind, they sailed into the open sea.

A few winters earlier Ingólf and Hjörleif had gone out to settle Iceland, and men's mouths were now full of their voyage and how there was admirable land there. So Hœng sailed west overseas, making for Iceland. But when they came in sight of land their landfall was from the south. And because the wind was rough, with surf on the coast and no sign of a harbor, they sailed west along the land off the Sands. Then as the wind began to slacken and the surf to subside, there was a big river mouth in front of them, and they held on with their ships up into the river and put in to its eastern shore. That river is nowadays called Thjórsá: at the time we are telling of its course was much narrower and deeper than it is today. They unloaded the ships, set to and explored the land east of the river, moving their livestock after them. That first winter Hœng spent away beyond the outer Rangá. But in the spring he explored the land to the east and took land in settlement between Thjórsá and Markarfljót from the mountains to the sea, and settled down at Hof on the eastern Rangá. Ingun, his wife, bore a child in the spring, after they had spent that first winter there: the boy was named Hrafn. And even when the buildings were pulled down, the place continued to be called Hrafntoftir.

Hœng gave Baug land in Fljótshlíd down from Merkiá to the river out past Breidabólstad, and he lived at Hlídarendi. From Baug has come a great progeny in that countryside. Hœng gave land to his shipmates, or sold cheaply to some, and these are known as the Settlement Men.

One son of Hœng was named Stórólf, who owned Hválin and Stórólfsvöll. His son was Orm the Strong. A second of Hœng's sons was named Herjólf, who owned land in Fljótshlíd opposite Baug and out towards Hválslœk. He made his home under Brekka. His son was named Sumarlid, the father of Vetrlid the skald. Helgi was the third

of Hœng's sons. He lived at Völl and had land right to the upper
Rangá and on down to meet with his brothers. The fourth of Hœng's
sons was Vestar, who owned land east of Rangá, between there and
Thverá, together with the lower part of Stórólfsvöll. He married
Móeid, Hildir's daughter from Hildisey, and their daughter was that
Ásny whom Ófeig Grettir married. Vestar lived at Móeidarhváll.
Hœng's fifth son was Hrafn, who was the first Lawspeaker in Ice-
land. He lived at Hof after his father. Hrafn's daughter was Thórlaug,
whom Jörund Godi married: their son was Valgard of Hof. Hrafn was
the most famous of Hœng's sons.

24

Kveldúlf heard tell of the fall of Thórólf his son. He grew so heavy-
hearted at the news that he took to his bed for grief and age. Skallagrím often came and talked with him, bidding him take heart, and
reckoning that any course at all was more worthy of him than that he
should grow pithless and lie bedridden.

"A better plan is that we should seek vengeance for Thórólf. Maybe
we can get at some of those men who were present at Thórólf's fall.
And if not, there will still be men we can catch whose deaths will
bring no pleasure to the king."

Kveldúlf chanted a verse:

> (1) "I learned in a northern island
>   (Grim ally the Norn) too early
>   Chose Thunder-God my champion:
>   Thórólf by foe lay fallen.
>   Thór's wrestler, Age, Thought's rustler,
>   Slyly and sure as slowly
>   Quells vengeance, cozens Kveldúlf;
>   Hand lags, but how heart longeth!" [1]

That summer King Harald proceeded to the Uplands, and in the
autumn traveled west to Valdres and on as far as Vors. Ölvir Hnúfa
was of the king's company and often came to discuss with him
whether he would be willing to pay redress for Thórólf, and grant

Kveldúlf and Skallagrím an award of money or some such honor as might content them. The king did not wholly refuse this if only the father and son would appear before him. Later Ölvir set off on his journey north to the Firths, making no stay till he reached Kveldúlf and Grím at the close of day. They gave him a grateful welcome, and he remained with them for some time. Kveldúlf questioned Ölvir closely about the events which had taken place at Sandnes when Thórólf fell, and about this too, what Thórólf wrought for his fame before he fell, and also who bore weapons against him and where he had his greatest wound, and how his death came about. Ölvir told him everything he asked, and also how King Harald gave him that wound which in itself was enough for his death, and how Thórólf fell face-down near the king's feet.

"Your words are good," answered Kveldúlf, "for men of old have told how there would be vengeance for him who fell face-down, and the vengeance alight not far from who stood before him where he fell. Yet there is little prospect such luck will come our way!"

Ölvir told the kinsmen he believed that if they would go and see the king and ask for redress it would prove a venture full of honor. He begged them to try, urging it long and frequently.

Kveldúlf said that he was quite past it because of his age. "I shall stay home," he said.

"Will you go, Grím?" asked Ölvir.

"I think it no mission for me," replied Grím. "To the king I shall appear crude of speech. Nor do I think I shall make long work of it when asking for redress."

Ölvir said he would not need to. "We shall all be speaking up for you the best we can."

So because Ölvir pleaded his case so hard, Grím promised to go along as soon as he felt ready. He and Ölvir fixed a time between them when Grím should come and visit the king, and then Ölvir went on ahead to see the king.

25

Skallagrím now made his preparations for this journey which has just been mentioned. For it he picked those of his household and neighbors who were the most formidable in strength and the bravest of any men alive. One of them was named Áni, a rich farmer; the second Grani, the third Grímólf, with Grím his brother, members of Skallagrím's household; also the brothers Thórólf Crook and Thórd Beigaldi. (These were called Thórarna's sons. She lived a short distance from Skallagrím and was versed in magic.) Beigaldi was a slugabed who had grown into a hero. Yet another of them was named Thórir Thurs, and his brother Thorgeir Earthlong. There was also a man Odd Live-alone, and Gríss the freedman. They were twelve for the journey, all of them men of great strength, and many of them shape-changers.

They took a rowing-ferry which Skallagrím owned, traveled south along the coast and laid course into Ostrarfjörd; then they proceeded by the land-route up to Vors, to the lake which is to be found there, and their road so lay that they had to cross over it. They obtained a rowing boat there which met their need, rowed afterwards across the lake, and it was not far then to this residence where the king was being entertained. Grím and his men arrived there at a time when the king had gone to his food.

Grím and his men met someone to talk to outside the courtyard and asked what was the news. And when they were informed as to that, Grím said to call Ölvir Hnúfa to speak with him.

The man went inside the hall to where Ölvir was sitting, and, "Men have arrived outside," he told him, "twelve of them together, if men I shall call them; for they are more like giants in size and appearance than mortal men."

Ölvir rose at once and went outside, feeling he knew who had come. He gave his kinsman Grím a warm welcome and said for him to walk inside the hall with him.

"It will be the custom here," Grím told his comrades, "that men go weaponless into the king's presence. So six of us will go inside, but the other six stay out here and keep guard on our weapons."

With that they went inside. Ölvir walked before the king, and Skallagrím stood behind him.

Ölvir began to speak: "Well, here is Grím Kveldúlfsson. We shall be grateful now, King, if you make his journey here a profitable one —as indeed we expect it will be. Many get great honors from you, King, who are less deserving than he and nothing like as well endowed in most respects as he will prove; and this is one thing you can do, King, if only because it seems to me of the first importance—if that seems worth anything to you."

Ölvir spoke long and eloquently, for he was a man handy with words. Many of Ölvir's friends went before the king and strengthened his plea. The king looked all round, and saw there was a man standing behind Ölvir who was higher by a head than other men, and bald.

"Is this Skallagrím," the king asked, "the big fellow?"

Grím said that he named him correctly.

"I am willing for this much," said the king, "should you be asking redress for Thórólf, that you become my man and enter the fellowship of my bodyguard here and serve me. Maybe I shall grow so satisfied with your service that I will pay you reparation for your brother, or some honor or other not smaller than those I gave your brother Thórólf. But you must know better than he how to sustain it, if I make so great a man of you as he became."

"It is well known," replied Skallagrím, "that Thórólf was far superior to me in all ways, and he found no luck in serving you, King Now I will not follow this course, nor will I do you service, for I know I shall not find such good fortune in serving you as I should want and would be right and proper. I am sure there will be more to find fault within me than in Thórólf."

The king made no answer but turned red as blood to look on. Ölvir instantly swung away, ordering Grím and his men to get outside. This they did: they walked out and laid hold of their weapons. Ölvir now ordered them to get away as hard as they could go. He saw them on their way as far as the lake, and many of his men with him.

Before he and Skallagrím parted, "Kinsman Grím," said Ölvir, "this trip of yours to see the king has turned out very different from what I would have had it. I was strong for your coming here, but now I want to ask you something quite opposite, that you head for home as fast as you can, and this into the bargain, that you never return to visit King Harald unless the pair of you find yourselves on easier terms than now appears to me can be the case. And keep a good lookout for yourself against the king and his men."

Grím next crossed the lake with his comrades, but Ölvir and those with him went to where the boats were lying which had been drawn ashore at the lakeside, and so laid their axes to them that not one remained seaworthy, for they could see the movement of men down from the king's house. They were no small number, heavily armed, and moving at high speed. King Harold had sent these men after them to kill Grím.

The king had started speaking the minute Grím and his men had got outside. This is what he said: "I can see of this great baldhead that he is wolf to the throat of him, and he will be the destruction of some we should consider a great loss, should he lay hands on them. You men he reckons to have a grudge against can be sure of one thing, that this baldhead will spare no one of you, should he cross your path. Get after him now, and kill him!"

With that they set off and came to the lake but did not find a single boat there that was seaworthy. They then returned and told the king what had happened, and this in addition, that Grím and his men must by now have crossed the lake.

Skallagrím kept going with his comrades till he reached home. He told Kveldúlf of their adventures, and Kveldúlf approved of it, that Grím had not run this errand to the king just to abase himself before him. He declared now as before that harm alone, and no amendment, would come to them from the king. Kveldúlf and Skallagrím often talked over their plans together, and always reached agreement, reckoning they would no more remain there in Norway than those other men who were at loggerheads with the king, and that it would be advisable for them to get abroad; and it seemed to them a good plan to make for Iceland, for there was a favorable report of the land there. By this time friends and acquaintances of theirs had arrived there, Ingólf Arnarson and his comrades, and had taken their pick of land and residence in Iceland. Men could take land for themselves there without having to buy, and choose where to live. On the whole this was the plan they determined on, that they would abandon their home and depart the country.

In his childhood Thórir Hróaldsson had been fostered with Kveld-úlf, and he and Skallagrím were much of an age. Theirs was a most loving foster brotherhood. Thórir had become the king's landed man while all this was happening, but his friendship with Skallagrím held good at all times.

Early in the spring Kveldúlf and his household made their ships ready. They had a big and excellent choice of vessels; they fitted out two big ships of lading, and aboard each had thirty men who were brisk and able, and women and youngsters too. With them they took all the movable property they might get away with, but no one dare buy their estates for awe of the royal power. As soon as they were ready they sailed away. They sailed to those islands which are called the Sólunds. There are many of these islands, big and so indented with bays that there will be few men to know all the harbors.

26

Guttorm, Sigurd Hart's son, was uncle on the mother's side to King Harald. He was also the king's foster father and regent over his land, for Harald was in his infancy when first he succeeded to the throne. Guttorm was commander of King Harald's forces when he subdued the country, and took part in all the king's battles when he overran Norway. When Harald had become sole king over the whole land and settled to a life of quiet, he gave his kinsman Guttorm Vestrfold and East Agdir and Hringaríki, together with all the territory his father, Hálfdan the Black, had possessed. Guttorm had two sons and two daughters, the sons named Sigurd and Ragnar, and the daughters Ragnhild and Áslaug.

Guttorm fell ill, and as his end drew near he sent messengers to King Harald, asking him to look after his children and his territory. Soon afterwards he died, and once the king heard tell of his death he had Hallvard Hardfarer and his brother summoned before him, and informed them that they must go an errand for him east to Vík.

At this time the king was in residence in Thrándheim. The brothers
prepared for their voyage with all the splendor they could, picked
their crew and took the very best ship they could find—that same ship
Thórólf Kveldúlfsson had owned and which they had seized from
Yelling-Thorgils. When they were all set for their voyage the king
explained their mission to them, how they were to go east to Túnsberg.
That was a market place in those days, and it was there that Guttorm
had had his seat. "You must fetch me Guttorm's sons," the king told
them, "but his daughters shall be brought up there until the day I
bestow them in marriage. I must moreover appoint men to take charge
of the kingdom and foster the girls."

As soon as the brothers were ready they set off and had a following
wind. They arrived in Vík in the spring, east at Túnsberg, and announced their business there. Hallvard and his men took charge of
Guttorm's sons and a lot of personal goods, and as soon as they were
ready made off back. This time they were a little slower getting a
good wind, but nothing worth telling of happened on their journey
until they sailed north past the Sognsær with a good breeze and bright
weather, and all of them merry as crickets.

27

Kveldúlf and Skallagrím and their men kept watch all that summer
along the sea's highway. Of all men alive Skallagrím was the sharpest
sighted. He spotted the passage of Hallvard and his men and recognized their ship, for he had seen her before this when Thorgils sailed
in her. Skallagrím kept watch on their movements, where they put
into harborage that evening. Next he returned to his followers to tell
Kveldúlf what he had seen, and this too, how he recognized the ship
Hallvard and his men had seized from Thorgils (the one Thórólf had
owned), and that there must be some along with her who would
prove a good catch. After that they put themselves in readiness, preparing both the boats and having twenty men in each. Kveldúlf captained the one, and Skallagrím the other. Next they rowed away to
hunt down the ship, and when they came to where she was lying
they put ashore.

Hallvard and his men had rigged awnings over their ship and then settled down to sleep. But when Kveldúlf and his men launched their attack, the watchmen who were stationed at the end of the gangway started up and shouted back to the ship. Get up, they called to the crew—an enemy was upon them! Hallvard's men made a rush for their weapons, but once Kveldúlf and his crew reached the gangway-end he drove on out to the rear gangway and Skallagrím forward to the fore. In his hand Kveldúlf had a double-headed spiked axe, and as soon as he got on board he ordered his men to work their way round the ship's side and cut the awning from its forks, but he himself raged towards the raised deck aft, and report has it that he ran mad there, and there were yet more of his comrades who ran mad too. They killed everybody they found in their path. And Skallagrím, wherever he trod the deck, he did the same. Father and son did not let up till the whole ship was cleared. And when Kveldúlf reached the raised deck aft he swung up the spiked axe, smiting Hallvard through helm and head, so that it sank in right to the haft. He then tugged it towards him so hard that he jerked Hallvard aloft and slung him overboard. Skallagrím emptied the prow and killed Sigtrygg. A lot of them jumped into the water, but Skallagrím's men took the boat they had brought there and rowed after them and killed every man they found swimming.

All in all more than fifty of Hallvard's men lost their lives. But Skallagrím and his men seized the ship Hallvard had been sailing and all the wealth that was in her. They took prisoner two or three men who seemed of least note, gave them peace and had news of them, inquiring what men had been on board, and this also: What was the purpose of their voyage? Once they felt assured of the truth of all this, they looked over the slain who lay on board ship. They found then that a greater number of men had jumped over the side and perished than had died on board. Those sons of Guttorm—they too had jumped overboard and perished, the one of them twelve years old at the time, and the other ten, and the most promising young men.

Next Skallagrím had those men freed to whom he had given quarter, ordering them to go and find King Harald and tell him every tittle of news that had happened there, and tell him too who had

been present at its making. "And you shall carry to the king," he
said, "this ditty:

> (2) Now hersir's righted,
>   And king requited;
>   Wolf and the erns
>   Tear Yngling's bairns.
>   Billows embrace
>   Hallvard's hewn face;
>   Grey eagle rends
>   Smartfarer's wounds."

Next Grím and his men moved vessel and freight out to their own
ships, then changed ships, loading her they had just captured and
emptying the one they had had before, which was smaller; they
carried stones on board and broke holes in her and sank her, and
afterwards sailed out to sea the moment they got a wind.

It is told of those men's state who were werwolves, or who went
berserk, that while the fit was on them they were so strong that nothing could withstand them, but the minute it was past they became
weaker than their wont. This was the case with Kveldúlf, that once
his madness left him he felt exhausted from the onslaught he had
made, and he was now quite enfeebled, so that he must take to his
bed. A following wind was bearing them out to sea. Kveldúlf was in
charge of the ship they had taken from Hallvard and his men. They
had a good wind and kept close together in their sailing, so that they
were in sight of each other constantly.

But once the open sea had been traversed, his sickness gained on
Kveldúlf. When it came to such a pitch that he looked like dying,
he spoke with his shipmates, telling them he thought it likely that
soon their ways must part. "I have not," he said "been one to ail, but
if it should happen that I die—and I think it only too likely—then
make me a coffin and let me go over the side, and it will prove other
than I have been thinking it would be if I do not reach Iceland and
take land there in settlement. You shall bear my greetings to my son
Grím once you fall in with each other, and tell him this too, that if
it so happens that he reaches Iceland, and it should turn out—unlikely

as it may appear—that I come to see it first, then let him make his home as near as ever he can to where I came ashore."

A little later Kveldúlf died. His shipmates did as he had requested: they put him in a coffin, then shot it overboard.[1] There was a man named Grím, the son of Thórir, Ketil Keelfarer's son, a rich man of good family, who was a member of Kveldúlf's crew. He had been a friend of that father and son of old, and had been on voyages both with them and with Thórólf—which was reason enough to earn the king's displeasure. It was he who captained the ship after Kveldúlf died.

When they arrived off Iceland they approached the land from the south. They sailed west along the coast, for they had heard how Ingólf had found himself a home there; but once they came past Reykjanes and saw the firth opening up they headed into the firth with both ships. The weather grew wild, with much rain and fog, and the ships parted company. They sailed in along Borgarfjörd till the skerries came to an end, then dropped anchor till the wind fell and the weather cleared. They waited there for high water. Afterwards they moved their ship up into a certain river mouth (the one now called Gufuá), and brought the ship up river as far as they could. Later on they carried their freight off the ship, and that was where they made their home that first winter.

They explored the land alongside the sea, both up and down the firth. And when they had gone only a short way they discovered in an inlet where Kveldúlf's coffin had been washed ashore. They shifted the coffin to the headland that stood there, where they laid it to rest and piled it with stones.

2 8

Skallagrím came to land where a big headland ran out into the sea, and beyond the headland a narrow isthmus. They carried their cargo ashore there, calling the place Knarrarnes.[1] Next Skallagrím explored the countryside: there was a lot of marshland there and spacious forest, with plenty of room between mountains and sea, ample seal-

hunting and good fishing. When they explored the country southwards along the sea they found a great firth in front of them; they
proceeded in along this firth and did not desist from their travels till
they came across those comrades of theirs, Grím the Hálogalander
and his shipmates. This was a joyful meeting of theirs. They informed
Skallagrím that it was there that Kveldúlf had come ashore and they
had buried him. Later they led him to the place, and it looked to
him as though just a short way off would be a fine place to raise a
home. And with that off he went, back to his own crew, and each
party spent the winter where it had come ashore.

Then Skallagrím took land in settlement between mountains and
sea, the entire Mýrar out to Selalón and inland to Borgarhraun, also
south to Hafnarfjall—the whole area marked out by its rivers falling
seawards. The following spring he brought his ship south to the
firth and into the inlet nearest to the spot where Kveldúlf had come
ashore. Here he established house and home, calling it Borg and the
firth Borgarfjörd; and the countryside inland from there, that too
they named after the firth.

To Grím the Hálogalander he gave a dwelling-place south of Borgarfjörd, at the place they called Hvanneyr. A short way further down
there stretched inland a not very big arm of water where they found
a lot of ducks, so called it Andakíl, and Andakílsá the river which
flows into the sea there. Up from that river to the river which was
called Grímsá, there in between Grím owned land.

In the spring, when Skallagrím had his livestock driven in along
the sea, they came on a little ness; they caught some swans there, so
called it Álftanes.

Skallagrím gave land to his shipmates. To Áni he gave land between Langá and Háfslœk, and he lived at Ánabrekka. His son
was Önund Sjóni. Grímólf was the first to live at Grímólfsstadir;
Grímólfsfít and Grímólfslœk get their names from him. His son was
that Grím who lived south of the firth; and his son the Grímar who
lived at Grímarsstadir—the one Thorstein and Tungu-Odd fell out
over. Grani lived at Granastadir in Digranes. To Thorbjörn Krum he
gave land up along Gufuá, and so with Thórd Beigaldi. Krum lived
at Krumshólar and Thórd at Beigaldi. To Thórir Thurs and his
brother he gave land up from Einkunnir and seawards along Langá.

Thórir Thurs lived at Thursstadir. His daughter was Thórdís Staff
who later lived at Stangarholt. Thorgeir lived at Jardlangsstadir.

Skallagrím explored the countryside inland over the whole area,
proceeding in along Borgarfjörd first till the firth came to an end, and
thereafter west along the river he named Hvítá (for those comrades
had never before seen waters which had run off glaciers: the river
struck them as a most peculiar color).[2] They continued up along Hvítá
until they were confronted by a river flowing from the mountains to
the north. This they named Nordrá, then kept up along it till once
more there was a river in front of them—this time a small stream.
Fording it, they continued once more up along Nordrá, soon saw
where the small stream ran out of some ravines, so called it Gljúfrá.
Later they crossed Nordrá, returned to Hvítá, and continued up along
it. Soon there appeared yet another river in front of them which
crossed their path and ran into Hvítá. This they called Thverá. They
came to know that all the waters there were full of fish. Later they
returned seawards to Borg.

29

Skallagrím was a great man for work. He always kept a lot of men
on hand, and sought busily after such supplies as might be found
thereabouts which could prove useful to them; for at first they had
little livestock compared with what was needed for the number of
men they had there. However, what livestock there was found its
own food in the forest through the winter. Skallagrím was a great
shipbuilder, nor was there any shortage of driftwood west of the
Mýrar. He had a farm built at Álftanes, and had a second home
there, from which he had men go out rowing for fish and seal-hunting
and egg-collecting, for there was abundance of all these provisions,
and also driftwood to be fetched back home. At that time too there
were numerous whale-strandings, and harpooning them was free for
all. And all creatures were at their ease in the hunting-grounds, for
men were unknown to them.

The third home he had was by the sea in the western Mýrar. This
was even better situated for waylaying driftwood; and he had ground

sown there and called it Akrar. Offshore lay islands where whales
were to be found, and these they called Hvalseyjar. Skallagrím also
had men of his up on the salmon rivers for the fishing. He put Odd
Live-alone on Gljúfrá to look after the salmon fishing there; he lived
under Einbúabrekkur, and it is from him that Einbúanes gets its
name. Then there was a man called Sigmund whom Skallagrím put
on Nordrá. He lived at the place which used to be called Sigmund-
arstadir but is nowadays known as Haugar. From him Sigmundarnes
gets its name. Later he shifted his dwelling over to Munodarnes,
where he found it handier for the salmon fishing.

Once Skallagrím's livestock showed a substantial increase, all the
sheep went up on the high ground for the summer. He could see a
big difference, how the stock which went on the heath grew better
and fatter, and also how sheep did well over the winter in the high
valleys, even if they were not fetched down. As a result, Skallagrím
had a farm built up by the fell, and owned a house there, and had his
sheep tended there. It was Gríss who looked after this house, from
whom Grísartunga gets its name. Skallagrím's estate was now standing on more legs than one.

Not long after Skallagrím had come to Iceland, a ship put from the
sea into Borgarfjörd, her owner's name Óleif Hjalti. He had his wife
and children with him, and a band of other kinsmen besides; and he
meant by this voyage of his to win himself a home in Iceland. Óleif
was a rich man of good family, and wise and prudent too. Skallagrím
invited Óleif to stay with him together with his entire company.
Óleif accepted, and it was at Skallagrím's that he spent his first winter
in Iceland. Then later, in the spring, he directed Óleif to land south
of Hvítá, from Grímsá up to Flókadalsá. This he accepted, and moved
his entire household there to establish a home at the place called
Varmalœk. He was a noteworthy man. His sons were Ragi of Laugar-
dal and Thórarin Ragi's brother who succeeded Hrafn Hœngsson to
the Lawspeakership of Iceland. Thórarin lived at Varmalœk. He
married Thórdís, daughter of Óláf Feilan and sister to Thórd Bellow.

30

King Harald Fairhair drew into his clutches all those estates which Kveldúlf and Skallagrím had left behind in Norway, together with any other wealth he could get his hands on. Further, he hunted busily after the men who had been admitted to their plans or secret counsel, or had been of any help to Skallagrím and his people in the deeds they wrought before quitting the country; and the enmity the king felt for that father and son went to such extremes that he pursued with his hatred their kinsmen and connections, as well as any he knew had shared close friendship with them. Some underwent punishment at his hands, while many fled seeking a refuge, some within the bounds of Norway itself, but others clean away out of the country.

Among these men we are now telling of was Yngvar, Skallagrím's father-in-law. What he settled to do was to turn his entire wealth into movable goods, provide himself with a sea-going vessel and her crew, and prepare for the Iceland voyage, for he had heard how Skallagrím had made his fixed abode there, and there would be no lack of choice land with Skallagrím. So when they were ready and the wind blew fair he sailed to sea, had a good passage, and made his landfall to the south of Iceland. He held west past Reykjanes, sailed into Borgarfjörd, then entered Langá and continued up the river as far as the waterfall, where they carried their freight off board. And when Skallagrím heard tell of Yngvar's arrival he went immediately to find him, inviting him to come and stay at his home with as many others as he chose. Yngvar accepted his offer, their ship was drawn ashore, whereupon he proceeded to Borg with a number of men to spend the winter there with Skallagrím. In the spring Skallagrím offered him choice land indeed, presenting him with that house he owned on Álftanes and the land inland as far as Leirulœk and outwards to Straumfjörd. Later he moved out there to this house and took possession of it. He was a fine worthy man and had abundance of wealth. Skallagrím then built a house at Knarrarnes and owned a place there for a long time afterwards.

Skallagrím was a great ironsmith and did a lot of smelting in

winter. He had a smithy built by the sea, a long way off from Borg
(where he thought the woods too far off), at a place called Raufarnes.
But when he found no stone there which proved hard and smooth
enough to impress him as good for beating iron on (for there are no
sea-boulders there: there are fine sands right along the sea), it happened one evening when the rest of them went to sleep that Skallagrím walked to the sea and pushed out an eight-oared boat which
he owned, then rowed out to the Midfjardareyjar, and dropped his
anchor-stone from her bows. Next he stepped over the side and dived
and brought a stone up with him and hoisted it aboard. Afterwards
he clambered back into the boat, rowed to land, and carried the stone
to his smithy, to set it down outside the smithy door, and afterwards
beat his iron on it. That stone is still lying there, with a lot of slag
alongside, and it can be observed of the stone that it is hammer-
marked on top, and that it is surf-worn rock and not like the other
rock which is thereabouts, and nowadays four men will not lift a
bigger.

Skallagrím went hard to work at his smithying, but his housecarles
grumbled and felt they were early afoot. Then he composed this
verse:

> (3) "Sound reason for soon rising;
>   Ironbeater who'd win better
>   Many a mint of money
>   With bellows windybellied.
>   Yelling sledge and yellow sludge
>   Of metal's ore are mated
>   By hand of mine, and meantime
>   Whinnies forth the wind there."

31

Skallagrím and Bera had a lot of children, but at first it so happened
that they all died. Then they begot a son who was sprinkled with
water and named Thórólf. And when he grew up he was soon tall
of stature and of the handsomest features. Every one said that he

would be a man just like Thórólf Kveldúlfsson, after whom he was named. Thórólf was far beyond those of his own age in strength, and as he grew up he became adept at most feats and skills then the vogue with men of ability. Thórólf was a happy-natured man. He was early so perfected in strength that he was judged fit to stand with other men. He was soon popular with everybody, while his father and mother loved him dearly.

Skallagrím and his wife had two daughters, one named Sæunn and the other Thórunn. These too showed promise as they grew up.

Once again Skallagrím and his wife had a son. He too was sprinkled with water and had a name given him. He was called Egil. But as he grew up it might soon be seen of him that he would prove a rare one for ugliness and black-haired like his father. When he was three years old he was as big and strong as other boys who were six or seven. He was a talker from the first, and clever with words. He was rather awkward to manage when he was at play with other youngsters.

That spring Yngvar came to Borg. His errand was to invite Skallagrím to a feast out at his place, and for this outing he bespoke Bera his daughter, Thórólf her son, and any others she and Skallagrím chose to bring along. Skallagrím gave a promise to come, whereupon Yngvar returned home to make preparations for the feast, and have ale brewed. When the time came for Skallagrím and Bera to go along, Thórólf got ready to go with them, together with some housecarles, so that they were fifteen in the party.

Egil had a word with his father, how he too wanted to go. "I have the same ties there as Thórólf," he maintained.

"You are not going," Skallagrím told him, "for you simply do not know how to behave yourself in company where there is heavy drinking—you who are not found very manageable even when you are sober."

With that Skallagrím mounted his horse and rode off, but Egil was thoroughly disgruntled. He walked from the house and found a cart-horse belonging to Skallagrím, clambered on its back, and rode after Skallagrím and the others. He found it rough going through the mires, for he did not know the right path; all the same he often caught sight of Skallagrím and his people riding when no mound or forest stood between them. There is this much to tell of his journey,

that he reached Álftanes late in the evening when men were seated
at the drinking. He walked into the hall, and when Yngvar saw Egil
he gave him a warm welcome and asked why he arrived so late? Egil
recounted what he and Skallagrím had had to say to each other.
Yngvar found Egil a seat right alongside him: they were seated opposite Skallagrím and Thórólf. It was held good sport there at the
drinking that men should chant verses. Then Egil chanted a verse:

> (4) "Still young, a march I've stolen
>   Brings me to Yngvar's homestead;
>   Fain am I to find him,
>   That lingthong's bedgold-giver.[1]
>   Know, goodly man, goldgiver
>   (The land of lindworm lightwhorled),
>   Ne'er shall you find a finer
>   Songsmith of some three summers."

Yngvar made a great to-do about this verse and thanked Egil warmly
for it. And the following day Yngvar fetched him in reward for his
skaldship three seasnail shells and a duck-egg. So next day at the
drinking Egil chanted a second verse, about his poet's pay:

> (5) "The raven's friend, the ravener,
>   Has given word-eager Egil
>   Three ever-silent seasnails
>   As guerdon for song's guardian.
>   Shipshaper, seasteed-steerer,
>   A gale of joy to Egil
>   He'll fan with his fourth favor,
>   (Nor dock again), a duck-egg."

   Egil won thanks from many a man for these poems of his. But
nothing more worth telling of happened on their outing, till he returned home with Skallagrím.

32

In Sogn there had been a powerful hersir named Björn living at
Aurland. He had a son Brynjólf, who took the entire inheritance
after his father. Brynjólf's sons were Björn and Thórd, who were
young men when these events took place. Björn was a great ven-
turer, was sometimes out raiding, and sometimes on trading voyages.
He was the very ablest of men.

It happened one summer that Björn was present at a crowded
feast in the Firths where he saw a beautiful girl with whom he fell
in love. He made inquiry as to what family she came from, and was
told that she was sister to Thórir Hróaldsson the Hersir, and that her
name was Thóra Lace-arm. Björn made his bid and asked for Thóra,
but Thórir refused him the match, and on those terms they
parted. That same autumn Björn got himself a crew and went
north to the Firths with a fully-manned skúta, so contriving it that
he reached Thórir's when he was not at home. Björn carried
Thóra off and brought her back with him to Aurland. They stayed
there over the winter, and Björn was anxious to marry her, but Brynjólf his father disapproved of what Björn had done, considering it a
disgrace, since up to then there had been long-lasting friendship between Thórir and Brynjólf. "So much the less, Björn," vowed Brynjólf, "shall you marry Thóra here at my house without her brother
Thórir's consent, that she shall be as well looked after here as if she
were my daughter and your sister." And that was the way it had to
be, even as Brynjólf stipulated, there in his own home, whether Björn
liked it or not.

Brynjólf sent messengers to Thórir, offering him atonement and
redress for what Björn had done. Thórir told Brynjólf to send Thóra
home, saying there would be no atonement otherwise; but Björn
would on no account let her go from him, however much Brynjólf
urged it.

In this fashion the winter wore away, but with the coming of spring
Brynjólf and Björn were talking over their affairs one day when
Brynjólf asked what he was planning to do.

Björn said the likeliest thing was that he would go abroad. "What I most fancy," he said, "is that you should fit me out with a longship and a crew to go with it, and that I then set off a-viking."

"There is no question of my fitting you out with a warship and a great crew," Brynjólf told him, "for I don't know but that you would then embark on the very course I least want you to follow—and there is trouble enough already on our hands because of you. But I will let you have a merchantship, and merchandise as well. Make south thereafter, for Dublin. That is the voyage now most talked about. I will find you a good ship's company too."

Björn's reply was that he would have to put up with things even as Brynjólf wished. So he now had a good merchantship fitted out and found a crew for her. Björn made preparations for his voyage, but was not ready in good time. When he was all set and the wind blew fair, he boarded his boat with twelve men and rowed in to Aurland, where they went up to the house, to his mother's bower there. She was seated indoors with a great many women. Thóra was there too. Björn said that Thóra was to go with him, and they led her away; but his mother told the women not to make so bold as to let this become known to those inside the hall. Brynjólf, she declared, would raise trouble if he knew of it, and the stage would then be set for great calamity between father and son. Thóra's clothes and valuables were all laid there ready to hand, and Björn and his men carried everything away with them. They then moved by night out of their ship, hoisted sail at once, and sailed out along the Sognsær and thereafter to the open sea.

They got an ill wind, had no choice but to run before it, and tossed long on the deep, for they were resolved to get the farthest they could from Norway. It happened one day that they were sailing east of Shetland in wild weather and damaged their ship making land on Mosey. They carried off their freight and made for the township there, carrying in all their wares, then drawing their ship ashore and repairing what was broken.

33

Shortly before winter a ship from the south reached Shetland from Orkney. They brought this news, how a longship had come to the Isles that autumn; on board were messengers of King Harald's with this message for Earl Sigurd, that the king wanted Björn Brynjólfsson put to death wherever he might be caught; and he sent similar instructions to the Hebrides, on down as far as Dublin. Björn heard this news, and heard also how he had been outlawed in Norway. As soon as he arrived in Shetland he had married Thóra. They spent the winter in Moseyjarborg, but in the spring, once the sea began to abate, Björn launched his ship and got her ready with all dispatch. And the minute he was ready and had a following wind he made for the open sea. They got a strong wind and were out only a short time before reaching Iceland from the south. The wind was blowing on to the land; then it bore them west along the coast and then out to sea, but later, when the wind favored them, they sailed towards the land. There was not a single man on board who had visited Iceland before. They sailed on into a remarkably big firth and thereafter stood in to the west shore. Landwards they could see nothing but breakers and harborless coasts; they beat as close as they could into the wind east along the land till there was a firth confronting them, and they sailed in along this firth till all the skerries and the surf came to an end. Then they lay up at a certain headland. An island lay on the outside, with a deep strait in between, where they secured their vessel. An inlet ran up west of the headland, and up above the inlet stood a big rock bastion.

Björn got into a boat and men with him. Björn warned his comrades that they must be on their guard against telling anything of their voyage which might get them into difficulties. Björn rowed to the farm with his men and there found people to talk to. The first thing they asked was where they had come ashore. They were told that the name of the place was Borgarfjörd, that the house there was named Borg, and its master Skallagrím. Björn remembered him instantly, set off to see Skallagrím, and they talked together. Skallagrím asked who might they be? Björn gave his own name, then his father's, and Skallagrím recalled Brynjólf very well and offered Björn all the furtherance he needed. Björn accepted this gratefully. Then Skallagrím asked what other notable persons might be on board. Thóra Hróald's daughter was there, replied Björn, the sister of Thórir Hersir, and at this Skallagrím was delighted, saying how right and proper it was for his foster brother Thórir's sister that he should give her all such help as she needed and he could provide, and he invited both her and Björn into his home with all their shipmates. This too Björn accepted. Then the freight was carried from off shipboard up into the home-meadow at Borg. That was where they set up their booths, but the ship was drawn up into the brook which is to be found there; and the place is called Bjarnartodur where Björn and his people had their booths.

Björn and his entire crew went to lodge with Skallagrím, and at no time had he fewer than sixty fighting men about him.

34

It happened that autumn, when ships had reached Iceland from Norway, that a rumor came with them that Björn had run off with Thóra without her family's consent, and for this the king had outlawed him from Norway. When this came to Skallagrím's ears, he sent for Björn and asked what was the truth about his marriage—had it been made with her family's approval?

"This is something I did not expect from a son of Brynjólf's," he said, "that I would not get the truth from you."

"Grím," answered Björn, "I have told you nothing but the truth, and you cannot blame me for telling you no more than you asked. Still, what is true had best be admitted. You have heard quite correctly that this marriage was not made with her brother Thórir's approval."

"But why," asked Skallagrím, incensed, "make so bold as to come here visiting me? Did you not know what friendship there was between Thórir and me?"

"I knew," Björn agreed, "that there was foster brotherhood between you, and close friendship too. But the reason why I visited you at your home was because I was driven ashore here, and I knew then that it was idle for me to try and steer clear of you. It now lies in your hands what my fate shall be, but I am hoping for the best, if only because I am a member of your household."

With that Skallagrím's son Thórólf stepped forward to put in a good word, urging his father not to press this charge against Björn, now that he had accepted him on friendly terms. Many others put in their word too, so now it came about that Grím grew less warm, and agreed that Thórólf should have his way in this.

"Take Björn, if that is what you want, and be as kind to him as you choose."

35

That summer Thóra gave birth to a child, a girl, who was sprinkled with water and given the name Ásgerd. Bera got a woman to take care of the child.

Björn and all his shipmates spent the winter with Skallagrím. Thórólf made a great friend of Björn and was forever in his company. So when spring came it happened one day that Thórólf went to talk with his father and ask him what plan he had to propose for Björn, his winter guest, or what help he was willing to give him. Grím asked Thórólf what he himself had in mind.

"On the whole," said Thórólf, "I think Björn would like to go to Norway, if he could live in peace there. It strikes me, father, that the best thing would be for you to send messengers to Norway to offer atonement for Björn, for your word will carry great weight with Thórir."

Thórólf so prospered in his persuasion that Skallagrím gave way and allotted men to go abroad that summer. These went with their messages and tokens to Thórir Hróaldsson and tried for an atonement between him and Björn. And as soon as Brynjólf knew of this errand he also set to with all his heart to offer atonement for Björn. The outcome was that Thórir took such atonement, for he could see that by this time events had taken such a turn that Björn had nothing to fear. Then Brynjólf agreed to atonement for Björn. Grím's messengers remained with Thórir over the winter, and Björn spent the winter with Skallagrím; but the following summer Skallagrím's messengers returned, and when they reached home in the autumn they announced how Björn was taken into atonement in Norway.

Björn spent yet a third winter with Skallagrím, but the following spring he made ready for his departure with the crew of men who had accompanied him there. When he was just ready to be off, Bera said she wanted her foster daughter Ásgerd to stay behind; Björn and his wife agreed to this, so the child stayed and was brought up there with Bera and Skallagrím.

Skallagrím's son Thórólf decided to take passage with Björn, and Skallagrím fitted him out for his voyage. He went abroad with Björn that summer. They had a good crossing and put in from the open sea at Sognsær. Björn sailed on into Sogn and later went home to his father, taking Thórólf along with him. Brynjólf gave them a delighted welcome. Next, word was sent to Thórir Hróaldsson, and he and Brynjólf arranged a meeting between them. Björn too came to this meeting, and he and Thórir confirmed the atonement between them. Later Thórir paid out the wealth which belonged to Thóra but happened to be in his keeping, and from there on Thórir and Björn built up a friendship between them quite apart from their ties by marriage. Björn was now living at home in Aurland with Brynjólf. Thórólf lived there too in high favor with father and son.

36

For a long time King Harald had his seat in Hördaland or Rogaland, at those great houses of his at Útstein or Ögvaldsnes or at Fitjar, at Alreksstadir or Lygra or Sæheim. But this winter we are now telling of the king spent in the north country. Now when Björn and Thórólf had spent a winter in Norway and spring came in, they prepared a ship, got her a crew, and went on a viking cruise that summer to the Baltic, returning home in the autumn after making great gains. But when they returned home, they learned that King Harald was in

Rogaland where he would be spending the winter. King Harald had now taken to age greatly, while many of his sons were grown men. King Harald's son Eirík, who was called Bloodaxe, was now in his early manhood. He was being fostered with Thórir Hróaldsson the Hersir. Of all his sons the king loved Eirík best. Thórir was at this time on the most affectionate terms with the king.

When they returned home Björn and Thórólf and their men went first to Aurland, then later they set off on their journey north into the Firths to visit Thórir Hersir at his home. They had a karfi¹ which twelve or thirteen men rowed aside, and had almost thirty followers. This ship they had captured whilst out viking in the summer. She was richly stained down to the waterline, and was the handsomest vessel.

When they reached Thórir's they got a good welcome and spent some time there, with their ship afloat under awnings in front of the farm. It happened one day as Thórólf and Björn were going down to the ship that they noticed how Eirík the king's son was there, now walking out on to the ship, now back ashore, then standing and studying the ship closely.

"The king's son is greatly struck with the ship," Björn told Thórólf. "So ask him to accept her from you, for I am sure it will help us greatly with the king if Eirík is on our side. I have heard tell that the king has hard feelings towards you because of your father."

Thórólf agreed that this would be a good plan, so with no more ado they continued on down to the ship. "You are running a close eye over the ship, Prince," said Thórólf. "What do you think of her?"

"Highly," he replied. "She is a lovely vessel."

"Then I will give you her," said Thórólf, "if you will accept her."

"That I will!" replied Eirík. "You will think it no great return though I promise you my friendship—yet that will bear fruit if I live."

Thórólf said such a return seemed to him worth far more than the ship. That was their parting, but from then on the king's son was on the most cordial terms with Thórólf and his men.

Björn and Thórólf found occasion to ask Thórir what he thought, whether it was true that the king felt hostile towards Thórólf. Thórir did not hide that this was what he had heard.

"Then I should like you to go and see the king," said Björn, "and put Thórólf's case to him, for it must go one and the same way for me and Thórólf. That was how he acted by me when I was in Iceland."

So it came about that Thórir promised to go and see the king, but he suggested they try whether Eirík the king's son was prepared to go along with him. And when Thórólf and Björn came to discuss this with Eirík, he promised to lend a hand with his father. Later Thórólf and Björn went off into Sogn, but Thórir and Eirík the king's king and found him in Hördaland. He gave them a glad welcome. They stayed there for a while and watched for an opportunity to meet the king when he was in a good frame of mind; they then set their business before him, announcing how a man had arrived there in Norway whose name was Thórólf—the son of Skallagrím. "We were wanting to ask, King, that you should recall how well his kinsmen have done by you, and not make him pay for his father's deeds, though he did avenge his brother."

Thórir talked of this mildly, but the king gave him a curt anwer, saying that they had suffered great mischief from Kveldúlf and his sons; and he gave it as his opinion that this Thórólf would be of the same temper as his kinsmen.

"They are all," he said, "arrogant men, devoid of moderation, and care not a rap with whom they contend."

But now Eirík struck in, telling him how Thórólf had made friends with him and given him a noble treasure, that same ship they had there.

"I have promised him my unqualified friendship. There will be few to make friends with me if I am not to have my way in this. You cannot let things turn out this way, father, for the very first man to give me such a treasure!"

So by the time they left off it came about that the king promised them that for his part Thórólf should live in peace. "Though I am not willing for him to come and see me. But you, Eirík," he said, "can take him as close to your heart as you like, and still more of that family too. But it will prove one or the other, either they will be softer-handed with you than they have been with me, or you will regret this request of yours, and this also, that you let them make long stay with you."

Later Eirík Bloodaxe and his men returned with Thórir to the Firths, whereupon they sent off a message to let Thórólf know how their mission to the king had turned out. That winter Thórólf and Björn spent with Brynjólf, but for many a summer they would be off on viking cruises, spending the winters with Brynjólf, or sometimes with Thórir.

37

Next, Eirík Bloodaxe assumed the royal power. He held the visitation of Hördaland and over the Firths as well. It was now that he picked men for his bodyguard and kept them about him. One spring Eirík prepared an expedition to Bjarmaland, taking great pains over his force for this journey. Thórólf decided to go with him; he was in the stem of his ship and carried his standard. Thórólf was by now bigger and stronger than all other men, and in that respect just like his father. Plenty to tell of happened on that expedition. Eirík fought a great battle in Bjarmaland on the Dvína, winning the victory there, as is recorded in the poems about him; and it was on this expedition that he won Gunnhild, Özur Tóti's daughter, and brought her home with him. Gunnhild was the loveliest and cleverest of all women, and was deeply versed in magic. Thórólf and Gunnhild were on very loving terms together. Thórólf was always wintering with Eirík, but would be out viking in the summers.

The next thing that happened was that Björn's wife, Thóra, fell ill and died, but a little later Björn found himself a new wife, whose name was Álof, the daughter of Erling the Rich from Ostr. They had a daughter whose name was Gunnhild.

There was a man named Thorgeir Thornfoot, who lived in Hördaland, at Fenhring: the place is called Ask. He had three sons, one of them named Hadd, and the second Bergönund, while the name of the third was Atli the Short. Bergönund was bigger and stronger than

other men, and hard and covetous. Atli the Short was not a tall man,
but square-built and strong of body. Thorgeir was a man with abundance of riches. He was a confirmed idolator and highly skilled in
magic. Hadd kept himself busy with viking cruises and was rarely at
home.

38

Thórólf Skallagrímsson prepared for a trading voyage one summer,
proposing what he indeed made good, to go to Iceland and see his
father. He had been away a long time now, and possessed wealth
uncounted and many a precious treasure. When he was ready for his
journey he went to see King Eirík, and at their parting the king
handed Thórólf an axe which he said he would like to give to Skallagrím. The axe had a halfmoon blade; it was big and decorated with
gold, the shaft inlaid with silver: it was indeed a treasure. Thórólf
set off as soon as he was ready, had a good crossing and brought his
ship into Borgarfjörd, and at once went briskly home to his father.
That was a great and joyful meeting when they saw each other. Later
Skallagrím went to the ship to collect Thórólf's goods, had her drawn
ashore, and Thórólf went home to Borg with eleven men. And when
he got there he gave Skallagrím King Eirík's greetings and handed
him the axe the king had sent him. Skallagrím took the axe; he held
it up and stared at it for a while without saying a word, and then hung
it up by his bed.

It happened at Borg one autumn day that Skallagrím had a great
many oxen driven home which he intended for slaughter. He had two
oxen led together under the side of the house, and placed so that their
necks were crossed. He took a big stone slab and slid it under their
necks. Then he went up to them with the axe, the king's gift, and
smote both the oxen at once, so that he took the head off either, but
the axe smashed down on to the stone, so that the blade's edge was
shattered and the hards ripped right through. Skallagrím stared at the
cutting-edge without saying a word, then walked into the hall
and, stepping up on to a beam, flung the axe up on to the cross-pieces
over the door, where it lay for the winter.

But in the spring Thórólf announced that he meant to go to Norway that summer. Skallagrím dissuaded him, saying it was good to drive home with a whole wagon.

"You have gone a great and glorious journey," he told him, "but there is a saying, 'Too often range, there'll come a change.' Take here and now so great a portion of wealth as you think will enable you to play a chieftain's part in the land."

Thórólf said he wanted to go one more voyage. "I have a pressing reason for going. But when I come back next time I shall be settling down here. But Ásgerd your foster daughter must go with me to Norway to see her father. He charged me with that when I came from the east."

Skallagrím said Thórólf would have his own way. "Though I have a feeling that if we part now we shall never meet again."

Later Thórólf went to his ship and put it in readiness. And when he was quite ready they moved the ship out to Digranes and lay there for a wind. Ásgerd now went down to the ship with him. But before Thórólf left Borg, Skallagrím went and took down the axe, the king's gift, from the doorbeams and walked outside with it. By this time the shaft was blackened with smoke and the axe rusted. Skallagrím stared at the axe's edge. Then he handed the axe to Thórólf. Skallagrím chanted a verse:

> (6) "Many a riving roughens
> My weapon's edge, my woundwolf;
> Woodgriever's soft—it would be!
> Ill-hatched this evil hatchet.
> Let snaghorn sneak to giver,
> Shift back with shaft thus smokebaked.
> What sense to send it hither?
> This was a princely present!"

39

It happened while Thórólf had been abroad and Skallagrím was living at Borg that one summer a merchant-ship from Norway came into Borgarfjörd. At that time shore-berths were employed in most cases for merchant-ships, either in the river or in the mouths of brooks or in dykes. The man who owned this ship was named Ketil, and nicknamed Ketil Blund. He was a Norwegian, of good family and rich. Geir was the name of his son, who was fully of age by this time and on board ship with him. Ketil was planning to find himself a place to live in Iceland. He came out late in the summer. Skallagrím knew all about him, and offered him lodgings together with all his company. Ketil accepted and spent the winter with him. That winter Geir, Ketil's son, asked for Thórunn, Skallagrím's daughter, in marriage; there was agreement as to the match, so Geir married her. Then later, in the spring, Skallagrím directed Ketil to land inland from Óleif's land on Hvítá, from Flókadalsárós on to Reykjadalsárós, with all that tongue of land which lay between, up to Raudsgil, and all Flókadal above the slopes. Ketil lived at Thrándarholt and Geir in Geirshlíd. He had a second home in Reykjalal at the upper Reykir. He was called Geir the Rich. His sons were Blund-Ketil and Thorgeir Blund. The third of them was that Thórodd Hrísablund who was the first to live at Hrísar.

40

Skallagrím found great pleasure in trials of strength and games, and liked talking about such things. Ball games were then all the fashion. The neighborhood was well blest with strong men at the time, yet not one of them had strength to compare with Skallagrím. He was now beginning to bend with the years.

Thórd was the name of Grani's son down at Granastadir. He was a most promising man, still young, and greatly attached to Egil Skallagrímsson. Egil was always wrestling. He was head-strong and quick-tempered, and everyone had learned to teach their sons that they should back down before Egil.

A very crowded ball game took place in Hvítárvellir at the beginning of winter, and men made their way there from all over the district. Quite a number of Skallagrím's household went to this game, and it was Thórd Granason who was their leader. Egil asked Thórd to let him go with him to the game. He was now in his seventh year. Thórd indulged him in this and carried him on horseback behind him. When they arrived at the playmeet men were sorted into sides for the game. A lot of small boys had come there too, who worked up a second game for themselves. In their case too there was a sorting. It fell to Egil's lot to play against a lad whose name was Grím, the son of Hegg of Heggsstadir. Grím was ten or eleven years old and powerful for his age, and as they played together Egil proved the less strong of them. Grím, too, made the most he could of these odds. Then Egil lost his temper, swung up the bat and gave Grím a clout, but Grím got hold of him and fetched him a heavy tumble and played rather rough with him, swearing he would do him a mischief if he did not behave himself. So once Egil got to his feet he left the game, and the boys catcalled him.

Egil went to find Thórd Granason and told him what had happened.

"I will go with you," promised Thórd, "and let you and me wreak vengeance on him." He handed him a beard-axe he had been holding (these weapons were then all the fashion), and they went to where the boys' game was taking place. Grím had just caught the ball and was running away, and the other boys were chasing him. Egil ran at Grím and sank the axe into his head, so that it instantly pierced the brain. Egil and Thórd made off afterwards towards their own people, whereupon the Mýramen raced for their weapons, and so with either party. Óleif Hjalti ran towards the men of Borg with all the men of his following, which made them by far the stronger party, and that was how they parted. From this arose the quarrel between Óleif and Hegg. They fought it out at Laxfit by Grímsá; seven men fell there; Hegg was hurt to death, and his brother Kvíg lost his life.

When Egil reached home, Skallagrím showed little liking for any of it; but Bera declared that Egil was of true viking stuff; and this would lie ahead, she vowed, that as soon as he was old enough he should be provided with ships-of-war. Egil chanted a verse:

> (7) "That mentioned my mother,
>   My ship they should buy me,
>   A fleet one, fair-oared one,

To fare out with vikings;
Stand up in the stem there,
Steer the dear sea steed,
Hold on to her haven,
Hew this man and that man."

By the time Egil was twelve years old he had grown so big that there were few so large or so dowered with strength that he could not beat most of them in the games. That winter which was his twelfth he was always at the games. Thórd Granason was by now twenty years old and of great bodily strength. It happened often in the course of the winter that Egil and Thórd were matched against Skallagrím. On one occasion that winter it happened that the ball game was at Borg, south in Sandvík. Thórd and he were matched against Skallagrím in the game, and he tired before them, so that it went easier for them. But in the evening after sunset it began to go worse for Thórd and Egil. Grím now grew so strong that he picked up Thórd and dashed him down so hard that he was all shattered and died on the instant. Next he caught at Egil.

Thorgerd Brák was the name of a bondwoman of Skallagrím's who had fostered Egil in his childhood. She was a big woman, strong as a man, and up to her eyes in magic.

Said Brák: "Do you now run mad at your own son, Skallagrím?"

At this, he loosed Egil and snatched at her. She dodged and ran off with Skallagrím after her. They made their way so to the outer edge of Dígranes, when she jumped off the cliff out into the strait. Skallagrím flung a big stone after her, landing it between her shoulders, and neither stone nor woman ever came up again. The spot is now known as Brákarsund.

Later in the evening, when they returned to Borg, Egil was in a black rage. And when Skallagrím and people in general had sat down to table, Egil had still not come to his place. Instead he had gone into the hall, to a man there who had control of both work and moneys for Skallagrím, and was a great favorite of his. Egil struck him his deathblow, and then went to his place at table. Skallagrím said never a word, and there the matter rested from that day on, with father and son speaking not one word about it, neither good nor bad.

In such fashion the winter passed. It was the following summer that Thórólf came home, as was reported earlier, and when he had spent a winter in Iceland, the following spring he again put his ship in readiness in Brákarsund. When he was all ready, it happened one day that Egil came looking for his father with a request that he fit him out for a voyage abroad.

"I want to go to Norway," he said, "with Thórólf."

Grím asked whether he had discussed this at all with his brother? No, said Egil, he had not, so Grím told him to do that in the first place. But when Egil broached the matter to Thórólf he said there was no question of his taking him with him.

"If your father thinks there is no managing you here in his own house, I cannot trust to having you abroad with me, for it will never do to show the same temper there as here."

"Then maybe," said Egil, "neither of us goes."

The next night a fierce gale blew up, a south-wester, and during the night, when it was dark and the tide at the flood, Egil came down to the ship and made his way on board outside the awning. He cut through the ropes which were on the outer side; next went as fast as he could up on to the gangway, instantly thrust out the gangway, and cut those ropes which were secured to dry land, whereupon the ship drove out into the firth. When Thórólf and his men discovered that the ship was adrift they jumped into a boat,[1] but the weather was far too wild for them to get anything done. The ship drove over to Anda-kíl and up on to the banks there, while Egil made his way home to Borg.

When men learned of this prank which Egil had played, most took a poor view of it. But he swore he would leave off doing Thórólf more hurt and mischief for only the briefest while, if he would not agree to carry him abroad. So now men intervened between them, and it ended so that Thórólf put up with Egil and he went abroad with him that summer.

As soon as Thórólf had come aboard ship, once he had possession of the axe which Skallagrím had put into his hands, he flung it overboard into the deep, so that it never came up again.

Thórólf went his ways that summer, had a good crossing, and reached Norway at Hördaland, whence he at once headed north for

Sogn. The news there that winter was that Brynjólf had died of an illness and his sons had shared out the inheritance. Thórd had Aurland, the house their father had lived in. He had become the king's retainer and a landed man. Thórd's daughter was named Rannveig, the mother of Thórd and Helgi. Thórd was the father of Rannveig, the mother of that Ingiríd whom King Ólaf married. Helgi was the father of Brynjólf, the father of Serk from Sogn and of Svein.

41

Björn's portion was a second homestead, fine and noble. He did not become the king's retainer, and for that reason was known as Franklin-Björn. He was a man rich in gold and in every way lordly. Thórólf went to see Björn the moment he put in from sea and brought him Ásgerd his daughter. That was a happy meeting of theirs. Ásgerd was a most beautiful and accomplished woman, and wise and knowledgable.

Next Thórólf went to see King Eirík. When they met, Thórólf conveyed Skallagrím's greetings to King Eirík, saying that he had received the king's gift with gratitude. Later he produced a fine longship's sail which he said Skallagrím had sent to the king. King Eirík accepted this gift graciously, and invited Thórólf to stay with him that winter.

Thórólf thanked the king for his offer. "But first of all I must go to Thórir's. I have urgent business with him."

Later on Thórólf went to Thórir's, as he had said he would, and received the best of welcomes there. Thórir invited Thórólf to stay with him, and Thórólf said he would like to accept.

"But there is a man with me—he is my brother—who must have lodging wherever I happen to be myself. He has never been from home before, and he needs me to keep an eye on him."

Thórir said it was quite all right, though Thórólf wanted to have yet more men out there with him. "We reckon your brother," he said, "a useful acquisition, if he is anything like you."

Next Thórólf went back to his ship, had her drawn ashore and set to rights; but he himself went to Thórir Hersir's, and Egil with him.

Thórir had a son whose name was Arinbjörn, who was rather older than Egil. Quite early Arinbjörn was a fine man and highly skilled at feats of strength. Egil made friends with Arinbjörn and was forever in his company; but there was rather a coolness between the brothers.

42

Thórólf Skallagrímsson raised with Thórir the question of how he would take it if he asked to marry his kinswoman Ásgerd. Thórir could not have taken it better; he would certainly be a forwarder of his suit, he said. So later Thórólf went north into Sogn, taking a fine body of men with him. Thórólf reached Björn's house and got a good welcome there; Björn invited him to stay with him for as long as he liked. Thórólf soon set out his business with Björn: he made his proposal and asked for Ásgerd, Björn's daughter. He welcomed the match; it was easily won of him, and the result was that the betrothals went forward and a day was set for the wedding. The feast should take place at Björn's in the autumn. Next Thórólf returned to Thórir's to tell him the result of his journey, and Thórir was delighted that this match would be taking place.

When the time arrived for Thórólf to be on his way to the feast, he invited men to go along with him, asking Thórir first, and then Arinbjörn, together with their housecarles and chief farmers, so that there was a large and goodly company for the journey. But as the appointed day drew near when Thórólf should leave home, and the bridesmen had arrived, Egil fell so ill that he could not go along. But Thórólf and his people had a big longship fully-manned and went on their way as had been arranged.

43

There was a man named Ölvir, a housecarle of Thórir's and the manager and steward of his household. The calling in of debts was entrusted to him, and he was Thórir's treasurer. Ölvir was past his prime but the most active of men even so. It so happened that Ölvir had to make a journey from home to collect those of Thórir's land-rents which had been left over in the spring. He had a rowing-ferry, with twelve of Thórir's housecarles on board. And now Egil began to perk up and rose from bed, thinking it grown dull at home now that everyone had gone away. He came to have a talk with Ölvir, saying he would like to go along with him, and Ölvir agreed they would not be overloaded by another good man, for there was plenty of room in the boat. So Egil made the trip with them. He took along his weapons, sword, halberd, and buckler. They set off as soon as they were ready and got wearisome bad weather, with a fierce head wind, but they pressed boldly on their way and bent their backs to the oars.

Their progress was such that in the course of the evening they reached Atley, where they put to land. A short distance up on the island was a big house belonging to King Eirík, with a man named Bárd in charge. He had been nicknamed Atley-Bárd, and was a great man for business and a good workman. He was not of good family, but King Eirík and Queen Gunnhild were very fond of him. Ölvir and his men hauled their ship up past highwater-mark, and then proceeded to the house. They met Bárd outside and told him their adventure, and this moreover, that they would like to spend the night there. Bárd could see that they were very wet, so led them to some rest-hall or other which was apart and separate from the other buildings. He had a big fire built for them and their clothes were dried there.

Once they had taken to their clothes again back came Bárd. "We will now set a table for you here," he told them. "I know you will be ready for sleep. You are men worn out with bad weather."

This suited Ölvir very well. Next a table was set and food given them, bread and butter, and big bowls of skýr set out.

"It is a great pity," said Bárd, "that there is no ale in the place, so that I might entertain you the way I would like. But this time you must put up with such as there is."

Ölvir and his men were very thirsty and supped the skýr, whereupon Bárd had buttermilk brought in and they drank that too.

"I should be only too pleased," Bárd told them, "to give you better drink if there were any."

There was no lack of straw inside, and he invited them to lie down now and sleep.

44

That same evening King Eirík with Gunnhild arrived on Atley, where Bárd had prepared a feast in readiness for him. There was to be a sacrifice to the goddesses there, with the best of banquets and heavy drinking inside the hall.

The king asked where might Bárd be? "I don't see him anywhere."

"Bárd is outside," was the reply, "serving his guests."

"What guests are those," the king asked, "since he considers that more of an obligation than to be indoors here with us?"

The man told him that housecarles of Thórir Hersir had come there.

"Then go after them as quick as you can," ordered the king, "and summon them here inside."

This was done, and they were told that the king would like to see them. So with that they went. The king had a gracious greeting for Ölvir and told him to sit opposite him in the high-seat and his comrades outwards from him. They did so, Egil sitting next to Ölvir. Then they were brought ale to drink. Many a toast followed, and a horn must be drained at each toast. In the course of the evening it came about that many of Ölvir's comrades grew helpless; some were spewing there inside the hall, while some got themselves out through the door. Bárd kept hard at it plying them with drink. Then Egil got hold of the horn which Bárd had handed to Ölvir and drank it off. Bárd swore he was mighty thirsty, and instantly fetched him the refilled horn, telling him to drink *that* off. Egil caught hold of the horn and chanted this verse:

(8) "You told your troll-foe[1] stranger,
      Once floods flowed free for Dísir,
      Strong ale was lacking strangely:
      I grant your guile, gravebreaker!
      Concealed next, unrevealing
      (A bad trick, Bárd, you played us)
      Thought's mischief and heart's malice
      From men unknown, unknowing."

Bárd told him to drink and give over these flytings. Egil was down-
ing every cup that came his way, and for Ölvir too. So off went Bárd
to the queen and told her that there was a man present who brought
shame on them, and never drank so much that he could say he was
no longer thirsty. The queen and Bárd then mixed the drink with
poison, and afterwards carried it inside. Bárd signed the cup, bringing
it next to the cup-bearer, who fetched it to Egil and invited him to
drink. Egil plucked out his knife and stabbed at his palm. He took
hold of the horn, graved runes on it, and spread them with blood.
Then he chanted:

(9) "Grave we runes on horn now,
      With red blood make words ruddy;
      Here are the words I'm wanting
      On tree of aurochs' ear-root:[2]
      Drain we what drink we crave for
      When merry maidens pour;
      Learn if fares foul or fairly
      The ale this Bárd has hallowed."

The horn split apart and the drink ran down into the straw. Then
Ölvir began to grow faint. Egil stood up and led Ölvir off to the door,
but kept a grip on his sword. As they reached the door Bárd came
after them, asking Ölvir to drink his parting-toast. Egil seized it and
drank, then chanted a verse:

(10) "I'm half-seas over, Ölvir
      With ale is turning paler,
      Beerfoam from aurochs' horn runs
      Frothing through my mouth's front.

> Rainspeeder of the spearcloud,
> Your wiles yourself bewilder:
> Here's rain of skalds a-roaring,
> And pelting down my poem!" [3]

Egil flung away the horn, but snatched at his sword and drew. It was dark in the front hall. He drove the sword through Bárd's middle, so that the bloody point came out at his back. Down he fell, dead, with blood spurting from his wound. Then Ölvir keeled over, the spew gushing out of him. At this same moment Egil rushed out and away from the hall. It was pitch dark outside. Egil instantly set off at a run from the farm.

Inside the front hall men could see that Bárd and Ölvir had both fallen. Then out came the king and had light fetched and men could see what had happened: how Ölvir lay there speechless, but Bárd had been killed and the whole floor was swimming with blood.

The king asked where might that big fellow be who had been the heaviest drinker there that evening? He was told that he had gone outside. "Search for him," ordered the king, "and have him appear before me." A search was made for him right through the house, but he was nowhere to be found. But when they came inside the rest-hall a lot of Ölvir's men were lying there. The king's men asked whether Egil had maybe passed that way? He had rushed in, they admitted, and snatched up his weapons. "But out he went after that."

This was reported to the king, who ordered his men to be off at their smartest and seize all the ships that were on the island. "And in the morning when it is light we will comb the whole island and then kill this man."

45

Egil kept going through the night and hunted for where there were ships; but whatever part of the seashore he came to, there were men everywhere. He kept going the whole night and could get a boat nowhere. As it grew light he found himself on a headland.. Then he saw an island, and there was a strait in between—and quite a wide one. So what he decided to do was to take helmet, sword and spear, and break off its shaft and fling it out to sea, but the weapons he rolled up in his cloak, thus making a bundle of it and tying it on his back. Then he plunged into the strait and made no stay till he reached the island. It was called Saudey. It was not a big island and was overgrown with scrub. There was livestock on it, cattle and sheep which belonged to Atley. And when he reached the island he wrung out his clothes. It was now daylight and the sun risen.

King Eirík had the island of Atley combed as soon as it was light. This was slow work, for the island was a big one, nor was Egil to be found. They then went by ship to other islands to look for him. It was in the evening that twelve men rowed to Saudey to look for Egil, though there were many islands near by. He saw this ship which was making for the island; and how nine men came ashore and shared out the search. Egil had lain down in the scrub and taken cover before the ship reached land. Three now went in each search party, but three were minding the ship. When a rise in the ground came between them and the ship, Egil stood up and walked towards her. Those who were guarding the ship noticed nothing till Egil was upon them. He instantly struck one his death blow, but the second ran off; there was a bank there which had to be scaled, and Egil swept after him and took off his leg. One jumped on to the ship and thrust off with the pole, but Egil hauled in the cable and jumped aboard, and they were not long swapping blows before Egil killed him and pitched him over the side. Then he took to the oars and rowed the boat away. He kept going the whole night and following day, and did not stop till he reached Thórir Hersir's.

But the king let Ölvir and his comrades go in peace from these disturbances. As for the men who were on Saudey, they were there many nights and slaughtered cattle for food, kindled a flame and built a fire-pit. They built one so big that it might be seen back home, got their fire going, and made a beacon. And when it was seen, men rowed out to them. By then the king had taken himself off. He was bound for another feast.

Ölvir and his men arrived home ahead of Egil, when Thórir and Thórólf had just returned from the wedding. Ölvir told his news, the killing of Bárd and everything that had happened there, but he did not know what had become of Egil. Thórólf was deeply depressed, and Arinbjörn as well, fearing that he would never come back. But the following morning Egil arrived home. When Thórólf learned this, he got up and went to find Egil and inquired how he had got away, and what had happened worth telling of in the course of it. Then Egil chanted a verse:

> (11) "I beat retreat from Listi's[1]
> Landguardian and from Gunnhild
> With daring (there's no danger
> I'll preen myself too proudly).
> This follows: three fine fellows,
> Spry thanes of this sprig Eirík,
> In Hel's high hall now halted
> Shall dawdle, now and always."

Arinbjörn commended what he had done, maintaining that his father was in duty bound to bring Egil into atonement with the king.

"People will agree that Bárd got only what he asked for when he was killed," said Thórir. "All the same, it is too much part of Egil's family history to think over-lightly of incurring the king's anger. For most men that proves too heavy a burden. Still, I will bring you into atonement with the king, this once."

So Thórir went to see the king, but Arinbjörn sat tight at home. It must go one way for all, was his attitude. When Thórir had audience of the king he offered terms for Egil, including himself as security and the king's right to make his own award. King Eirík was very angry indeed, and it was no easy task to reach terms with him. What his father had told him would prove true, he said: one should be slow to trust to any of the breed.

Arrange matters this way, he told Thórir—"For though I make an agreement of sorts, Egil shall make no long stay in my kingdom. Still, for your sake, Thórir, I will take payment for those men."

The king awarded such fines as he thought fit, and Thórir paid them in full. He then went home.

46

Thórólf and Egil stayed with Thórir on cordial terms, but in the spring they fitted out a big longship, found her a crew, then sailed to the Baltic in the summer, to harry there and win immense wealth; they had many battles. They held on out to Kúrland where they put ashore for a fortnight's peace and trading. When that was over they began raiding again and made landings in various places.

One day they landed at a big river mouth. There was a large forest there. Their plan was to go up inland, so they broke up into groups of twelve. They marched to the forest, and it was no distance before the settlements began. They robbed there, killing some people too, but the inhabitants ran away and they met with no real opposition. In the course of the day Thórólf blew the recall for his followers to get down to the sea. His men, wherever they happened to be, then returned to the forest, but their strength could be checked only when they reached the shore.

By the time Thórólf had got down to the sea, Egil had not shown up, but the night had now begun to darken and they felt they could not go looking for him. Egil had crossed the forest with his twelve men, when they caught sight of some big flats and settlements. Only a short way from them stood a farm, so they pushed towards it, and as soon as they got to it dashed into the house; they found no one there, but carried off such wealth as was transportable. There were a lot of buildings, so they spent a good while over this, and by the time they were out and away from the buildings a force of men had got between them and the forest, and attacked them. There was a high fence erected between them and the forest. Egil ordered them to stay close, so that they might not be got at on all sides. Egil advanced at their head, and then each after the other so close that no one could thrust between them. The Kúrir attacked them briskly, for the most part with spear-casts and missiles, but did not come to close quarters. Egil and his men could see nothing amiss as they advanced along the fence, but a second fence came to enclose them on the other side, till they could make no headway. The Kúrir herded them into the dead end, some harassing them from the far side with spear thrusts and swords through the fence, while others threw clothes over their weapons. They were wounded, and the next thing, captured and all bound, and so led back to the farm.

The man who owned the farm was important and rich. He had a grown-up son. There was a discussion later as to what they should do with them. The farmer said it seemed to him a good plan to kill them off one by one; but the farmer's son said that the night was growing dark and they could not now have any fun torturing them. He was for letting it wait till morning, so they were thrown into an outhouse and firmly tied. Egil was tied hand and foot to a post. Next, the house was strongly secured, and the Kúrir went into the hall, where they ate, drank, and were merry. Egil jerked about testing the post, until it loosened up out of the floor. Then the post fell, and Egil worked himself free of it. Next he untied his hands with his teeth, and once his hands were free untied the fastenings off his feet. Then he untied his comrades.

When they were all freed they hunted through the house for the likeliest place to get out. The place was constructed with walls of huge logs, but at one of its two ends stood a flat partition wall. They dashed against this and so broke through. There was then a second room which they came into, and here too there were log walls all round. They could hear men's voices down under their feet, so they hunted about and found a trap door in the ground. This they opened, and down under there was a deep pit. It was from there they had heard men talking. Egil asked who in the world was there, and the person who replied said that his name was Áki. Egil asked whether he would like to come up out of the pit, whereupon Áki said they would like nothing better. So Egil and his men lowered the rope they had been tied with into the pit and hauled up three men. Áki said the others were his two sons, and that they were Danes who had been taken prisoners-of-war last summer.

"I was well treated," he admitted, "last winter. I was employed in great part to look after the farmer's property, but the boys were made serfs and hated it. In the spring we decided to run away, but were retaken and were then put here in this pit."

"The plan of the house must be familiar to you," said Egil. "Where are we likeliest to get out?"

Áki said that there was a second partition wall. "Break that open. You will then come out into a granary, and from there can get into the open at will."

Egil and his men did this, broke through the partition, went next into the granary, and from there into the open. It was pitch dark. His comrades were now of opinion that they should make tracks for the forest.

"If you know your way around the place," Egil reminded Áki, "you should be able to lead us to some pickings."

Áki agreed that there was no lack of good things in the place. "There is a big loft here where the farmer sleeps. There is no lack of weapons inside."

Egil told him to lead the way to the loft, but as they reached the top of the stair they could see that the loft stood open. There were lights inside, and some serving men making up the beds. Egil ordered some of his men to stay outside and watch that no one got away, but he himself dashed into the loft, grabbed weapons there (for there was no lack of them inside), and killed every man in the place. They all helped themselves to a full rig of weapons; then Áki went to where there was a trapdoor in the floorboards and pulled it open, saying that they should descend there into the lower chamber. They took lights and went that way. The farmer's money-boxes were there, fine treasures besides, and a lot of silver. They loaded themselves with these, then carried them outside. Egil hoisted a big mead-cask in the crook of his elbow and carried it off under-arm. They then made for the forest, but no sooner were they inside it than Egil called a halt.

"This is a feeble and unsoldierly way of doing things," he told them. "We have stolen the farmer's goods in such a fashion that he knows nothing about it. Such shame shall never be ours. So back to the farm we go and let them know what is happening."

Everyone spoke against this. They wanted to make for the ship, they said. But Egil set down the mead-cask, made off at a run, and went racing back to the farm. When he got back there he could see how servant lads were walking from the kitchen with trenchers and carrying them into the hall. There was a big fire, he noticed, in the kitchen, with various pots on it. That, then, was the way he went. Big logs had been fetched home, and fires built as is the practice there, so that one end only of the log is set alight, and the log consumes that way. Egil picked up such a log and carried it to the hall and stuck the end which was ablaze under the eaves and so up into the birch-bark. The fire spread quickly through the faggots, but those who sat drinking noticed nothing till flame ran right through the roof. They rushed for the doorway, but there was no easy way out, both because of the faggots and this in addition, that Egil was guarding the door. He killed men both in the doorway and out in front of the door; and it was only a second or two before the hall burned so that it fell in. The whole company which was inside perished, but Egil got back to the forest and found his comrades there. He said he would take the mead-cask he had carried off for his private booty; and, as a matter of fact, it proved to be full of silver.

Thórólf and his men were overjoyed when Egil came down to the ship. As soon as morning broke they put to sea forthwith. Áki and his sons stayed with Egil's troop. As the summer wore on they sailed to Denmark, and once again lay in wait for merchant-ships and robbed wherever they had the chance.

47

Harald Gormsson had assumed the royal power in Denmark, for Gorm his father was dead. The land was now a prey to strife, and vikings lay in ambush pretty well everywhere off Denmark. Áki knew his way about Denmark both by sea and land. Egil questioned him closely which would be the places where great booty lay for the taking, and when they reached Eyrarsund, Áki said that up inland was a big market place called Lund; he claimed that there was a good chance of profit there, but that it was likely there would be opposition from the townsmen. The case was put to their followers to decide whether they would go ashore or not. Men took it different ways: some were for it, while some hung back; so the decision was left to the leaders. Thórólf was all for going ashore. Then there was a discussion with Egil as to what he thought advisable. He chanted a verse:

(12) "Raise glaive and let sword glitter,
My warrior, wolftooth-stainer:
We've doughty deeds to do now
This summer, dalesnake-season.
Let every lad to Lund then,
Briskly no less than bravely,
Let's sing there long ere sunset
The soursweet song of spears."

Next men made ready to put ashore and marched upon the town. But once the townsmen were aware of hostilities they moved against them. There was a wall of logs around the town; they set men to defend it, and the battle was joined. Egil was the first to go in over the wall, and at that the townsmen fled. There was a great slaughter of men there. They pillaged the town, then set fire to it before they went away, and afterwards marched down to their ships.

48

Thórólf held north off Halland with his following and put into harbor there when the wind checked them. They did no robbery there. A short way inland there was an earl, Arnfid by name, who, when he heard that the vikings had arrived off the coast there, sent men of his to meet them; their errand was to discover whether they wanted sanctuary or war. When these messengers had found Thórólf with their message, he said that they would not be harrying there, adding that they had no call to harry or go plundering, for the land was not rich. The messengers returned to the earl and told him the result of their mission. And when the earl felt assured that he need not assemble an army on their account, he rode down without a guard to meet the vikings. And when they met their talk went off well. The earl invited Thórólf to a feast with him, with any of his men whom he chose, and Thórólf promised to go.

At the appointed time the earl had riding horses sent down for them. Both Thórólf and Egil decided to go along, and they took thirty men with them. When they came into the earl's presence he

gave them a good welcome: they were escorted into the hall, where
good ale was instantly fetched in and served for them to drink. They
stayed on for the evening, and before it grew time to remove the
tables the earl suggested that they should take their seats by lot, and
be drinking man and woman together so far as they went, and any
who were left over on their own. Lots were then cast into the skirt
of a cloak and the earl picked them up. The earl had a most handsome daughter, now in the flower of her youth. The lot decreed that
Egil should sit by her during the evening. She was walking about the
floor, diverting herself. Egil got up and walked to the place where
the earl's daughter had been sitting during the day, but as men took
their seats she walked to her own proper place, chanting:

> (13) "Why sit, my lad, in *my* seat?
>   For seldom you'll have served
>   Warm carrion into wolfmouth;
>   Alone I'd be, all on my own!
>   No raven you've seen raving
>   In fall o'er blood of fallen,
>   And nought you've wrought where swordblades
>   Shellfine shall foin together."

Egil caught hold of her and drew her down alongside him, chanting:

> (14) "With blade I've fared all bloody
>   (Woundgrouse had grace to follow),[1]
>   Feared for my yelling spear
>   In viking rush voracious.
>   Our battle bleak and bitter,
>   Blazed fire in every farmstead,
>   We hewed and heaped up corpses
>   In every guarded gateway."

They drank together throughout the evening and were most merry.
The feast was everything it could be, and so too on the following day.
Then the vikings went to their ships. The earl and they parted good
friends and they exchanged gifts. Thórólf and Egil held on with
their crews for the Brenneyjar, at this time a favorite haunt of vikings,

because a lot of merchant-ships sailed through these islands. Áki went home with his sons. He was a man with abundance of gold and owned many a house in Jutland. They parted on good terms, pledging full friendship between them. At the beginning of autumn Thórólf and Egil sailed north off Norway and came on to the Firths where they put in to see Thórir Hersir. He gave them a good welcome, and Arinbjörn his son a still better. He suggested that Egil should spend the winter there, an offer Egil accepted with thanks.

But when Thórir learned of Arinbjörn's offer he reckoned it a rather hasty one.

"I don't know how King Eirík is going to like it," he said, "for after Bárd's killing it was his sentence that he would not have Egil remain in Norway."

"But, Father," said Arinbjörn, "you can easily arrange matters with the king so that he has no quarrel with Egil's stay. In any case you will be inviting your kinsman Thórólf to stay here, and Egil and I must have one and the same home this winter."

From this conversation Thórir saw that Arinbjörn meant to have his way in this. Father and son then offered Thórólf winter-quarters there, and he accepted. They spent the winter there with twelve men.

The names of two brothers are given as Thorvald the Haughty and Thorfid the Strong. They were closely related to Franklin-Björn and had been brought up with him. They were big strong men, very active and assertive. They accompanied Björn so long as he went on viking cruises, but later, when he settled down, the brothers came over to Thórólf and went raiding with him. On his ship they were in the stem, but when Egil got command of a ship Thorfid was his fore-castleman. The brothers accompanied Thórólf at all times, and he thought more of them than of any of his shipmates. They were in his following that winter, and their seats were next to the brothers'. Thórólf sat in the high-seat and took his drink with Thórir, but Egil sat as drinking-mate to Arinbjörn. They used to walk on the floor there for every toast.

That autumn Thórir Hersir went to see King Eirík. The king gave him an excellent welcome. When they came to talk matters over, Thórir asked the king not to find fault with him for having Egil with him that winter.

The king made a gracious answer, saying that Thórir could get from him anything he liked. "But it would not turn out this way if anyone else had taken Egil into his keeping."

But when Gunnhild got wind of what they were discussing, "To my way of thinking, Eirík," she said, "it is the case now as only too often that you are easily taken in with talk, nor do you long carry in mind the wrongs men do you; and you are now going to humor the sons of Skallagrím till they again kill off some close kinsman of yours. But act though you may as if you reckon Bárd's killing of no importance, that is not what I think!"

"Gunnhild," said the king, "more than any living soul you goad me into cruelty. Yet Thórólf has had more kindness from your hands than now appears the case. I am not going back on my word regarding these brothers."

"Thórólf was all very well," she retorted, "till Egil spoiled him. But now I see no difference between them."

Thórir returned home when he was ready and told the brothers of the king's words, and the queen's words too.

49

There were two brothers of Gunnhild's by the name of Eyvind Brag and Álf Askman, sons of Özur Tóti. They were big men and very strong and active, and just now were in high favor with King Eirík and Gunnhild. They were not all that popular with people in general, were still young, and yet come to their full strength. It happened that spring that arrangements were made for a great summer-sacrifice at Gaular. This was a most famous head-temple. A great many men made their way there out of the Firths and from Fjalir and Sogn, almost all of them notable persons. King Eirík went along too.

Gunnhild had this to tell her brothers: "I want you so to contrive in this press of men that you get one or other of Skallagrím's sons killed. And best of all, were it the pair of them!" They promised it should be so.

Thórir Hersir made ready for his journey there. He called Arin-björn to talk with him. "I am off now to the sacrifice," he said, "but

I don't want Egil to go. I know Gunnhild's gifts of persuasion, and Egil's madheadedness, and the king's power, and how it will not be easy to watch out for them all together. Yet Egil will not agree to be left unless you too stay behind. But Thórólf shall accompany me," he said, "and the rest of those comrades. Thórólf shall make sacrifice and seek good fortune for both brothers."

Later Arinbjörn told Egil that for his part he would be staying home. "You and I together," he told him. Egil agreed that it should be so. But Thórir and his people went to the sacrifice, and there was a considerable body of men there, and big drinking sessions. Wherever Thórir went, Thórólf went with him, and they were never separated day or night. Eyvind told Gunnhild that he could not get at Thórólf, so she ordered him to kill one of his men—"Rather than we suffer a dead loss."

It happened one evening when the king had gone to sleep, and Thórir and Thórólf too, but Thorfid and Thorvald sat on, that the brothers Eyvind and Álf came up and sat down beside them and were merry, and at first they drank as a party. Next it came about that they should drain the horn half and half. Eyvind and Thorvald were drinking together, and Álf and Thorfid. As the evening wore on there was unfair drinking, and following that sharp words, and then big talk. Then Eyvind jumped up, whipped out his dagger, and stabbed at Thorvald so that it sufficed for his death wound. Both parties started up, the king's men and Thórir's housecarles, but every one in the place was unarmed, for it was temple-holy there, and men intervened to part those who were maddest. Nothing more to tell of happened that evening.

Eyvind had wrought manslaughter in a sanctuary, had become wolf and outlaw, and must away at once. The king offered payment for the dead man, but Thórólf and Thorfid vowed that they had never taken such payment—nor would they take it now. On these terms they parted. King Eirík and Gunnhild sent Eyvind south to Denmark to King Harald Gormsson, for he could not legally remain on Norwegian soil. The king was very glad of him and his following. Eyvind had taken a very big longship with him to Denmark, and later the king set Eyvind to guard the land from vikings, for he was a great fighting man.

Once springtime succeeded to winter Thórólf and Egil prepared to go viking. When they were ready they held once more for the Baltic. After reaching the Vík they sailed south off Jutland and raided there; next they went to Frísland where they made a long stay that summer, and then once again shaped course back to Denmark. As they reached the boundary where Denmark and Frísland meet, and were lying off shore, it happened one evening when men were settling down to sleep on the ships that two men came to Egil's ship, claiming that they had a message for him. They were brought before him. They said that Áki the Rich had sent them there with this message, that: "Eyvind Brag is lying out at sea off Jutlandssída, and planning to waylay you as you travel from the south. He has assembled so strong a force that you stand no chance against him if you encounter the whole of it; but for himself he is traveling with two light ships, and is now hardly any distance from you."

When this news reached Egil he had them instantly strike their awnings, issuing orders for them to proceed with stealth, which they did. They came up with Eyvind and his men at dawn, where they were lying at anchor, and attacked them immediately, letting fly with both stones and weapons. Many of Eyvind's followers perished there, but he himself jumped overboard and got to land by swimming, and so with the rest of them that got away. Egil and his men seized the ships, their clothes and their weapons, and returned that same day to his own following and met Thórólf. He asked Egil where on earth had he been, and where he had picked up those ships they traveled in. The ships had been Eyvind Brag's, said Egil, but they had taken them from him. Then Egil chanted:

> (15) "We found some pretty fighting
> 'Foretime off Jutland's foreshore;
> The warrior who was warden
> Of Denmark made deep dintmark;
> Till brash of wit the Braggart
> (His hands all close behind him)
> Overborne leapt overboard
> To breast these eastern breakers."

"I think you have done such a deed here," said Thórólf, "that it will be inadvisable for us to go to Norway the whole autumn."

Egil agreed it was just as well, though they now looked round for new quarters.

50

Alfred the Great was a ruler over England. He was the first of his line to be sole king of England (this was in the time of Harald Fairhair, king of Norway). After him his son Edward was king there, who was the father of Athelstan the Victorious, the fosterer of Hákon the Good. At the time we are now speaking of Athelstan became king of England in succession to his father, though there were other brothers too, sons of Edward. Now no sooner had Athelstan become king than those chieftains started hostilities who had earlier lost their power to his ancestors. They judged now would be the easiest time to claim their own, while a young king was in charge of the country These were the Welsh and Scots both, and the Irish too. But King Athelstan assembled an army, and gave war-pay to all men, both foreign and native, who chose to have that for their gain.

The brothers Thórólf and Egil were holding south off Germany and Flanders when they heard how England's king found himself in need of men, and how there was prospect of great profit ahead. They decided to hold that way with their crews, and kept traveling that autumn till they fell in with King Athelstan, who gave them a good welcome, guessing there would be powerful reinforcement in their following. The king of England soon came to the point, invited them to take his pay and become his land's defenders, and between them they settled that they would become King Athelstan's men.

England was Christian when these events took place, and had been so for a long time. King Athelstan was a good Christian: he was called Athelstan the Faithstrong. He requested Thórólf and his brother that they should have themselves primesigned, for this was a common custom of the time among traders and those who went on war-pay along with Christian men; for those who were primesigned held full communion with Christians and heathens too, yet kept to the faith which was most agreeable to them. Thórólf and Egil did this at the king's request; they both had themselves primesigned. They had three hundred men of theirs there who took the king's war-pay.

51

Óláf the Red was the name of the king in Scotland. He was Scottish on the father's side but Danish on the mother's, and come of the line of Ragnar Lodbrók. He was a very great man. Scotland was reckoned a third of the kingdom as compared with England. Northumberland is reckoned a fifth of England, and it lies furthest to the north, neighboring Scotland on the east side. Danish kings had held it in the old days. York is the chief town there. Athelstan was lord over that territory, and had set two earls in charge of it, one of them named Álfgeir and the other Godrek. They stayed there as defenders of the land against attack by both Scots and Danes and Norwegians too, who raided continually in the land and considered they had strong claim to the land there—for in Northumberland were only those men (if they were anybody at all) who were of Danish descent by father or mother, and many of them by both.

Over Wales reigned two brothers, Hring and Adils, who were tributary to King Athelstan, and it followed that when they were on war service with the king they and their forces should be in the forefront of the battle, before the king's standards. These brothers were very fine soldiers, but men not all that young.

Alfred the Great had deprived all tributary kings of their titles and power. Those were now styled earls who earlier had been kings or kings' sons. That lasted out his time and Edward, his son's, but Athelstan came to the kingdom young, and they reckoned to stand in less awe of him. Many grew untrusty then who earlier were full of service.

5 2

Óláf, the Scots' king, assembled a great army and afterwards marched
south to England, and when he reached Northumberland he ravaged
the whole way. When the earls who were ruling there heard this,
they summoned a force together and marched against the king. When
they met there was a great battle, and it ended in King Óláf winning
the victory; Earl Godrek perished and Álfgeir took to his heels with
the biggest part of the army which followed them and had got away
from the battle. Álfgeir could now make no stand against him, and
King Óláf subdued the whole of Northumberland.

Álfgeir went to find King Athelstan and told him of their disaster,
and as soon as the king heard tell how so great an army had made
entry into his kingdom, he immediately dispatched messengers and
mustered an army, sending word to this effect to his earls and other
great lords. The king instantly moved off with such force as he
obtained and marched against the Scots; but when it became known
that Óláf the Scots' king had won the victory and subdued a large
part of England, he then found himself with a far greater force than
Athelstan, for a lot of the leading men came over to him. And when
Hring and Adils heard of it (they had drawn together a strong body
of men) they threw in their lot with King Óláf. By this time they
had strength uncounted. So when Athelstan heard all this, he held
a meeting with his leaders and counselors and debated what was best
to do, telling them all plainly what he had learned of the Scots' king's
doings and of his strength in men. Everyone there expressed the
same opinion, that Earl Álfgeir had played the shabbiest part in this,
and held it only right to strip him of his honors. But this was the
plan adopted, that King Athelstan should turn back into southern
England, and then collect an army on his way north through his
territories; for they saw that it would be slow work assembling such
a great force as was needed, unless the king collected the army himself.

The king put Thórólf and Egil in command of the army which

had already been mustered. They were to lead the force which the vikings had brought to serve with the king, but Álfgeir still held command of his own troops. The king appointed such additional leaders of companies as he thought fit. When Egil returned from the meeting to his comrades, they asked what news he had to tell them about the Scots' king. He chanted:

> (16) "How's Óláf's foes all left him!
>   One fled, one slain (the slow one),
>   Unmanageable monarch,
>   That Scot soon had them scattered!
>   What foul ways Godrek follows,
>   Treading the road the dead trod;
>   While harried by Scots' harrow
>   Ache half of Álfgeir's acres."

Later they sent messengers to King Óláf, inventing this as their errand, that King Athelstan wanted to hazel a field for him and offer battle at Vínheid beside Vínuskógar, and he requested them not to go raiding in his land, but let him who won victory in battle rule the realm of England. He gave a week's notice of their encounter, and whichever of them should come first, let him wait a week for the other, for it was the custom in those days that as soon as a field was hazeled for a king he might not go plundering free from shame till the battle was over. King Óláf did just that: he halted his army and did no plundering, but waited for the appointed day. Then he moved his army to Vínheid. North of the heath stood a stronghold. King Óláf occupied this stronghold and kept the biggest part of his forces there, for there was a roomy countryside next at hand, and he judged it more convenient there for laying in those provisions the army must needs have. But he sent men of his up on the heath where the field was appointed for battle. They must choose places for tents and make ready there before the armies arrived. And when men reached the place where the field was hazeled, hazel poles were set up everywhere as landmarks where the precise place was where the battle should be fought. It was necessary to take pains over the place, that it should be level, since a great army must be drawn up for battle. This was the shape of things where the battle should take place, that there the site was level, but on one side a river fell away, and on the other there was a big forest.

Where the distance was shortest between the forest and the river (and that was quite a long way), it was there that King Athelstan's men had pitched their tents. Their tents stood the whole distance between the forest and the river. They had pitched so that there were no men in every third tent, and few indeed in any. But when King Óláf's men came visiting them, they had men crowding in front of all the tents, and they were unable to go inside. Athelstan's men said how their tents were all full of men, so that they had nothing like room enough for their following. The tents stood so high that no one could see over them, whether they stood many deep or few, and they concluded that there must be a multitude of men assembled there. King Óláf's men pitched their own tents north of the hazels, and in that direction the ground fell away somewhat. Athelstan's men were saying too from one day to the next that their king would come or had come to the stronghold which was south under the heath. Strength gathered to them both day and night.

When the appointed time had run out, Athelstan's men sent ambassadors to meet King Óláf with these words, that King Athelstan was ready for battle and had an immense army, but he sent King Óláf this message, that he was not willing that they should make so great a slaughter as now threatened, urging him rather to return to Scotland; but Athelstan would find him by way of friendly gift a silver shilling for every plough throughout the whole of his kingdom, and was desirous that they should be joined together in friendship.

When the messengers reached King Óláf, he was beginning to put his army in readiness and planning to ride out to battle. But when the messengers set out their business, the king postponed going for that day, sat then in council, and his army commanders along with him. Men had very different ideas about this. Some were most eager that the offer should be accepted, maintaining that it had then turned out a great and glorious venture that they should return home after exacting so big a tribute from Athelstan. Some hung back, maintaining that Athelstan would offer far more the second time if this were not accepted. And theirs was the plan decided on.

Then the messengers asked King Óláf to give them a respite to go and find King Athelstan a second time and try whether he was willing to pay a bigger tribute so that there might be peace. They requested a truce for one day for riding home, a second for deliberation, and a third for their return. The king agreed to this. The messengers returned home and came back the third day, as had been arranged; they informed King Óláf that Athelstan would give everything he had promised before, and this in addition for distribution among King Óláf's following: a shilling to every free-born man, a mark of silver to every group-leader who had charge of twelve men or more, a mark of gold to every leader of the bodyguard, and five marks of gold to every earl.

The king had this put to his army. It happened as before that some hung back and some were for it, but finally the king gave this ruling, that he would accept the offer should it be included that King Athelstan would let him have the whole of Northumberland with all rents and rights pertaining thereto. The messengers asked for a further respite of three days, and this besides, that King Óláf should send emissaries of his to hear King Athelstan's decision, whether he would accept that offer or not, adding that they thought he would let few things stand in the way of their getting peace. King Óláf agreed to this and sent emissaries to King Athelstan. The messengers rode all together and found the king in the stronghold which stood close to the heath to the south. King Óláf's messengers laid their business and their peace-offer before him. In turn, King Athelstan's men reported with what offers they had gone to King Óláf, and moreover, that this was the device of wise men to delay the battle for as long as the king had not come.

King Athelstan made a quick ruling in the case, instructing the emissaries thus: "Carry these words of mine to King Óláf, that I will give him leave to return to Scotland with his army; yet let him make restitution of all the wealth which he has wrongfully seized here in my dominion. After that let us make peace between our countries, and neither go ravaging the other. This too shall follow, that King Óláf shall become my liegeman and hold Scotland at my hand, and be my under-king. Now go back," he told them, "and tell him how matters stand."

The messengers returned posthaste that evening and reached King Óláf near midnight; they roused the king and at once informed him of King Athelstan's words. The king had his earls and other leaders summoned to him forthwith, and had the messengers come in and announce the result of their mission and the words of King Athelstan. When this was made known to the army, they said with one voice that what lay ahead was to prepare for battle. The messengers reported too that Athelstan had a multitude of men and had arrived at the stronghold that very day the messengers arrived.

"It has now turned out, King," said Earl Adils, "just as I maintained, that they would prove tricky customers, these English. We have sat around a long while here, waiting till they have gathered all their strength about them—and their king could have been nowhere near when we ourselves came here. And now they will have assembled a great body of men while we have been standing idle. It is my suggestion, King, that my brother and I ride out this same night with our troop. Maybe by now they are in no fear for themselves, since they have learned how their king is close at hand with a vast army. Let the two of us fall upon them and once they are put to flight they will lose their strength and thereafter be less bold in attacking us."

The king thought this plan well devised. "We will put our army in readiness once it is light, and come to join you."

They decided on this plan and so ended their meeting.

53

Earl Hring and Adils his brother put their troop in readiness and promptly proceeded by night south to the heath. As it grew light Thórólf's sentries saw where the army was on the move. A trumpet-blast was blown and men put on their armor, then began to deploy their forces; they were in two divisions. Earl Álfgeir commanded the one and a standard was borne before him. In that division were the troops who had served with him earlier, and also the strength which had assembled there from the country round about. It was a far more numerous force than that which followed Thórólf.

Thórólf was so equipped that he had a broad, stout shield, a very strong helmet on his head, and was wearing the sword he called Long, a fine big weapon. He had a halberd in his hand, whose blade-feather was two ells long and mounted with a four-edged spike, and in its upper part the blade was a broad one, the socket both long and stout. Its shaft was not so long but that the hand might reach to the socket, but it was unusually thick. There was an iron prong in the socket, and the shaft was wired round with iron. Such spears were called byrnie-bolts.

Egil had the same sort of gear as Thórólf. He was wearing the sword he called Adder, which he had come by in Kúrland. It was a splendid weapon. Neither of them wore a mailshirt.

They set up their standard, and it was Thorfid the Strong who bore it. Their whole company had Norse shields and none but Norse war-gear. In their army served all the Norwegians there present. Thórólf and Egil deployed their division near the forest, but that of Álfgeir moved alongside the river.

Earl Adils and his brother could see that they would not take Thórólf unawares. At that they began to deploy their forces, and they too were in two divisions and had two standards. Adils took up position opposite Earl Álfgeir, and Hring opposite the vikings, where-upon the battle began. Each side went bravely forward. Earl Adils pressed on fiercely till Álfgeir had to give ground, whereat Adils's men advanced as boldly again. It was not long before Álfgeir fled, and there is this to report of him that he rode off south over the heath, and a band of men with him. He rode till he came near the strong-hold where the king was waiting.

"I am not thinking for us to call at the stronghold," said the earl. "We had quite a scolding last time we faced the king, when we came off beaten from King Óláf, and our state will not strike him as much mended by our present action. There is no need to think of honors where he is concerned."

With that he rode for the south, and there is this to tell of his move-ments that he rode day and night till they reached Jarlsnes in the west, where the earl got passage south across the sea and so reached France. He had half his ancestry there. He never set foot in England again.

At first Adils pursued the fleeing foe, but before long turned back to where the fighting was, and delivered his attack. When Thórólf saw this, he swung round to encounter the earl and bade carry the standard in that direction, ordering his men to follow each other bravely and keep in close order.

"Let us move over to the forest," he said, "and let it protect our rear, so that they cannot get at us from all sides."

They did so, and moved alongside the forest. There was bitter fighting now. Egil advanced upon Adils and there were furious exchanges between them. The odds were great, but with it all, more were falling among Adils's host. Thórólf now grew so battle-mad that he swung his shield onto his back and seized his spear in both hands, then ran forward, cutting and thrusting both right and left. Men fell back on either hand, but there were many he killed, so clearing a path forward to Earl Hring's standard. Nothing could now stop him; he killed the man carrying Hring's standard and cut down the standard-pole, then thrust with his spear at the earl's breast, through mailshirt and body, so that it came out between his shoulders, hoisted him up on the halberd over his head, then jammed the spear-butt into the ground, and the earl perished there on the spear, and every one saw it, his own men and his foes too. Next Thórólf plucked out his sword and cut right and left, while his men too gave the assault. Many of the Welsh and Scots fell at this time, while some turned and fled.

When Earl Adils saw his brother's fall and the great slaughter in his ranks, and how some were fleeing and he himself looked to be in sore straits, he too turned to flight and ran off to the forest, and into the forest he fled, both he and his troop. Then the whole army which had accompanied them began to flee. A great toll was taken of the men in flight, and those who fled were by now strewn wide over the heath. Earl Adils had dashed down his standard, and no one was sure whether it was he who fled there or someone else. Soon the night began to grow dark and Thórólf and Egil turned back with their men to their war-booths; and at this same moment up came King Athelstan with the whole of his army and set up field-tents and made them ready.

A little later, up came King Óláf with his army. They pitched their tents and made them ready where their own men had set up tents. King Óláf was now informed that both his earls, Hring and Adils, had fallen, and a great multitude of the rest of his men.

54

The previous night King Athelstan had spent in the stronghold which was mentioned earlier, and there he heard tell how there had been a battle on the heath. He at once made ready with his entire army and proceeded north to the heath, where he received a clear account of how the battle had gone. Then the king came to see the brothers, Thórólf and Egil. He thanked them warmly for their valor and the victory they had won, pledging them his full friendship. They all remained there together that night.

Next morning King Athelstan roused his army at first light, held a meeting with his commanders and described how the army should be ordered. First he drew up his own division, and in its forefront he set those troops who were keenest. Then he announced that Egil should command that part of the army.

"But Thórólf," he said, "shall stay with his own troop and that other force I am placing with it. It shall be the second division of our army, the one he leads, for the Scots use at all times a loose formation, running this way and that, and coming on now here, now there. They often prove dangerous if men are not on their guard, but are unsteady on the field if they are turned on."

"I don't want Thórólf and myself parted in the fighting," Egil answered the king. "Though I am content enough that we be posted where the greatest need and hardship seem to lie."

"Let the king decide where he wants to post us," said Thórólf. "It is our part to give him the service he requires. But if you like, I am ready to take over where you are posted."

"You must have your way this time again," said Egil, "but for the rest of my life I shall repent this battle order of ours."

Men now entered into their divisions, as the king commanded, and the standards were raised. The king's division took up position on the wide stretch to the river, but Thórólf's proceeded higher up

along the forest. Then King Óláf began to deploy his forces, once he
could see that Althelstan had deployed his. He too drew up two
divisions, and let his standard and the army he himself commanded
proceed against King Athelstan and his array. Each side had now so
big a host that there was nothing in it which was the stronger in
men; but King Óláf's second division advanced near the forest against
the force commanded by Thórólf. The leaders there were Scottish
earls, most of their troop were Scots too, and theirs was a formidable
body of men. Next thing, their divisions clashed together and soon
there was bitter fighting. Thórólf made a strong attack and had his
standard advanced alongside the forest, for he had it in mind to press
so far forward that he might get at the unshielded flank of the king's
division. They were holding their shields before them, and the forest
was on their right where they were content for it to protect them. Thórólf pressed so far forward that there were few of his men ahead of
him, and, when he was least expecting it, Earl Adils and the troops
who followed him came charging out of the forest; they bore many
halberds at once against Thórólf, and he fell there alongside the
forest. Thorfid, who was carrying the standard, retreated to where
the men stood thicker, but Adils came forward against them, and
there was severe fighting there. The Scots roared their victory-roar
once they had felled the commander.

When Egil heard that roar and could see how Thórólf's standard
was withdrawn, he knew that Thórólf himself would not be in its
wake. He went running in that direction, out between the divisions,
and the moment he reached his own Norsemen learned what had
happened. He then rallied the company strongly to the attack, and
was the foremost in their van. He had his sword Adder in hand and
pressed forward, hewing right and left, and killing a lot of men. Close
behind him Thorfid carried the standard, and the rest of their force
came following on behind it. There was the bitterest fighting there.
Egil kept moving forward till he encountered Earl Adils. They exchanged only a blow or two before Adils fell and a lot of men with
him, and after his fall the force which had followed him turned to
flight, and Egil and his troops pursued them and killed every man
they could catch, for it was useless to ask for quarter. The Scottish

earls too made no long stand once they could see how the rest of their comrades were fleeing; they took to their heels in a trice.

Egil and his men now drove on to where King Óláf's division stood, and came against their unshielded flank and quickly made great slaughter there. Then the army broke rank and was all scattered. Many of Óláf's men now fled, and the vikings roared their victory-roar. And once King Athelstan came to feel that King Óláf's army was beginning to break, he rallied his own force and had his standard advanced, and made so hard an assault that Óláf's force reeled before them and a great slaughter took place. King Óláf fell there, and the main part of that army King Óláf had commanded; for those who turned to flight and were caught were put to the sword every man of them. King Athelstan won there a resounding victory.

55

King Athelstan now withdrew from the battle, while his men pursued the fleeing host. He rode back to the stronghold and took no night-quarters before he reached it; but Egil pursued the fleeing host, hunting them for a long time and killing every man he laid hands on. Later he turned back with his troops and went to where the battle had taken place and there lighted on his brother Thórólf, dead. He took up his body and washed it, seeing to it afterwards as was their practice. They dug a grave there and set Thórólf in it with all his weapons and clothes. Next Egil clasped a gold ring about each of his arms before he parted from him; then they piled him with stones and scattered earth on top. Then Egil chanted a verse:

> (17) "Fearless he went as peerless
>   To Thunder's wondrous war-roar;
>   Earl's bane but boon to England,
>   High-hearted Thórólf fell.
>   Green will grow earth by Vína,
>   Grass cover brother's grave there;
>   Most searing of my sorrows
>   With silence I must seal."

And a second time he chanted:

> (18) "Westward a load of warslain
> I stacked before the standards;
> Fierce warfare forced together
> Bleak Adils and black Adder.
> Young Óláf dinged all England,
> Could still hear cold steel's thunder;
> Hring toiled at Thing of weapons,
> Not long the raven hungered."

Next Egil went with his troop to find King Athelstan, and at once went into the king's presence as he sat at the drinking. There was a great noise of rejoicing there. Once the king could see that Egil had come inside, he ordered that the lower dais should be cleared for them, saying that Egil should sit there in the high-seat opposite the king. Egil sat down there and drew his shield in front of his legs. He wore helm on head and set his sword across his knees, and from time to time slid it halfway out and then slammed it home into the scabbard. He sat upright, but his head was deeply bowed. Egil had strongly marked features, was broad of forehead, heavy-browed; the nose not long but very thick, his lips wide and long, the chin notably broad and so throughout the jaw, thick-necked and big-shouldered, so that in that respect he surpassed what other men were: hard-faced and forbidding to look on when he.was angered. He was powerfully built and taller than any man else, the hair wolfgray and thickset, and he had become bald early. And while he sat as has already been described, he was twitching one eyebrow down on to his cheek and the other up into his hair-roots. Egil was black-eyed and with brows of dark brown. He would drink nothing, though drink was fetched him, but twitched his eyebrows up and down, now this way, now that.[1]

King Athelstan was sitting in the high-seat. He too had laid his sword across his knees, and when they had been seated so for a while, the king drew his sword out of the scabbard and, taking a fine big gold ring off his arm, drew it over his sword's point, stood up and walked on to the floor and reached it across the fire to Egil. Egil stood up, plucked out his sword, and walked on to the floor. He stuck the sword in the round of the ring, drew it towards him, then went back to his place. The king sat down in the high-seat. When Egil sat down he drew the ring on to his arm, and with that his eyebrows fell into line. He then put down sword and helm, took hold of the horn which was brought him and drank it off. Then he chanted:

(19) "King, corslet's god, has given me
A ringing springe for clawtongs,
To swing from hawktrod hangtree,
Handgallows goldenhaltered.
Aloft on sword I lift it,
My gallows-spar of spearstorm;
This swordhand's snare wins favor
And fame for ravens' feeder." [2]

From then on Egil drank his full share and conversed with other men. Later the king had two chests carried in, and it took two men to carry either. They were both full of silver. "Egil," said the king, "you shall take these chests, and if you reach Iceland you shall convey the money to your father, to whom I am sending it as payment for his son. But some of the money you shall share out among those of your and Thórólf's kinsmen who seem to you of most account. You yourself shall receive payment for your brother here along with me, land or movables, whichever you prefer; and if you are content to stay with me for the future, then I will provide you with such glory and honor here as you yourself can name to me."

Egil took the money and thanked the king for his gifts and friendly words. From then on Egil began to grow cheerful, and chanted:

(20) "My browcrags griefbruiséd
O'erhilled my eyehollows;
Yet forehead's rough furrows
Were smithied to smoothness.
The prince has now prised up
(Gold armrings' despoiler)
High edge of my eyecliffs
From maskland of face."

Later on those men who though wounded yet kept alive were

healed. Egil spent the winter following the death of Thórólf with King Athelstan, and received very great honors from the king. All that force was still with him which had earlier accompanied the two brothers and had come alive from battle. Egil then composed a drápa³ upon King Athelstan, in which will be found these lines:

> (21) Landlofty man, warlifter,
>   Of many a king main kinsman
>   (Falls land in Ella's line now),
>   Brought three proud princes crashing.
>   Great Athelstan wrought further:
>   We flaunt this, waveflame-breaker,
>   That all the world louts lowly
>   To king so named, so kinfamed.⁴

And this is the refrain in the drápa:

> (22) Now falls each loftiest deerfell
>   To valiant Athelstan.

Further, Athelstan now gave Egil as a reward for his poetry two gold rings, each weighing a mark, and in addition a costly cloak which the king himself had worn before.

But when spring came Egil informed the king that he was proposing to leave for Norway that same summer, to find out what had happened to Ásgerd—"the woman my brother Thórólf married. Great wealth has been building up there, but I do not know whether any of their children are alive. It is for me to look after them if they are, but the whole inheritance is mine if Thórólf has died childless."

"Egil," said the king, "it will be for you to decide on leaving us, if you think you have pressing business. But I think the other course best, that you should make your home here with me, on just such terms as you care to ask for."

Egil thanked the king for his words. "But first I must follow that course to which I am bound. Still, it is more likely than not that I shall return here for the fulfillment of those promises, once I can arrange it."

The king told him to do that. Afterwards Egil made ready to be off with his following, though a number stayed behind with the king.

Egil had a big longship, with all of a hundred men on board, and when he was ready for his voyage and had a following wind, he held for the open sea. He and King Athelstan parted in great friendship. He told Egil to return as soon as he could, and he promised it should be so. He afterwards set course for Norway, and once he reached land made as briskly as he could for the Firths. He learned this news, how Thórir Hersir was dead and Arinbjörn had taken up the inheritance and become a landed man. Egil went to visit Arinbjörn and got the best of welcomes from him. Arinbjörn invited him to stay with him, and Egil accepted. He had his ship laid up and his people lodged, but Arinbjörn found room for Egil and eleven men, and he stayed with him over the winter.

56

Bergönund, son of Thorgeir Thornfoot, had by this time married Gunnhild, the daughter of Franklin-Björn. She had gone to keep house with him at Ask. But Ásgerd, whom Thórólf Skallagrímsson had married, was now living at her kinsman Arinbjörn's. She and Thórólf had one young daughter, whose name was Thórdís, and the child was there with her mother. Egil told Ásgerd of Thórólf's death and offered to take care of her. Ásgerd was very downcast at his story; she had a kind answer for his offer, but did not commit herself to anything.

In the course of the autumn Egil suffered great unhappiness, and often would be sitting with his head sunk under the hem of his cloak.

One day Arinbjörn went to find him and asked what caused his unhappiness. "For though you have now suffered great loss in your brother, it is a man's part to bear it well. 'Man must live after man.' And what verses are you making now? Let me hear!"

Egil said that he had just composed this verse:

> (23) "The goodly hawkcliff's goddess
>   Can find no show of fondness.
>   In days departed durst I
>   Heave up my heavy forehead;
>   But now this skald unskilled is

(Touching Berg-Onar's girdle)
To move from under mantle
Brow's pedestal, braw nosepiece." [1]

Arinbjörn asked who might this woman be on whom he made love
songs. "You have concealed her name in this verse!"
Then Egil chanted:

(24) "Seldom do I conceal
In verse, the Narfasons' nurture,[2]
Fame of my kinswoman's name,
That stronghold of seaflame gold.[3]
What grieves her now will leave her
As soon as the warriors discern,
Skalds with their skilful fingers,
What truth's entrusted to song."

"Here we find," said Egil, "as the old saw has it, that all can be
told to a friend. Yes, I will tell you what you are asking, this woman
I make verses on. She is your kinswoman Ásgerd, and I should like
to have your backing here, so that my marriage bid may prosper."

This, said Árinbjörn, was surely a happy thought. "I must certainly put my oar in here, so that the match comes to something."

Later Egil put the matter to Ásgerd, but she referred it to the decision of her father and her kinsman Arinbjörn. Next Arinbjörn talked
it over with Ásgerd, and she made the same answer, while Arinbjörn
was strongly for it. Next Arinbjörn and Egil went to see Björn, and
Egil made his proposal, asking for Ásgerd his daughter. Björn welcomed it, but suggested that Arinbjörn should have the main say. So
because Arinbjörn was entirely in favor, the matter ended so that
Egil and Ásgerd were betrothed. The wedding was to take place at
Arinbjörn's, and when the day came there was a magnificent feast
when Egil was married. He was in high spirits for what was left of
the winter.

In the spring Egil fitted out a merchant-ship for the Iceland voyage.
Arinbjörn warned him that he ought not to make his home in Norway so long as Gunnhild's power was so great.

"For she has a heavy grudge against you," Arinbjörn told him, "and it ruined everything when you and Eyvind clashed off Jutland."

So once Egil was ready and had a favoring wind he sailed to the open sea and had a good crossing. He reached Iceland in the autumn and held for Borgarfjörd. He had been abroad twelve years, and Skallagrím was by this time grown into an old man. He was the happiest man alive when Egil came home. Egil went to lodge at Borg, and Thorfid the Strong along with him, indeed a great many of them all told, and they stayed with Skallagrím over the winter. Egil had wealth past counting, but it is not recorded that he shared the silver which King Athelstan had entrusted to him either with Skallagrím or with anybody else.

That winter Thorfid married Skallagrím's daughter Sæunn, and later, in the spring, Skallagrím found them a home at Langárfors, with land inwards from Leiruloek between Langá and Álftá, right up to the mountains. The daughter of Thorfid and Sæunn was Thórdís, whom Arngeir of Hólm married, the son of Godless Bersi. Their son was Björn the Hitdalers' champion.

This time Egil spent some winters with Skallagrím. He took charge of the stock and household affairs no less than Skallagrím himself. Egil was growing still barer of pate. The country was now beginning to be settled far and wide. Hrómund, brother of Grím the Hálogalander, settled in Thverárhlíd at this time with his shipmates. Hrómund was father to Gunnlaug, the father of Thuríd Dyllu, mother of Illugi the Black.

Egil had now been at Borg while many a winter ran its course. Then it happened one summer when ships came from Norway to Iceland, that news was heard from the east how Franklin-Björn was dead. The story continued that his son-in-law Bergönund had taken over all the wealth Björn had owned. All transferable goods he had removed to his own home, but he had let the estates and had apportioned the whole of the rents to himself. He had also confiscated all the estates which Björn had owned. When Egil heard this, he inquired closely whether Bergönund would have gone ahead with this of his own accord, or had he received the support of others more important? He was informed that Önund had come into great friendship with King Eirík and into still greater favor with Gunnhild. Egil let it lie quiet for the autumn, but, once winter was past and spring had begun, he had that ship of his launched which had been laid up in the boat-house by Langárfors, fitted her out and found her a crew. Ásgerd his wife was set on going, but Thórólf's daughter Thórdís stayed behind. As soon as he was ready Egil put to sea. There is nothing to tell of his journey till he reached Norway, where he set off post-haste to find Arinbjörn. Arinbjörn gave him a warm welcome and invited Egil to stay with him. He accepted, and both he and Ásgerd went along, and a number of others with them.

Egil soon struck into talk with Arinbjörn regarding these claims on property which Egil considered he had there in Norway.

"The case looks unpromising to me," Arinbjörn confessed. "Bergönund is a hard man and awkward to deal with, unjust and greedy after money, and he has strong backing from the king and queen. Gunnhild is your biggest enemy, as you already know, and she will not be putting pressure on Önund to reach a fair solution."

"The king will let us have law and justice in this suit," Egil assured him, "and with your help I have no misgivings about going to law with Bergönund."

What they decided on was that Egil should man a skúta. Almost twenty of them went aboard; they proceeded south to Hördaland and so reached Ask. They went up to the house, where they met Bergönund. Egil set out his business, demanding from Önund a share of Björn's inheritance, and maintaining that in law Björn's daughters were equal claimants to the inheritance.

"Though it would seem to me," added Egil, "that Ásgerd will appear far better born than your wife Gunnhild."

Önund had a very sharp answer for him. "What an unspeakably impudent fellow you are, Egil, that you make your way here, King Eirík's outlaw, into his land and see fit to molest his men. Remember this, Egil: I have given a tumble to men as good as you, and for less cause than I reckon this, when you claim to inherit on your wife's behalf. For the whole world knows that she is born of a bondwoman on her mother's side."

Önund carried on violently for a time. But once Egil could see that Önund wanted no fair solution of the case, he summoned him to the Thing, referring the suit to the Gulathing Law.

"I shall come to the Thing," promised Önund, "and my wish is that you'll not get away from there undamaged."

Egil retorted that he would risk coming to the Thing despite that. "Be it then as it may, how our suits end."

After that Egil and his men took themselves off, and when he arrived back home he gave Arinbjörn an account of his trip and of Önund's rejoinders. Arinbjörn was very angry that anyone should call his father's sister a bondwoman. Arinbjörn went to see King Eirík and put the case before him, but the king gave it rather a hostile reception, commenting that Arinbjörn had long been a warm backer of Egil's suits.

"He has you to thank that I have let him stay here in Norway, but I shall not regard it as a friendly act if you uphold him when he molests my friends."

"You must let us have law in this case," replied Arinbjörn.

The king was far from cordial in the matter. Even so, Arinbjörn could tell that the queen would prove more hostile by far. He returned home to report that it was turning out none too promisingly.

The winter passed away and it grew time to go to the Gulathing. Arinbjörn took a crowd of men to the Thing, and Egil kept him company. King Eirík was there too, and had a big body of men. Bergönund was in the king's troop with his brothers, and they had a strong following. And when there should be decision in men's lawsuits, both sides proceeded to where the court was established, to set out their proofs. Önund was now all big talk. Where the court was established there was a level field, with hazel poles set down in the field in a ring, and ropes in a circuit all round. These were called the hallowed bands. Inside the ring sat the judges, twelve out of Firthafylki, twelve out of Sognfylki, and twelve out of Hördafylki. It was for these three twelves to reach a verdict in men's lawsuits. Arinbjörn decided who were the judges from Firthafylki, and Thórd of Aurland those from Sogn. They were all in the one party. Arinbjörn had brought a powerful body of men to the Thing. He had a fully-manned snekkja, and had a lot of small ships, skútur and rowing-ferries of which his tenants had control. King Eirík had a big force there too, of six or seven longships. There was also a big gathering of farmers there.

Egil began his suit by calling on the judges to pronounce lawful judgment in his suit against Önund. He then set forth what proofs he had for his claim to this property which had belonged to Björn Brynjólfsson. He stated that Ásgerd, the daughter of Björn and own wife to Egil, had title to the inheritance and that she was odal-born and landed-born in all branches of her family, and born of princes early in her line. He asked the judges to award Ásgerd half of Björn's inheritance, both lands and movable goods.

But once he stopped talking, Bergönund set to work. "My wife Gunnhild," he said, "is the daughter of Björn and Álof, the woman Björn had lawfully taken in marriage. So Gunnhild is Björn's rightful heir. For that reason I took charge of all the property which had belonged to Björn, because I knew that she alone was Björn's other daughter who had no right to inherit. Her mother was carried off as a captive and later taken for leman, without consent of her family, and carried from land to land. Now you are planning to act here, Egil, as everywhere else you have come with your arrogance and injustice. But this time they are not going to serve you here, because King Eirík and Queen Gunnhild have promised me I shall get my due in every suit wherever their power extends. I propose to bring forward true witness before king and judges that Thóra Lace-arm was taken from home as a captive from Thórir her brother's, and a second time from Aurland, from Brynjólf's. She then departed the land with vikings and king's outlaws, and in that outlawry she and Björn begot this daughter Ásgerd. Now it is an odd thing about Egil, when he thinks to make void King Eirík's every word, that first, Egil, you have visited here in the land since King Eirík outlawed you; and second, though you have married a bondwoman, you reckon her fit to inherit. I shall call on the judges to this end, that they award me the whole of Björn's inheritance but adjudge Ásgerd the king's bondwoman, for such was her begetting that her mother and father were in the king's outlawry at the time."

Then Arinbjörn started to speak. "We will produce witness, King Eirík, to this, and have oaths accompany it, that it was insisted on in the atonement between Thórir my father and Franklin-Björn that Ásgerd, daughter of Björn and Thóra, was brought into the inheritance after Björn her father; and this besides, as you yourself know, King, that you set Björn free from outlawry, and the dispute was then in every respect concluded which earlier had stood between the atonement of men."

The king made no very quick answer to this plea of his. Then Egil chanted:

> (25) "He calls, this Thornfoot's thorn,
> My hallhorn girl thrallborn;
> This Önund pleads he's needy,
> Nor grudges to read greedy.
> Spearthrower! you'd best know
> My cloakclasp Norn's trueborn.[4]
> An oath, king's son? We'll make it.
> Our tale's oathtrue. You take it!"

Arinbjörn then had twelve men bear witness, and all of them selected for that purpose, for they had all heard the atonement of Thórir and Björn, and offered now to king and judges to swear to it. The judges were ready to accept their oaths if the king did not ban it. The king declared he would do neither: pronounce leave nor ban for this.

Then Queen Gunnhild began to speak. "It is a wonder, King," she said, "how you let this great Egil muddle every case for you. And would you not speak out against him though he demanded the very kingship from you? But though you are not prepared to give a ruling when it is such a help to Önund, I shall not suffer Egil so to tread my friends underfoot that he deprives Önund of this property by his injustice. Where are you, Askman? Get with your troop to where the judges are, and do not let this evil come to judgment."

At that Askman and the men of his troop ran to the court, cut through the hallowed bands and broke down the poles, scattering the judges abroad. A great uproar broke out at the Thing, but everyone was weaponless there.

"Can Bergönund hear my words?" asked Egil then.

"I hear," said he.

"Then I am challenging you to holmgang, that we fight here at the Thing. Let him have the property, land and movable goods, who wins the day. And be every man's dastard if you dare not."

It was King Eirík who answered. "If you are spoiling for a fight, Egil, we can promise you that here and now."

"I neither want to fight with you," retorted Egil, "nor with impossible odds. But from an equal strength of men I'll not run off, should such be offered me. Nor shall I then make any odds who my opponents are."

"Let us be off," said Arinbjörn to this. "We can do nothing useful here just now." With that he turned away and all his followers with him. But Egil turned back. "I bid you take notice, Arinbjörn," he cried, "and you, Thórd, and all who can now hear my words, landed men and lawmen and all folk in full, that I set ban on all those estates which Björn owned, to let and to work. I set ban on you, Bergönund, and on all other men, native and foreign, titled and untitled. And any man who acts in this, I charge him with law-breach of landrights and truce-wrecking and wrath of the gods."

Next Egil took himself off with Arinbjörn. They went to their ships over some rising ground, by reason of which the ships could not be seen from the Thing. And when Arinbjörn reached his ship he said: "It is known to you all what an ending there has been to the Thing, and how we have had no law. The king is so incensed that I fear our men will get rough handling from him if he can contrive it. I want every one of you now to get to his ship and go home." Then he turned to Egil. "As for you, get aboard your ship with your comrades, and be off. And look out for yourselves, for the king will try to bring about a meeting between you and him. But come and find me after, whatever takes place between you and the king."

Egil did as he said. Thirty of them got aboard a skúta and made off as hard as they could. This ship was exceptionally fast. There rowed out of the harbor a swarm of other ships which belonged to Arinbjörn, skútur and rowing-ferries, with a longship of Arinbjörn's bringing up the rear, for she was the heaviest under oars. But Egil's skúta forged quickly ahead. Then Egil chanted a verse:

> (26) "This inheriting traitor
>   (Heir to Thornfoot rightly)
>   Disinherits me by betrayal;
>   His hate I meet, his hot words,

When brisk to bring him justice
I ask acres, oxen's sorrow.
Fought we for (or thought we)
Tranceland's gold of serpents."

King Eirík heard these concluding words of Egil's which he spoke last of all at the Thing, and grew very angry. But every one had gone unarmed to the Thing, for which reason the king made no move to attack. He ordered all his men down to the ships, and they did as he commanded. Then the king called a meeting and declared his purpose.

"We shall now have the awnings cleared from our ships, for I am going to find Arinbjörn and Egil. And I want to make this plain to you—I intend to take Egil's life if we get a chance at him, and spare no one who tries to stand in our way."

After that they got aboard and made ready as fast as they could, thrust out their ships and rowed to where Arinbjörn's ships had been. Then the king had them row in pursuit north into the sounds, and when they reached Sognsær they caught sight of Arinbjörn's fleet. Then the longship and its fellows turned in towards Saudungssund, so the king turned that way too. He came up with Arinbjörn's ship there, and the king instantly made up to her and hailed her. The king asked whether Egil was on their ship.

"He is not on ship of mine," Arinbjörn answered. "You can see that for yourself, King, and quickly. Only those are on board here whom you will recognize. Nor will Egil be skulking below deck when you do catch up with him."

The king asked what was the last Arinbjörn knew of him, and he replied that Egil was aboard a skúta with thirty men. "They were making their way out to Steinssund." The king and his men had noticed that many ships had been rowing for Steinssund, so he now gave orders that they should row into the inner sound and so try to come up with Egil and his crew.

There is a man to be mentioned now, one Ketil, a member of King Eirík's bodyguard. He set course for the king's ship, but it was Eirík himself who steered her. Ketil was a big-bodied man, handsome in appearance and the king's near kinsman; and everyone said how alike in looks he and the king were.

Egil had had his own ship launched and her freight carried on
board before he left for the Thing, and he now made for where she
lay and they went up on board; but the skúta floated, with her rudder
ready, between the land and the ship, and the oars lay ready in the
thongs. In the morning, when it had hardly grown light, those who
were keeping watch noticed how there were big ships rowing towards
them. When Egil heard this news he was on his feet at once, and soon
saw that hostilities were come upon them. There were six longships
heading in their direction. Egil ordered everybody to jump into the
skúta. He picked up the two chests which King Athelstan had given
him (and which he always carried around with him), and into the
skúta they jumped. He and the rest of them quickly armed themselves,
and they rowed off between the land and that warship which was
traveling closest inshore—which was King Eirík's ship. And because
everything happened so suddenly, when there was hardly any light,
the ships ran past each other; and as the raised decks came into line
one with the other Egil flung a spear and it struck the man's middle
who sat steering, and that was Ketil the Hadalander. Then King Eirík
shouted out, ordering men to row in pursuit of Egil. As the ships ran
past the merchant-ship the king's men jumped up on board; and those
of Egil's men who stayed behind and did not jump into the skúta
were all killed who were caught, though a few escaped ashore. Ten
men perished there from Egil's crew. Some of the ships rowed on
after Egil and his men, while some plundered the merchant-ship. All
the wealth was seized which was on board, but the ship they set on
fire.

Those who were rowing after Egil and his men gave hot chase,
pulling two to an oar. There was no lack of power on their ships, but
Egil's was thinly manned. There were now eighteen of them on the
skúta. The distance was closing between them. But inshore of the
island, between it and another island, there was a certain shallow
wading-strait. The tide was now at the ebb. Egil and his men drove
the skúta into this shallow strait, but there was not sufficient clearance
for the warships, and the two parties lost contact there. The king
then turned back south, but Egil headed north to find Arinbjörn.
Then Egil chanted a verse:

(27) "Now must fierce warfire's master
Have felled ten of our fellows.
Contumely untimely
I miss yet, for my message
(So calls a skald that quivering
Shaft of woundsalmon's goddess),[5]
Pierced sharp my spear's point
Curved ribcage of Ketil."

Egil came to find Arinbjörn and told him what had happened. Arinbjörn assured him that he had expected nothing better from his dealings with King Eirík.

"But you shall not lack for money, Egil. I intend to compensate you for the ship and find you another on which you can have a good voyage out to Iceland."

Ásgerd, Egil's wife, had been staying at Arinbjörn's ever since they went to the Thing. Arinbjörn provided Egil with a ship which was admirable for ocean-going, and had her loaded with timber. Egil fitted her out for sea, and even now had almost thirty men. He and Arinbjörn took friendly leave one of the other. Then Egil chanted:

(28) "Let gods so give quital,
Arraign my ransackers;
Great Ones lour grimly,
Drive king from his kingdom.
Let Freyr bring folk freedom,
Njörd work realm-riddance;
Thór make thought sicken
At sanctuary-spoiler." [6]

57

Harald Fairhair set his sons in power in Norway as he began to grow old, making King Eirík supreme king over all his sons; and when Harald had been king for seventy winters he handed over his realm to Eirík his son. Just then Gunnhild gave birth to a son, whom King

Harald sprinkled with water and endowed with his own name, letting it be known at the same time that he should become king after his father, if he lived so long. Then King Harald settled to a quiet life, and for the most part lived in Rogaland or Hördaland. Three years later he died in Rogaland, and a funeral-mound was erected for him alongside Haugasund.

After his death there was great dissension among his sons, for the Vík-dwellers chose Óláf as their king, and the Thrándmen Sigurd. But Eirík slew both his brothers in Túnsberg one winter after the death of King Harald. It was one and the same summer that King Eirík proceeded out of Hördaland with his army east into Vík to fight against his brothers and, earlier, Egil and Bergönund had clashed at the Gulathing, along with those other events which have just been recounted.

Bergönund remained at home when the king went campaigning, for he thought it asking for trouble to leave home so long as Egil had not left the country. He had his brother Hadd there with him at the time.

There was yet another man, by the name of Fródi, a kinsman of King Eirík's and his foster son. He was the handsomest person, young in years and yet a grown man. King Eirík had left him behind for Bergönund's protection. Fródi stayed at Álreksstadir, at the king's own house, and kept a troop of men there.

There was a son of King Eirík and Gunnhild whose name we are told was Rögnvald. He was now ten or eleven years old, a youngster of the fairest promise. He was staying with Fródi when these events took place.

Before King Eirík rowed off on this campaign he made Egil an outlaw from one end of Norway to the other, and every man's prey. Arinbjörn went campaigning with the king, but before he left home Egil set his ship to the open sea and held for that outer fishing-station which is called Vitar, out beyond Aldi, and lying off the sea's highway. There were fishermen there, and it was a good place to pick up news. He learned that the king had made him an outlaw, whereupon he chanted this verse:

(29) "Lawbreaker not lawmaker
On long ways bids me languish;
Bride-murmurer, brothers' murderer,
Makes me outlaw (Hear me, Land-Elf!).
His guilt stems all from Gunnhild,
Main axle of mine exile;
Yet, king, while young I countered
All venomed acts with vengeance!"

The weather was calm, with a wind off the high ground by night and a sea-breeze by day. One evening Egil and his crew sailed out to sea, and at that the fishermen who had been set there to spy on Egil's movements rowed to land. They had this much to report, that Egil had put out and sailed to sea and was off and away. They had this information conveyed to Bergönund, and the minute he heard the news he sent away all the men he had kept there earlier for protection. He then rowed in to Álreksstadir and invited Fródi to come and visit him, for Bergönund had a lot of ale at home. Along went Fródi, taking a number of other men with him. They held a fine feast there and had the merriest time. Everybody there was now free from misgiving.

Rögnvald the king's son had a karfi which six men rowed aside. She was color-stained right down to the waterline. He had with him the ten or twelve men who accompanied him on every occasion. No sooner had Fródi left home than Rögnvald took the karfi and they rowed out to Herdla twelve together. There was a big house of the king's there, and in charge of it a man known as Skegg-Thórir. As a child Rögnvald had been fostered there. Thórir was delighted to see the king's son. Nor was there much shortage of drink there either.

Egil sailed out to sea overnight, as was recorded earlier, but as morning came the wind sank and a calm befell. They then set her to drift, and let her drift for a few nights. But once a sea-breeze sprang up Egil said to his shipmates: "We will now sail for the land, for if heavy weather overtakes us I am not sure where we shall come ashore, and there is rather an unpeaceful prospect ahead in most places." The seamen told Egil to order their movements. They afterwards set sail and sailed in towards Herdluver, where they found a good harbor and set awnings over the ship and hove to overnight. They had a small boat on board, and Egil got into this with a couple of men. He rowed in towards Herdla by night, where he sent a man up on to the island to ask for news. When he came back down to the boat, he reported that Rögnvald the king's son was present at the farm with his men.

"They were sitting drinking. I met one of the housecarles, a fellow drunk as a lord on ale, and he reckoned that there should be no less drinking here than at Bergönund's, though Fródi would be over there for the festivities with his party of five." There was no company there apart from the household, he added, except for Fródi and his men.

Next Egil rowed back to the ship and ordered his men to look lively and take their weapons. They did so, moving the ship out to ride at anchor. Egil had twelve men guard the ship, but himself set off in the ship's boat, and they were eighteen men all told. Afterwards they rowed in along the sound, and so arranged matters that they reached Fenhring late in the day and ran into a hidden creek there.

"I shall be going up on to the island on my own now," said Egil, "and see what I can find out. You wait for me here."

Egil had those weapons of his which he commonly had, helmet and shield, a sword belted round him, and a halberd in his hand. He now went up on to the island and forward alongside some woodland. He had pulled a long hanging hood over his helmet. He came to where there were some boys, and big sheepdogs with them and when they struck into talk together he asked where they were from and why they were there, and why they had hounds so big?

"You must be a fool," they told him. "Haven't you heard how a bear roams the island here, the biggest robber going, and is killing both men and livestock here, and there is a price set on his head? We keep watch every night here at Ask over that stock of ours which is enclosed in fold. For that matter, why are you moving about by night, and armed too?"

"I am frightened of the bear," he replied, "and they are few, I fancy, who now travel unarmed. The bear has chased me a long time tonight—and look at him now, there he goes, in the spur of the wood! Is everyone asleep at the farm?"

The boy reckoned that Bergönund would still be drinking. "They sit drinking every night."

"Then tell him where the bear is," said Egil. "As for me, I must run off home."

With that he made off, but the boy ran back to the farm to the hall where they were drinking. By then matters stood this way, that everybody had gone to sleep there except for those three, Önund, Fródi and Hadd. The boy described to them where the bear was to be found. They reached for their weapons which were hanging there beside them and instantly ran out and up to the forest. There were spurs of woodland jutting out thereabouts from the forest, with bushy growths here and there. The boy told them just where the bear had been in the bushes. They could see how the branches were stirring and felt sure that the bear would be there. Bergönund ordered Hadd and Fródi to run ahead between this and the main piece of woodland and watch that the bear did not escape to the forest.

Bergönund ran forward to the copse. He had helmet and shield, was wearing a sword, and carried a halberd in his hand. But it was no bear but Egil who confronted him inside the copse, and once he could see where Bergönund was he drew his sword. There was a loop on the mid-hilts which he pulled over his hand, then let the sword hang. Catching hold of his halberd he ran forward to encounter Bergönund, and when Bergönund saw this he quickened his pace and drew his shield in front of him, and before they met together each flung his halberd at the other. Egil parried the halberd with his shield, holding it aslant so that it scraped off the shield and shot into the ground; but Egil's spear struck the shield's center and pierced it the length of the blade-feather, so that the spear stuck fast in the shield. Önund's shield grew unwieldy, and Egil snatched quickly at the mid-hilts of his sword. Önund too began to draw sword, but before it was half out Egil thrust him through with his blade. Önund staggered with the thrust, whereupon Egil hauled the sword hard back and cut at Önund, almost severing his head. Then Egil plucked his halberd out of the shield.

Hadd and Fródi saw Bergönund fall. They ran that way, and Egil turned to meet them. He flung the halberd at Fródi, on through his shield and into his breast, so that the point came out at his back. He at once fell backwards, dead.

Egil next got a grip on his sword and turned against Hadd, and they exchanged only a few blows before Hadd went down. Then up came the boys.

"Look after Önund your master here," Egil told them, "and these comrades of his, so that no beast or bird despoils their dead bodies."

Egil then took himself off, but got no great way before eleven of his comrades came to meet him (for six were keeping watch on the boat). They asked him how he had got on. He chanted:

> (30) "Far too long had I forborne
>   Resistance to oppression
>   (I was once a better guardian
>   Of my gear from goldgirt men),
>   Ere these death-wearied warriors
>   Felt death. I first felled Önund;
>   Then Hadd and his friend Fródi
>   With red coif made Earth ruddy."

"And now we will turn back to the farm," said Egil, "and play the man there, kill everybody we catch and seize all the wealth we can lay hold of."

They made for the farm and dashed into the house, killing fifteen or sixteen men there. Some few escaped their onset. They plundered all the wealth there and spoiled whatever they could not carry off. The farm beasts they drove down to the shore for slaughter, loaded into the boat as much as it would hold, and then took themselves off and rowed out along the island strait. Egil was now so furious that there was no speaking with him. His seat in the boat was by the tiller. And as they headed out into the firth towards Herdla, there came rowing in towards them Rögnvald the king's son, some thirteen of them together on that painted karfi. By now they had learnt how Egil's ship lay at Herdluver, and were intending to fetch Önund news of Egil's movements. When Egil saw the ship he recognized her instantly. He steered dead straight at her, and as the ships ran together the beak of the skúta struck the karfi's bows, and she so heeled over that the sea poured in on the far side, filling the ship. With that Egil sprang on board, gripping his halberd and shouting to his men that they should not let a single man get away alive who was aboard the karfi. By now this was easy, for all opposition was at an end. They were killed in the water, all of them, and not a soul got away. Rögn-vald and his companions perished there, the whole thirteen of them. Egil rowed on with his men to the island of Herdla. Then Egil chanted a verse:

> (31) "We battled with a boatload
>   (I minded no man's menace),
>   Let Bloodaxe' son's red lifeblood
>   (And Gunnhild's) gush o'er gunwale.
>   Fell now thirteen fellows,
>   Seamoon's firs, fine seamen,
>   Carved in one royal karfi;
>   I've dealt them dole enough now."

When Egil and his men reached Herdla they immediately ran all armed up to the farm. But when Thórir and his household saw this, they ran away hot-foot from the farm, and all who could shift saved themselves, both men and women. Egil and his men robbed all the wealth there they could lay hands on, then set off to their ship. Nor had they long to wait till a fair wind blew off the land. They made ready to sail, and when they were with sail set Egil went up on to the island. He took a hazel pole in his hand and went to a certain jutting rock facing the mainland. Then he took a horse's head and set it up on the pole.

Afterwards he recited a formulary, saying these words: "I here set up a scorn-pole,[1] and I turn this scorn against King Eirík and Queen Gunnhild." He turned the horse's head landwards. "I turn this scorn upon the landspirits which dwell in this land, so that they all fare wildering ways, and none light on or lie in his dwelling till they drive King Eirík and Gunnhild out of the land."

Next he jammed the pole down into a crack in the rock and let it stand there. The head he turned landwards, but he graved runes on the pole, and they state all that formulary.

After that Egil went on board ship. They set sail and sailed out to sea. The breeze began to stiffen and the weather grew sharp with a following wind. The ship went grandly. Then Egil chanted:

(32) "Fronting our stem storm's giant,
     Treeshaker, files seabreakers,
     Ridging stembullock's road
     With stormsped chops of chisel.
     Like forestwolf the frostwind
     Rasps Gestil's swan unresting;
     With icegust stroke incises,
     Fronting our beak, the fo'c'stle." [2]

Next they sailed to the open sea and had a good crossing, and from the open sea reached Borgarfjörd. There he held on with his ship to the harbor, where they carried their baggage ashore. Egil went home to Borg, but his shipmates found themselves lodgings. Skalla-grím had now grown old and infirm with age, and Egil took over the management of the estate and charge of the household.

58

There was a man by the name of Thorgeir who was married to Thórdís Yngvar's daughter, the sister of Bera, Egil's mother. Thorgeir lived at Lambastadir, inwards along the coast from Álftanes. He had come out to Iceland along with Yngvar. He was rich and men thought a lot of him. It was their son Thórd who was living at Lambastadir in succession to his father when Egil now returned to Iceland. It happened that autumn, a little before winter, that Thórd rode in to Borg to meet his kinsman Egil and invite him to his house for a feast. He had been brewing ale out there. Egil promised to go along, and it was fixed for about a week's time. When the time came round Egil made ready for his journey, and Ásgerd his wife with him. They were some ten or twelve together.

When Egil was quite ready, Skallagrím went outside with him and embraced him before Egil climbed on horseback, and—"Slowly, Egil," he said, "you seem to me to have paid over the money King Athelstan sent me. What are you planning to do with that money?"

"Are you so short of money then, father?" inquired Egil. "That is something I did not know. I will let you have silver any time I know you need it. And yet I know you must still have a chestful or two in safe-keeping."

"It strikes me," said Skallagrím, "you must think you have now carved up the personal property between us. So you will be easy in mind though I do as I like with what stays my own."

"And you," retorted Egil, "will think you need ask no consent of mine for that; for you will follow your own bent, whatever I say."

With that Egil rode away till he reached Lambastadir, where he got a good and joyful welcome. He was to spend three nights there. That same evening Egil had left home Skallagrím had his horse saddled and rode from home when the rest of them were going to sleep. When he rode off he was carrying a mighty big chest across his knees and a copper cauldron under his arm, and ever since men have believed that he let one or both drop into the quag at Krumskelda, then dropped a big stone slab on top of them. About midnight he returned home and went to his bed and lay down in his clothes. In the morning, as it grew light and men were dressing, Skallagrím was sitting on the platform-edge, dead, and so stiff that men could neither straighten him out nor lift him, though every method was tried.[1]

Then a man was set on horseback, and rode his hardest till he reached Lambastadir. He went instantly to find Egil and told him what had happened. Egil took his weapons and clothes and rode home to Borg that same evening, and as soon as he dismounted he went inside and along the passage which lay around the hall, for there were doors leading inwards from this passage to the bed-platforms. Egil stepped onto the platform from the rear, gripped Skallagrim by the shoulders and forcibly bent him backwards, laid him down and paid his body its rites. Then Egil said to take picks and break through the wall to the south. And when that was done Egil lifted Skallagrím's head and shoulders, while others lifted him by the legs; they carried him across the house, and so out through the wall which had been broken open in readiness.[2] Next they whipt him off down to Naustanes, where an awning was put over him for the night. But in the morning at high tide Skallagrím was laid in a ship and rowed out to Digranes. Egil had a howe built there, on the point of the headland. Skallagrím was laid inside it, with his horse and his weapons and his smith's tools.

It is not recorded that any loose money was laid in the howe beside him.

Egil took the inheritance there, both land and movable goods, and full control over the household. Thórdís, the daughter of Thórólf and Ásgerd, continued to live there along with Egil.

59

King Eirík ruled Norway a single winter after the death of his father King Harald before Hákon, Athelstan's foster son, another son of King Harald, came east to Norway from England—and that same summer Egil Skallagrímsson went to Iceland. Hákon proceeded north to Thrándheim and was chosen as king there, so that winter both he and Eirík were kings in Norway. But later, in the spring, each assembled an army. Hákon had by far the bigger following, and Eirík saw no alternative but to flee the land. He went abroad with his wife Gunnhild and their children.

Arinbjörn Hersir was King Eirík's foster brother and his child's fosterer. He was dearest to the king of all his landed men. The king had made him lord over the whole Firthafylki. Arinbjörn left the country with the king. First they crossed the sea west to Orkney, and it was then that Eirík gave Ragnhild his daughter in marriage to Earl Arnfinn. Next he sailed with his following south off Scotland and raided there. From there he went south to England raiding, and when King Athelstan learned this he gathered an army and marched against Eirík. But when they met, words of treaty were carried between them, and it was part of the treaty that King Athelstan put Eirík in charge of Northumberland, and he should be the defender of King Athelstan's land against the Scots and Irish. King Athelstan had levied tribute of Scotland after the fall of King Óláf, and yet that nation was for ever untrue to him. King Eirík was at all times resident in York.

The tale runs that Gunnhild had a spell worked, and the burden of the spell was this, that Egil Skallagrímsson should never rest easy in Iceland till she might see him again. But the summer Hákon and Eirík had clashed together and fought over Norway there was a ban on travel to all lands out of Norway, so that summer no ship came to Iceland, and no news from Norway. So Egil Skallagrímsson spent it at home. But the second winter he spent at Borg after the death of Skallagrím Egil grew morose, and his uneasiness that much the more the longer the winter wore on. And once summer came, he announced that he intended to fit out his ship for a voyage abroad that summer. He picked his crew and had it in mind to sail for England. There were thirty of them on board. Ásgerd stayed behind to look after their household, but Egil proposed to go and visit King Athelstan and check those promises he had made him at their parting. Egil was late getting ready, and when he put to sea was late again getting a wind. Autumn was upon them and the weather growing rough. They sailed north of Orkney, where Egil was unwilling to put in, for he assumed that King Eirík's power would extend everywhere in the islands. They then sailed south off Scotland, and met with great storms and cross winds. They clawed their way past Scotland and the north of England too. But in the latter part of the day, as it began to grow dark, there was wild weather. They noticed nothing till there were shoal breakers to seaward, and forward too. There was nothing for it but to run for the land, so they did so, ran her ashore under sail, and came to land at the mouth of the Humber. All the men were saved, and the best part of their goods, except for the ship. She was broken to flinders. When they found men to talk to, they learned news which struck Egil as full of menace: how King Eirík was there, and Gunnhild, and they had the kingdom in their charge, and he was only a short distance off up in the town of York. He learned too that Arinbjörn Hersir was there with the king, and in high favor with him. Once Egil was sure of his news he made this resolve. Escape seemed to him hopeless, even though he should attempt to lie up and fare with hidden head so long a way as it would be before he could escape from Eirík's kingdom. Then he was so easy to recognize for anybody who saw him. He thought it paltry to be captured when fleeing. So he hardened his resolve and determined on this: as soon as they got there that night he found himself a horse and at once rode to the town. He arrived there late in the day, and instantly rode into the town. Over his helm he had a long hanging hood, and he carried all his weapons. Egil asked whereabouts in the town might be the house which Arinbjörn owned.

This was told him, and he rode on to the house. When he came to the hall he dismounted from his horse and met a man to talk to. He was told that Arinbjörn was seated over his food.

"I should like you, my good fellow," said Egil, "to walk inside the hall and ask Arinbjörn whether he had rather talk outside or in with Egil Skallagrímsson."

"It is little trouble to me to run this errand," replied the man. He went inside the hall and spoke on the loud side. "A man has arrived here outside the door," he said, "as big as a troll. He asked me to come inside and inquire whether you preferred to talk outside or in with Egil Skallagrímsson."

"Go and tell him to wait outside," said Arinbjörn. "Not that he'll need to wait long!"

He did as Arinbjörn ordered, went outside and said as he was told. Arinbjörn gave orders to take away the tables. Next he went outside, and all his housecarles with him. And when Arinbjörn met Egil he greeted him and asked why he had come there.

Egil told him in a few words the truth about his journey. "But it is now for you to settle what plan I shall adopt, if you are willing to help me a little."

"Have you met anyone in the town who may have recognized you," asked Arinbjörn, "before you reached the house here?"

"Not a soul," Egil assured him.

"Then let men take their weapons," said Arinbjörn.

They did so, and when they and all Arinbjörn's housecarles were armed he went to the king's house. When they reached the hall Arinbjörn rapped on the door and said to open up, announcing who was there. The doorkeepers at once opened the door. The king was seated at table. Arinbjörn then ordered twelve men to go inside, naming Egil and ten others. "And now you must bring King Eirík your head, Egil, and embrace his foot; but it is I who will plead your cause."

They now went inside. Arinbjörn walked before the king and greeted him. The king gave him greeting and asked what he wanted.

"I have brought here a man," said Arinbjörn, "who has come a long way to visit you at your home and be atoned with you. It is a great honor to you, Sire, when your enemies proceed of their own accord from other lands, finding themselves unable to endure your disfavor though you are nowhere near. Now, show yourself the great lord to this man! Let him win a noble atonement from you, because he has made your honor as great as now appears, braving many a sea and grievous road away from his own home. No need drove him to this journey—only goodwill to you."

The king looked about him, and over men's heads he saw where Egil was standing, and glowered at him, saying: "Why be so fool-hardy, Egil, as to dare come into my presence? You so took yourself off last time that you could not hope for life at my hands."

Then Egil went to the table and embraced the king's foot. He chanted:

> (33) "I steered Ívi's sea steed[1]
> On weary long waveroads
> To look on the landholder,
> Landwarder here in England.
> Now has woundflame's flaunter,[2]
> A swordsman hot, sought hither,
> Uncaring, over-daring,
> Heartstrand of Harald's strain."

"No need for me to count up my grievances against you," said King Eirík. "And yet they are so many and so big that any one of them is reason enough why you shall never escape alive. You can look for nothing but to perish here. You might have known beforehand you would win no atonement of me."

"Why is Egil not killed out of hand?" Gunnhild demanded. "Or do you not now remember, King, what Egil has done: killing your friends and kinsmen, aye more than that, your son, and heaping scorn on your royal person? Where did men hear tell of such affront to a *king!*"

"If Egil has spoken ill of the king," Arinbjörn countered, "he can put that right with words of praise which shall endure for all time."

"We have no desire to hear his praises," said Gunnhild. "King, have Egil led out and beheaded. I have no wish to hear his words or look on him."

"The king," replied Arinbjörn, "will not let himself be goaded into

all your wickedness. Nor will he have Egil killed tonight, for killing
by night is murder."

"So be it, Arinbjörn," said the king, "even as you ask: Egil shall
live overnight. Take him home with you—but bring him to me in the
morning!"

Arinbjörn thanked the king for his words. "We hope, Sire, that
from now on Egil's case shall take a better turn. And though he has
offended you deeply, yet look at this, how heavily he has suffered at
the hands of your family. Your father, King Harald, took the life of a
famous man, his father's brother Thórólf, because of the slander of
wicked men, and for no offence done. And you yourself, King, broke
the law to Egil for Bergönund's sake. More than that, you would have
had Egil a dead man, you killed men of his, and robbed him of all
his wealth, and more than that, made him an outlaw and drove him
from the land. But Egil is a butt for no man! And every case a man
shall judge, he must examine both reason and consequence. And
now," concluded Arinbjörn, "I will keep Egil by me in my house
tonight."

So it was. When they reached the house the two of them went into
a certain little loft and talked the matter over.

"The king was very angry just now," said Arinbjörn, "but on the
whole I thought his temper softened a little before it ended. Well,
luck must settle what is to happen now. I know that Gunnhild will
set her whole mind to spoiling your case. Now I want to offer you this
advice, that you stay awake tonight and compose a poem of praise
about King Eirík. It would seem best to me if it were a twenty-verse
drápa which you could recite in the morning when the two of us appear before the king. That is what Bragi my kinsman did, when he
incurred the anger of King Björn of the Swedes: he composed a
twenty-verse drápa about him in the course of one night, and received
his head in return. Now it might happen that we get such luck with
the king that this shall bring you into peace with him."

"I must try this plan," agreed Egil, "since you wish it, but the last
thing I had in mind was singing King Eirík's praises!"

Arinbjörn told him to try. He afterwards went away to his men,
and they sat drinking till the middle of the night. Then Arinbjörn
and his troop went to their sleeping-quarters, but before he undressed

he went up into the loft to Egil, and asked him how the poem was progressing. Egil said that nothing was done. "A swallow has sat here by the window and twittered all night, so that I have had never a minute's peace for it." At that Arinbjörn went away and out through a door by which one could get up on to the house, and sat down beside that window in the loft where the bird had sat before. He saw where some shape-shifter[3] left the house another way. Arinbjörn sat there by the window all night until it grew light; and once Arinbjörn had come there, Egil composed the whole drápa and had so got it by heart that he could recite it in the morning by the time he met Arinbjörn. They kept watch till it would be time to go before the king.

60

King Eirík went to table according to his custom, with a strong body of men about him. When Arinbjörn knew this, he went with his whole troop fully-armed into the king's house as the king sat at table. Arinbjörn demanded entry into the hall, and this was granted him. He and Egil went inside with half their following, and the other half took up position outside, in front of the door.

Arinbjörn greeted the king, and the king gave him a good welcome. "Well," said Arinbjörn, "here comes Egil now. He did not try to run away overnight. We want to know now, Sire, what his fate is to be. I am hoping for good things from you. For my part I have done only what was right, in that I have spared to do and say nothing in order that your glory might be greater than before. Further, I have left all my possessions and kinsmen and the friends I had in Norway, and stood by you when all your landed men deserted you—which is all proper enough, for you have treated me handsomely in so many ways."

"Be quiet, Arinbjörn," said Gunnhild then, "and don't make so long a tale of this. You have done King Eirík good service—and he has amply repaid you for it. You owe your loyalty more to King Eirík than to Egil, and it is not for you to demand that Egil gets off scot-free from this encounter with King Eirík, when he has wrought him such offense."

"King," continued Arinbjörn, "if you are determined, and Gunnhild with you, that Egil shall find no atonement here, then the manly thing is to grant him peace and safe-passage for a week, so that he may reach safety, seeing that he has made his way here of his own free will to find you, hoping for peace as a result. But from there on let your dealings together go as they will."

"I can see by this, Arinbjörn," said Gunnhild, "how your loyalty is rather to Egil than to King Eirík. If Egil is to ride off and away for a week in peace, by that time he will have reached King Althelstan. King Eirík need deceive himself no longer how all kings are today grown his lords and masters; yet even a short while since it would have seemed incredible that Eirík would have neither will nor nerve to avenge his injuries on such a man as Egil."

"No one," replied Arinbjörn, "will call Eirík a bigger man though he should kill a farmer's son from abroad who has thrown himself on his mercy. But if he wants to magnify himself this way, I must needs lend a helping hand, so that the tidings may be thought worth telling of; for Egil and I must now stand by each other, and be dealt with both at once. You will pay dearly for Egil's life, King, when we are all laid dead on the field, my followers and I. I should have expected something else of you than that you would rather lay me to earth than let me receive the one man's life I ask for."

"Arinbjörn," said the king to that, "you lay mighty great stress on helping Egil. I will be loth to do you harm if it comes to such an issue that you will rather lay down your life than see him killed. But my grievances against Egil are ample, whatever I have done with him."

And when the king had spoken these words, Egil stepped before him and began his poem,[1] chanted it aloud, and instantly had silence.

> "West sailed I to sea,
>   My freight poesy;
>   Words' breastfoam of Vidrir[2]
>   My skald's destiny.
>   Launched oak to main
>   When ice broke again;
>   Abaft unseen
>   Stowed poesy's pæan.

Next as king's guest
In verse him addressed;
I bear Ódin's toast[3]
To England's coast.
I praise this lord,
His honor applaud;
Silence afford
The king's high laud.

Heed now, O king
('Twill honor bring),
How well I sing,
Men hearkening.
Most have heard tell
Of warlord's quell;
Vidrir marked well
Where the dead fell.

Swordmetal pealed
On rim of shield;
Strife round him reeled
Who ranged that field.
Heard was the yell
Of bladefury fell,
Ironstorm's knell
Past far sea's swell.

Spearwoof of the fray
Sped not astray
From glittering array
Of king's shieldstay.
There bloodwet strand
Of surfbeaten land
Felt thunder resound
As pennants unwound.

Shore's dust they bit
When javelins hit;
Bright fame he gat,
Eirík from that.

Fresh praise I lend
If men attend;
More I've heard tell
Of deeds more fell.
Great wounds they gash
At prince's clash;
All swords a loss
On black shield's boss.

Crack whetstone's sharp loads[4]
On battlesun swords;
Woundgraver invades,
Bloodpoint of blades.
Deathcold it felt,
Ice of swordbelt;
Ódin's oaks crashed,[5]
By ironstorm lashed.

Edge and point fret
Where shrill swords met;
Bright fame he gat,
Eirík from that.

King reddened sword,
Came ravens a horde,
Bright lifeblood outpoured
As shafts flew abroad.
Scots' scourge bade feed
Trollwife's wolfsteed,
Hel trod with her feet
The eagles' nightmeat.

Flew battlecrane[6]
To heaps of warslain,
Woundmew[6] was fain
Of his red gain.
Wolf tore at wound,
Bloodbillows resound,
And loud ascend
To raven's beak end.

Gjalp's steed[7] knew free
Satiety.
Eirík o'er sea
Paid the wolves' fee.

Rouses war's maid
The Freyr of the blade,
Longship's shieldbraid
Dry music made.
Spearpoints shatter
And swordpoints natter,
Bowstrings mutter
As arrows flutter.

Shaft bit as it flew,
Peace shattered anew;
Elmbows they draw,
Wolf licks his maw.
Folkleader withstood
Death's welling flood;
Yewbow roared
At drawing of sword.

King bent the yew,
Woundbees[8] outflew;
Eirík o'er sea
Paid the wolves' fee.

Now will I again
Display to men
That leader's glory
(Yet speed my story):
This high lord flings
Gold freely, clings
Close to his lands
—Laud he demands!

Breaks armfire's glow[9]
His gold to bestow;
No miserly ways
Win ringbreaker's praise;
Has in his power
Hawkstrand's goldshower[9]
Many he'll dower
With Fródi's flour.[9]

Whetter of swordplay
Flings shield away,
Ringbounteous goldfay
Frees arm to slay.
Across seas leaps his fame
(Plain truth I declaim),
In Norway the same,
Eirík's great name.

Warrior, give thought
To that I have wrought.
Glads me this court
With silence fraught.
With my mind's mouth
I drew up the truth
From Ódin's sea,
Warlord, for thee.

King's fame I hailed
Till silence failed.
(Words' measure I ken
In halls of men.)
From joy's deep spirit
Praised prince's merit,
And forth did bear it
That most might hear it."

6 1

King Eirík sat bolt upright, glaring at him, while Egil chanted the poem. But once the drápa was ended, then the king spoke.

"The poem's *delivery*," he said "could not be bettered. And I have considered, Arinbjörn, now, what shall be the outcome of my case against Egil. You have pleaded Egil's suit with much heat, since you offered to fight out your differences with me; but for your sake I will do what you asked: Egil shall leave my presence safe and sound. But, Egil, so sort your travels that once you get away from this hall and out of my presence you never again come before my eyes or my sons', and never run into me or my people. But now, this once, I am giving you your head. If only because you put yourself in my hands I will not treat you basely; but you must know beyond any shadow of doubt that this is not a reconciliation with me or my sons or any of our family who desire to exact their dues of you."

Then Egil chanted:

(34) "I am not loth,
    Though it loathsome be,
    This helmcrag,[1]
    King, to grasp.
    Where's the man got
    A goodlier gift
    From any highminded
    Mighty king's scion?"

Arinbjörn thanked the king with courteous words for the honor and friendship he had shown him. Then Arinbjörn and Egil returned to Arinbjörn's house. Afterwards Arinbjörn had horses made ready for his men's riding. He rode away with Egil, and a hundred fully-armed men with him. Arinbjörn rode with that force till they reached King Athelstan and got a good welcome there. The king invited Egil to stay with him, and asked what had taken place between him and King Eirík. Then Egil chanted:

> (35) "That lawless warlock-warrior
> (Kinsman's true heart helped save me)
> Pledged me my blackedged eyebrows,
> A gift Egil was glad of.
> I hold now as of old high
> Before bale-adders' leader
> My highdescended headpiece,
> Highstool of Áli's helmet."[2]

At Arinbjörn's parting from Egil, Egil gave Arinbjörn those two gold rings which King Athelstan had given him, each weighing a mark; and Arinbjörn gave Egil the sword known as Dragvandil. Thórólf Skallagrímsson had given this to Arinbjörn, but earlier Skallagrím had received it from the other Thórólf, his brother. It was Grím Hairycheek, Ketil Hœng's son, who gave it to Thórólf. Ketil Hœng had owned this sword and used it in holmgangs, and it was the most biting of all swords. They parted with deep affection. Arinbjörn returned to King Eirík in York, where Egil's comrades and shipmates got a good peace and disposed of their wares under Arinbjörn's protection. But in the course of the winter they moved south to England and went to find Egil.

62

Eirík Allwise was the name of a landed man in Norway who had married Thóra, the daughter of Thórir Hersir and Arinbjörn's sister. He had holdings east in Vík. He was a very rich man and most distinguished and wise. Their son's name was Thorstein, who was reared by

Arinbjörn, and by this time was fully grown, though still a young man. He had gone west to England with Arinbjörn. But that same autumn Egil arrived in England news was heard from Norway how Eirík All-wise was dead, and the king's stewards had seized his inheritance and drawn it into the king's possession. When Arinbjörn and Thorstein heard this news, they decided that Thorstein should return to Norway and claim the inheritance; so in the course of the spring, when men who planned to travel from land to land were fitting out their ships, Thor-stein went south to London to see King Athelstan. He produced tokens and a message from Arinbjörn to the king, and likewise to Egil, request-ing him to plead his cause with the king, that King Athelstan should send a message of his own to King Hákon, his foster son, so that Thorstein might obtain his inheritance and property in Norway. King Athelstan was easily persuaded to this, for Arinbjörn was known to him as a fine man.

Then Egil too came to talk with King Athelstan and told him his plans.

"This summer," he said, "I want to go east to Norway to claim that property King Eirík and Bergönund robbed me of. At present the property is under Bergönund's brother, Atli the Short. I know that if a message of yours is brought to bear I shall get law in the matter."

The king agreed that Egil should decide his own movements. "But to me it would seem best that you stay on with me and be made warden of my kingdom and take command of my armies. I will pro-vide you with great revenues."

"This offer," said Egil, "seems to me a most desirable one to close with. I should like to accept it, not reject it. Still, I must go to Iceland first and see to my wife and the property I own there."

King Athelstan gave Egil a fine merchant-ship, and a cargo along with her. There were wheat and honey there as freight, and much wealth besides in other wares. As Egil was fitting out his ship for sea, this Thorstein Eiríksson who was mentioned earlier (he was later to be known as Thóruson) decided to go with him; and once they were ready they set sail. King Athelstan and Egil parted in the greatest friendship. Egil and his men had a good crossing and came east to Norway, to Vík, and held straight on with their ship into Oslóarfjörd. Thorstein had an estate on shore there, and on in as far as Raumaríki too. And once Thorstein was ashore, he laid claim to his father's inheritance against the stewards who had settled into his home. Many gave Thorstein their backing over this, and meetings were arranged. Thorstein had many noble kinsmen there. It ended so that it was referred to the king's ruling, while Thorstein took over the management of this property which his father had owned.

Egil went to Thorstein for winter quarters, as did twelve of them all told. Wheat and honey were fetched home there to Thorstein's. There was fine entertainment there that winter, and Thorstein lived in high style, for there were ample means for this.

63

King Hákon, Athelstan's foster son, ruled Norway at this time, as was recorded earlier. That winter the king had his seat north in Thrándheim. Towards the end of winter Thorstein set off on his journey, and Egil with him. They had almost thirty men. When they were ready they went first to the Uplands, from there north past Dofrafjall to Thrándheim, and there met with King Hákon. They set out their business before the king, and Thorstein gave a clear account of his case, producing witness to how he owned all that inheritance which he invoked. The king received this suit favorably; he let Thorstein recover his possessions, and at the same time he was made the king's landed man, just as his father had been.

Egil went to see King Hákon and laid his business before him, together with King Athelstan's message and his tokens. Egil claimed that property Franklin-Björn had owned, both land and movable goods. He claimed half of this property for himself and Ásgerd his wife, producing witnesses there and oaths for his case; he added too how he had put all this before King Eirík, and went on to say he did not get law on that occasion because of King Eirík's power and the prompting of Gunnhild. Egil expounded the whole state of the case as it had taken shape earlier at the Gulathing, and he then asked the king to let him have law in the case.

"I have heard tell, Egil," answered King Hákon, "how both Eirík my brother and Gunnhild would maintain that you flung a stone too heavy for you in your dealings with them. I think you can rest well content, Egil, that I take no part in the affair even though Eirík and I have not the good fortune to hit it off together."

"King," replied Egil, "you cannot stay silent about such great law-suits, for all men here in the land, both native and foreign, must give ear to your commands. I have been told that you decree law here in the land and rights for every one. Now I know you will let me have these like other men. I judge myself to have birth and sufficient family backing here in Norway to prove a match for Atli the Short. And there is this to tell you of my affair with King Eirík, that I stood in his presence and we parted so that he bade me pass in peace wherever I chose. I should like, lord, to offer you my help and service. I know there will be men here about you who will not appear more soldierly in the field than I. I have a feeling that no long time is going to pass before you and Eirík meet face to face—if both parties live so long. And I shall be very much surprised should it not then prove the case that Gunnhild seems to you to have raised a heavy crop of sons."

"You will not be made man of mine, Egil," the king assured him. "Your kinsmen have hacked notches in our line far too big for it to be any use for you to make your home here in Norway. Go out to Ice-land and busy yourself with your father's inheritance. Then no harm will come to you from us kinsmen. But here in Norway it can be expected all your days that our family will be the strongest. But for Athelstan my foster father's sake you shall have peace here in the land and get law and land-right, for I know King Athelstan has a warm regard for you."

Egil thanked the king for what he had said and asked that he should provide him with sure tokens of his to Thórd in Aurland or other landed men in Sogn and Hördaland. The king promised that it should be so.

64

Thorstein and Egil made preparations to leave as soon as they had finished their business, and then set off on the way back. But as they were traveling south past Dofrafjall, Egil said he wanted to go on down to Raumsdal and south thereafter by the coast road. "I want," he said, "to finish my business in Sogn and Hördaland, for it is my wish to fit out my ship this summer for Iceland." Thorstein told him to order his own movements, so he and Egil parted company. Thorstein proceeded south past Dalir and the whole of the way till he reached home, where he produced the king's tokens and message before the stewards, that they should surrender all the property they had seized there to which Thorstein laid claim.

Egil pressed on his way (there were twelve of them all told). They came on into Raumsdal, took passage there, and afterwards went south to Mœr. Nothing is told of their journey till they reached the island known as Höd and went for lodging to the farm called Blindheim. This was a notable farm. A landed man lived there, by the name of Fridgeir. He was young and had just taken over his father's inheritance. His mother's name was Gyda: she was Arinbjörn Hersir's sister, a great and noble lady. She managed the household for her son Fridgeir, and it was a great estate they had there. They received a most excellent welcome, and that evening Egil sat next to Fridgeir, and his comrades outwards from him. There was a lot of drink and costly entertainment. During the evening Gyda the housewife came to talk with Egil. She asked after Arinbjörn her brother, and after still more of her kinsmen and friends who had accompanied Arinbjörn to England. Egil informed her of what she asked. She inquired what had happened worth telling of on Egil's travels, and he told her the whole story. Then he chanted:

> (36) "Irksome I found that ugly
> Land-hungry king's anger.
> Not eager the gowk when the eagle
> Swings o'er him to linger.
> Ever there I found favor
> Where bears help Hearthstone's Bear;
> He'll fail not nor falter
> Who leans on such friends."[1]

Egil was in high spirits that evening, but Fridgeir and his household were rather quiet. Egil saw a handsome, well-dressed girl there who he was told was Fridgeir's sister.[2] The girl was sad and cried unceasingly throughout the evening—a circumstance they found very strange. They stayed there that evening, but in the morning there was a fierce gale and the sea impassable (they needed passage there from off the island). Then both Fridgeir and Gyda went to see Egil. They invited him to stay there with his comrades till the weather was good for traveling, and have from there the conveyance they needed. Egil accepted, and they spent three nights there weatherbound, and the entertainment was of the choicest. After that the wind dropped. Egil and his men rose early in the morning and made themselves ready, then went to eat and were given ale to drink, and they sat on for a while. Later they took their clothes. Egil stood up and thanked the master and housewife for their hospitality, and then they went out. The master and his mother went a short way with them.

Then Gyda had occasion to speak with her son Fridgeir, and talked with him quietly.

"Why do you weep, child?" Egil asked the girl. "At no time do I see you happy."

She could make no answer and cried all the more.

Fridgeir answered his mother out loud. "I don't want to ask this now, when they are just ready for their journey."

Then Gyda came up to Egil. "I will tell you, Egil," she said, "how matters stand with us here. There is a man named Ljót the Pale who is a berserk and holmgang man. He is hated by everybody. He came here and asked for my daughter, but we made a quick answer and refused him the match. At that he challenged my son Fridgeir to holmgang,[3] and they must come in the morning to the holm on the island which is called Vorl. Now I would like you, Egil, to accompany Fridgeir to the holm. It would be proved, if Arinbjörn were here in the land, that we need not suffer the violence of any such man as Ljót."

"I am bound, lady, for the sake of Arinbjörn your kinsman to go with your son, if that seems any advantage to him."

"Then you do well," said Gyda. "We shall now go inside the hall and be all one party the whole day through."

They and Egil then went inside the hall and drank. They spent the day there, and in the evening there came friends of Fridgeir's who had decided to make the journey with him, and there was a crowd of men there that night. They held a big feast, but the following day Fridgeir made ready for his journey, and a lot of men with him. Egil was of the party. It was good weather for traveling. They set off now and came to the island of Vorl. A short distance from the sea there was a fine field where their encounter should take place. The holmstead was marked out, with stones laid round about. Now Ljót came there with his following and made ready for the holmgang. He had shield and sword. Ljót was very big and very strong, and when he walked out on to the field at the holmstead the berserk fit came over him. He began to howl horribly and bite into his shield. Fridgeir was not a big man, but slight and handsome of appearance, and not strong. Besides, he had never taken part in combats.

When Egil saw Ljót he chanted a verse:

> (37) "No fit task this for Fridgeir
> (Come we to holm, my comrades,
> And ban this man the maiden)
> To browbeat him to battle
> With warmaid's swordstorm-stirrer;
> Libator of gods, good biter
> Of roughrimmed shield, the ruffian
> Stares bold with doomstark eyeballs!"

Ljót could see where Egil was standing, and heard his words and made answer. "You, the big fellow, step this way to the holm and take me on yourself, if you are all that eager, and let you and me try a bout together. That is a fairer match than for me to fight with Fridgeir, for I shan't think any more of myself though I stretch him on mother earth."

Then Egil chanted:

> (38) "This little boon, Ljót's bane,
> 'Twere churlish not to cherish;
> Playing with the pale one
> With quivering rod of corslets! [4]

> Put on your gear—but pity
> Is premise I'll not promise;
> Warrior, grant we wordsmith
> One merry bout in Mœr."

So now it was Egil who made ready for the holmgang with Ljót. Egil had the shield he was accustomed to have, and was wearing the sword he called Adder, but it was Dragvandil he carried in hand. He stepped in over the bounds where the holm-meeting should take place, but Ljót was not yet ready. Egil brandished his sword and chanted a verse:

> (39) "Hew we with polished hiltwands,
> Batter we shield with brand;
> Test we shining shieldmoon,[5]
> Redden we blade with blood.
> Lop we Ljót from living,
> Play we sore with pale one;
> Quell we the quarreler;
> Course, eagles, to his corse!"

Then Ljót advanced to the battlefield, and with that they ran at each other and Egil cut at Ljót, but Ljót countered with his shield. But Egil kept dealing one stroke after another, so that Ljót could not get in a single blow in return. He backed away for room to make his stroke, but Egil kept after him just as fast, still letting fly furiously. Ljót retreated past the boundary-stones, far and wide over the field. He asked for a rest, and Egil was content that it should be so. He chanted:

> (40) "Slinks off a little, methinks,
> The swordsman, spearflame's spurter;[6]
> Heartneedy as hoardgreedy,
> Helpless he shuns my onset.
> This speardew-shedder, ready
> For stern hits (heard we), stands not;
> Woe-boder is no bider
> On field before the Baldhead."

It was the law of holmgang in those days that he who challenged another man for anything at all, if the challenger won the victory he should have as his victory-prize that for which he had challenged; but should he not win the victory, then he must ransom himself by such a payment as might have been agreed on; while if he fell on the holm he had forfeited all his possessions, and he should inherit after him who had felled him on the holm. It was law too, if a man from abroad died who had no heir there in the land, then the inheritance went into the king's keeping.

Egil ordered Ljót to make ready. "I want us to get this holmgang settled." With that Egil ran at him and cut at him. He then pressed him so close that he fell back and his shield was lost to him. Then Egil cut at Ljót and caught him below the knee and took off his leg. Ljót fell down and at once breathed his last. Then Egil walked to where Fridgeir was standing with his men and received warm thanks for this deed. Egil chanted:

> (41) "Allworst of illworkers,
>   Wolves' feaster was felled;
>   Skald hacked Ljót's leg off,
>   To Fridgeir fetched peace.
>   Unregardful of guerdon
>   From brisk seaflame-breaker,[7]
>   For me passed for pastime
>   Spearplay with the pale one."

Ljót was little lamented by most, for he had been the cruelest of men. He was Swedish by descent and had no family there in Norway. He had just come there to win himself wealth by holmgangs. He had killed many a good farmer, after first challenging them to fight for their estates and odal rights, and by now had grown very rich both in land and movable goods.

Egil returned home with Fridgeir from this island-encounter, and spent a short time there before heading south for Mœr. Egil and he parted on terms of warm friendship. He instructed Fridgeir to lay claim to whatever estates Ljót had owned, then continued on his way and reached the Firths, whence he set off into Sogn to find Thórd at Aurland. Thórd had a warm welcome for him. He set out his business and King Hákon's messages. Thórd approved of what Egil had to tell him, and promised him his help in the affair. Egil spent a good while there that spring with Thórd.

65

Egil made his way south to Hördaland. For his journey he had a rowing-ferry with thirty men on board. One day they reached Fenhring, at Ask. Egil walked up to the house with twenty men, while ten kept guard on the ship. Atli the Short was present there with some men. Egil had him called outside and told that Egil Skallagrímsson had business with him. Atli took his weapons, as did all the men who were fit for arms there, and afterwards went outside.

"I am told, Atli," said Egil, "that you will have in your keeping the property which by right belongs to me and my wife Ásgerd. You will have heard tell of this before, how I reckoned the inheritance of Franklin-Björn mine which Bergönund your brother withheld from me. So now I have come to claim this property, the land and the movables, and to ask you to disgorge and pay it over to me."

"For a long time, Egil," said Atli, "we have heard what an unjust man you are, and I will now come to the proof of it, if you propose to claim from me this property which King Eirík assigned to Önund my brother, at a time when it was Eirík's prerogative to bid and ban here in the land. Indeed I was thinking, Egil, that you would have come here to offer me redress for those brothers of mine whose lives you took, and that you would want to make amends for the robbery you wrought here at Ask. I would give an answer in the case if you advance that errand, but to this I know no answer."

"I want to offer you," said Egil, "what I offered Önund, that the Gulathing's law shall decide our case. Your brothers I consider to have fallen past atonement through their own doing, in that they had earlier robbed me of law and land-right, and seized my wealth as spoils of war. I have the king's permission to have the law of you in this: I intend to summon you to the Gulathing and there get a legal ruling in the case."

"I will come to the Gulathing," promised Atli, "and there we can contest the case."

Egil went away afterwards with his company. He then went north into Sogn and in to Aurland to his kinsman-in-law Thórd's, where he remained till the Gulathing. But when men came to the Thing, Egil came there too. Atli the Short had also come. They then began to contest their lawsuit and set it out before the men who were to judge of it. Egil set out his claim to the property, but Atli presented a lawful defense to it, an oath of twelve that he did not have that property in his keeping which should be Egil's. As Atli proceeded to the courts with his oath-takers, Egil went to meet him, stating he was not prepared to accept his oaths in lieu of his property. "I want to offer you another law, that the two of us go on the holm here at the Thing, and let him who wins the victory take the property." For that too was law which Egil pronounced, and the custom of old, that it was every man's right to challenge another to holmgang, whether he would defend or prosecute a suit. Atli said he would not refuse to go on the holm with Egil. "For you are saying only what I had in mind to say, for I have injuries enough to avenge on you. You have stretched two of my brothers to earth, and I should come a long way short of holding a rightful cause if I relinquish my possessions unlawfully because of you rather than fight you when you make me the offer."

At that Atli and Egil struck their hands together and confirmed between them that they should go on the holm, and he who won the victory should have the estates they contended for before. After that they made ready for holmgang. Egil walked out and had helmet on head and shield before him, and a halberd in hand; but the sword Dragvandil he secured to his right hand. It was the practice of holm-gang-men, so as not to need draw their sword on the holm, rather to let sword keep with hand, so that the sword might be ready the instant he wished. Atli had the same equipment as Egil, and was well used to holmgangs. He was a strong and dauntless man.

A big old bull was led forward there, which was called the beast of sacrifice. He should slaughter him who won the victory. Sometimes it was the one beast, sometimes each who went on the holm had his own led forth.

When they were ready for the holmgang they ran at each other and shot first with their spears, and neither spear stuck fast in the shield; both were stayed in earth. Next they both took to their swords, and went hard at it swapping strokes. Nor did Atli give ground. They cut hard and fast and the shields were quickly made useless. When Atli's shield was quite useless he flung it from him, took his sword in both hands, and cut as fast as he could. Egil struck him on the shoulder, but the sword did not bite. He struck him a second time and a third. It was easy for him to find places to land on Atli, for he had no covering shield. Egil swung his sword with all his might, but it did not bite wherever he cut. He could now see that things would not do as they were, for his own shield had grown useless. Egil then abandoned sword and shield and rushed at Atli and grabbed hold of him with his hands. Their difference of strength grew manifest: Atli fell over backwards, but Egil flung himself down on him and bit through his windpipe, which was the end of Atli. Egil jumped up quickly to where the beast of sacrifice was standing, gripped at the muzzle with one hand and at a horn with the other, and wrenched so that the legs turned upwards and the neckbone cracked asunder. Next Egil walked to where his companions were standing, and chanted:

> (42) "The brand I drew, Dragvandil,
> Blackbladed failed on shieldrim;
> For that thank the short Atli,
> Who blade's edge had blunted.
> Strength's difference I stressed then
> 'Gainst wordmanly swordsman;
> My teeth saved me mischief,
> God's good ox I gained there."

Egil afterwards took possession of all the estates he had contended for and which he claimed Ásgerd his wife had stood to inherit after her father. It is not recorded that anything more worth telling of happened at that Thing. Egil then went first into Sogn and attended to the estates he had brought into his rightful possession. He remained there a very long time that spring. Later he proceeded with his following east into Vík. Then he went to see Thorstein and spent some time with him.

66

Egil put his ship in readiness that summer, and as soon as he was
ready, off he went. He held for Iceland and had a good crossing. He
made for Borgarfjörd and brought the ship only a little short of his
own farm. He had his wares carried home and laid up the ship. That
winter Egil spent at home. He had now brought considerable riches
out to Iceland and was a very wealthy man. He had a big and stately
household.

Egil was not meddlesome in men's affairs and was unoffending
towards most when he was here in Iceland. Nor did men try to interfere in his affairs. Egil now lived at home while no few winters ran
their course.

Egil and Ásgerd had children whose names are these: one of their
sons was named Bödvar, and another Gunnar, Thorgerd a daughter,
and Bera; Thorstein was the youngest. All Egil's children were promising and born with their wits about them. Thorgerd was the eldest of
Egil's children, and Bera the next.

67

Egil heard tell from east across the sea how Eirík Bloodaxe had
perished on a viking expedition in the west, but Gunnhild and their
sons had gone south to Denmark, and all that body of men was out
and away from England which had accompanied Eirík and them
there. Arinbjörn had now returned to Norway. He had secured his
revenues and those possessions which belonged to him, and had come
into great favor with the king. Egil decided it had now become a most
desirable thing to go to Norway. Part of the news too was that King
Athelstan was dead. His brother Edmund now ruled over England.

Egil fitted out his ship and found seamen for her. Önund Sjóni
decided to go with him, Áni's son from Ánabrekka. Önund was big
and the strongest of those men then in the neighborhood. It was by
no means agreed that he was not a werwolf. Önund had often been

on voyages from land to land. He was somewhat older than Egil. They had been good friends for a long while.

Once Egil was ready he put to sea. They had a good crossing and reached mid-Norway; and once they saw land they laid course for the Firths. When they got news from ashore, they were told that Arinbjörn was home at his residence. Egil held on there with his ship into harborage as near as might be to Arinbjörn's farm. Next Egil went to visit Arinbjörn, and there was a great and joyful meeting between them. Arinbjörn invited Egil there to lodge with him, and such of his comrades as he would like to bring along. Egil accepted this offer and had his ship drawn ashore, but the seamen found lodgings. Egil went to Arinbjörn's, as did some twelve of them altogether. Egil had had made a richly-worked longship's sail. He gave Arinbjörn this sail, and still further gifts which were worth the conveying. Egil spent the winter there and was made much of. Egil traveled south into Sogn that winter about his landrents, remaining there quite a long time. Later he went north to the Firths.

Arinbjörn held a big Yuletide feast, to which he invited his friends and the neighboring farmers. There was a big throng of men there and the best of entertainment. For a Yule gift he gave Egil a gown made of silk and much embroidered with gold, set all down the front with gold buttons. Arinbjörn had had this garment made to Egil's measure. Arinbjörn gave Egil a new-cut full rig of clothes at Yule, which were cut in English cloth of many colors. Arinbjörn gave friendly gifts of many kinds during Yule to the men who had come to visit him, for he was the most generous and lordly of men. Then Egil composed a verse:

> (43) Silk gown for skald's gain
> Our warrior freely awards me.
> Goldstudded it stood there;
> No better friend know I
> Now or forever, for never
> (Has not Arinbjörn borne
> Power where great kings lour?)
> His like shall again steal to light.

68

Egil suffered such grief after Yule that he couldn't utter a word. And when Arinbjörn noticed this he had a talk with Egil, asking what it could signify, this grief that was on him. "I want you," he said, "to let me know whether you feel ill or what else is the matter. Then we can find a remedy."

"I have no sickness," Egil told him, "but I am much exercised in mind how I shall lay hands on the property I won when I felled Ljót the Pale up north in Mœr. I am told that the king's stewards have confiscated all that wealth and drawn it into the king's possession. Now I should like to have your support for this claim."

"I hold it not far from the law of the land that you came to possess that wealth," admitted Arinbjörn, "but all the same the property now seems to me come into a tight place. 'Entry into the king's garth is wide, the exit narrow.' We have had a number of hardish property-claims to prosecute against over-bearing men, and at the time we sat in better shape with the king than is now the case. For our friendship with King Hákon is at an ebb, though I must needs do as the proverb says of old: 'He must cherish the oak who would live under it.'"

"Still," said Egil, "I feel that if we have the law on our side we should give it a trial. It may happen that the king will grant us our dues in this, for I am told he is a just man and fairly maintains those laws which he has established here in Norway. On the whole, I feel I should go and see the king and try out this business with him."

Arinbjörn admitted that he did not much care for this. "I think it will prove hard work, Egil, to reconcile your heat and stubbornness with the king's temper and strength. For I believe him to be no friend of yours, and indeed he thinks there is reason for that. I should prefer us to let this suit fall through and not make a start on it. However, if that is what you want, Egil, then I had better go and see the king myself and handle the affair with him."

Egil said he owed him gratitude and many thanks for this and would gladly accept his offer. Hákon was then in Rogaland, but from time to time in Hördaland, and it was not hard to get to see him. Nor was this much later than their talk had taken place. Arinbjörn made ready for his journey. It was made clear to everyone that he intended to visit the king. He manned with his housecarles a twenty-seater which belonged to him. But Egil was to stay at home, if only because Arinbjörn did not want him to go along.

Arinbjörn set off when he was ready and had a good journey. He found King Hákon and received a good welcome. And when he had stayed there a short while, he set out his business with the king and said how Egil Skallagrímsson had come there to Norway and considered he was the owner of all the wealth which had belonged to Ljót the Pale. "We are told, King, that in this Egil will have the law on his side, but your stewards have confiscated the property and drawn it into your possession. My request to you, Sire, is that Egil should get law in this matter."

The king answered his plea but was slow to speak. "I cannot think why you are acting on Egil's behalf in such a case. He came to see me once and I told him I would not have him stay here in the land, for reasons which are already known to you. Now Egil need not raise such claims with me as with Eirík my brother. As for you, Arinbjörn, there is this to tell you: you can stay here in the country only in so far as you set no greater store by men from abroad than by me or my commands. For I know that your thoughts lean to where your foster son Harald Eiríksson is; and your best plan is to go and find those brothers, and stay with them, for it is my foreboding that men like you will be ill stays for me if matters must needs be thrashed out between me and the sons of Eirík."

When the king took this suit so crossly, Arinbjörn could see that it would be idle to pursue it with him. He then prepared for his journey home. The king was rather distant and cold towards Arinbjörn once he had wind of his business; nor had Arinbjörn any disposition to humble himself before the king in this matter. It was on these terms that they parted. Arinbjörn returned home and told Egil how his mission had ended. "I shall not venture on such a business with the king again."

Egil wore a great scowl at this news; he thought he was losing a lot of money, and not justly either. A few days later it happened early one morning when Arinbjörn was in his room (there were not many

present at the time), he had Egil called to him, and when he came
in Arinbjörn had a chest opened up and weighed out forty marks of
silver, and spoke these words: "I am paying you this money, Egil, for
the estates which Ljót the Pale owned. It seems to me only fair that
you get this recompense from my kinsman Fridgeir and me, for you
redeemed his life from Ljót, and I know that you did it for my sake.
I am bound therefore not to let you be cheated of your lawful rights
in this suit."

Egil took the money and thanked Arinbjörn. Egil now grew quite
merry again.

69

That winter Arinbjörn spent at home, but later, in the spring, he
announced that he was planning to make a viking cruise. Arinbjörn
had a fine fleet of ships, and put three longships, all big ones, in
readiness in the spring. He had three hundred men. He had housecarles of his on his own ship, and it was notably well manned. He had
a lot of farmers' sons with him too. Egil decided to keep him company;
he had command of a ship, and with him went a great many of the
crew Egil had brought with him from Iceland. But the merchant-
ship which Egil had brought from Iceland he had moved east to
Vík, and found men to handle his wares. Arinbjörn and Egil held
south along the land with the longships. Later they headed their
force south for Germany, where they spent the summer raiding and
won themselves wealth. But at the beginning of autumn they held
back north and lay off Frísland.

One night, when the weather was calm, they laid course up into a
certain river mouth where there was poor hope of a harbor and a big
tide race outwards. Up ashore there were big flats, and it was only a
short way to the forest. The fields there were waterlogged, for the
rain had been considerable. They made plans for going ashore and
left behind a third of their force to guard the ships. They moved up
along the river, between that and the forest. Soon there was a village
in front of them, where many farmers were living. Once they were
aware of the invaders, the people ran from the village and inland

wherever they might, but the vikings gave chase. Later there was a second village, and a third. All the people fled who might do so. There was level ground there and big flats. Dykes were scored wide throughout the countryside, and there was water standing in them. They had enclosed their ploughland and pasture, but in some places great balks were set over the dykes where people should cross. There were bridges, with timbers laid over. The inhabitants there fled into the forest. But by the time the vikings had advanced a long way into the settlements the Frisians gathered together in the forest, and when they had more than three hundred men they headed against the vikings and were resolved to fight with them. A hard struggle took place, but it ended so that the Frisians fled and the vikings pursued the fleeing foe. The country people were scattered far and wide—those who escaped. So too were those who pursued. It thus came about that few of either side kept together.

Egil gave stern chase, and a few men with him, but there were a great many running before them. The Frisians came to where there was a dyke ahead and crossed over it. They afterwards took away the bridge. Then Egil and his men came up on the other side. Egil at once set to and jumped over the dyke, but that was not a jump for other men, and no one'thought to try it. When the Frisians saw this they attacked him, but their exchanges ended so that he felled them all. After that Egil shot the bridge across and then came back over the dyke. He could see how all their following had turned away to the ships. By now he was at a point near the forest. Next Egil carried on along the forest and so to the ships, so that he might have recourse to the forest if he needed it. The vikings had brought down huge booty and cattle for slaughter, and when they reached the ships some slaughtered the farmstock, some shifted their takings out to the ships, and some stood higher up with a wall of shields, because the Frisians had come down and were in great force, and were shooting at them. By this time the Frisians had a second army there. But when Egil came down to the sea and saw what was brewing, he ran at his fastest to where the rabble was standing. He had a halberd before him and gripped it with both hands, sweeping his shield on to his back. He drove forward with the halberd, and all fell back who stood in his way, so that a space was cleared for him ahead through their army.

By this means he made his way down to his own men. It seemed to them they had got him home from Hel. They next boarded their ships and stood away from the land, and then they sailed to Denmark.

When they came to Limafjörd and were lying off Háls, Arinbjörn called a meeting of his people and told them what he was proposing to do. "I will now," he told them, "seek a meeting with the sons of Eirík, with whatever force will follow me. I have just learnt that those brothers are here in Denmark and keep great forces, and go raiding in the summers but spend the winters here in Denmark. I will now give all men leave to go to Norway who prefer that to following me. And I think it wise, Egil, for you to return to Norway and make for Iceland as soon as you can, once you and I are parted."

Later men changed ships. Those who wished to return to Norway threw in their lot with Egil, but by far the bigger part of their force was that which followed Arinbjörn. Arinbjörn and Egil parted in love and friendship. Arinbjörn went to find the sons of Eirík, and threw in his lot with Harald Graycloak, his foster son, and stayed with him thereafter as long as they both lived.

Egil went north to Vík and held on into Oslóarfjörd. His merchant-ship was there, the one he had moved south in the spring. Also there were those wares and followers of his which had gone with the ship. Thorstein Thóruson came to meet Egil with an invitation to spend the winter with him, together with such men as he wanted to keep about him. Egil accepted, had his ships laid up and his wares put in store. Of the force which accompanied him some found themselves lodgings, but some went into the north country where they had their own homes. Egil went to Thorstein's, and they were ten or twelve together there. Egil spent the winter there with good cheer.

70

King Harald Fairhair had subdued Vermaland in the east. It was Óláf Woodcutter who first conquered Vermaland, the father of Hálfdan Whiteleg, who first of his kinsmen was king in Norway. King Harald was descended from him in the male ancestral line, and all those ancestors of his had ruled over Vermaland and levied tribute on it and set men over it for the land's defense. When King Harald grew old, there was ruling over Vermaland an earl named Arnvid. It then proved the case there, as in many another place far and wide, that the tribute paid worse than when King Harald was at his most active; and so too when the sons of Harald fought for power in Norway. Small attention was then paid to the tributary lands which lay far off. But once Hákon dwelt in peace, he made inquiry into all the dominion which Harald his father had had. King Hákon had sent men east to Vermaland, twelve of them together; they had obtained tribute from the earl, but as they were traveling back through Eidaskóg highwaymen attacked them and killed them all. It fared the same way with the second lot of messengers King Hákon sent east to Vermaland, that the men were killed and the wealth did not get back. It was some men's report that Earl Arnvid would set men of his to kill the king's men and have that wealth carried back to the earl.

Then King Hákon sent the third lot of men. At the time he was in Thrándheim, and they were to go east to Vík to find Thorstein Thóruson with these words: that he should go east to Vermaland to fetch tribute home to the king's hand, or else Thorstein should depart the land, for the king had heard tell how Arinbjörn, his mother's brother, had arrived south in Denmark and was with the sons of Eirík, and this too, how they had great forces there and were raiding in the summers. It seemed to King Hákon that they were altogether untrustworthy, for he had likelihood of hostilities from the sons of Eirík once they had any strength to rebel against King Hákon. He moved then against all kinsmen and relatives and friends of Arinbjörn: many of them he drove out of the country or appointed other hard terms for them. It came about too in respect of Thorstein, that the king set him this choice for the same reason.

The man who delivered the message was a man of all countries. He had spent much time in Denmark and in the kingdom of the Swedes, and knew everything to be known there, both about the roads and the people. He had also traveled far and wide throughout Norway. And when he conveyed this charge to Thorstein Thóruson, then Thorstein told Egil on what business these men had come, and asked how he should answer them.

"From this message it seems clear to me," said Egil, "that the king wants you out of the country, like the rest of Arinbjörn's kinsmen; for I call it a mortal mission for a man of your quality. My advice is that you should summon the king's messengers to talk with you, and I want to be by at your talk. We shall then get to the bottom of this."

Thorstein did as he advised, and brought them to talk. The messengers told the whole truth of their errand and the king's message, how Thorstein should undertake this mission or else be outlawed. "I see through your errand clearly," said Egil. "If Thorstein will not go, then it will be you who must go to fetch home the tribute?" The messengers agreed that he had guessed right. "Well, Thorstein will not undertake this journey, for there is no obligation on a man of his standing to undertake such miserable missions. On the other hand, Thorstein will do anything he ought, and serve with the king, at home or abroad, if the king wishes to call on him. Further, if you would like to have some men from here for this expedition, that will be arranged for you, and all the furtherance you care to tell Thorstein of."

Thereupon the messengers discussed this among themselves and reached agreement to accept the offer if Egil himself was prepared to make the journey. "The king," they said, "is ill-disposed towards him, and he will think our journey a memorable one if we contrive a way for him to be killed. For then, if he likes, he can drive Thorstein from the land."

They now told Thorstein that they would be satisfied if Egil went and Thorstein stayed at home. "So be it," replied Egil. "I will redeem Thorstein from this undertaking. How many of us do you reckon you need have from here?" "There are eight of us all told," they said. "We should like four men to go along from here, which makes us twelve." Egil agreed that it should be so.

Önund Sjóni and certain of Egil's followers had gone out to the sea, to see to their ship and the other wares they had given into safe keeping that autumn, and they had not returned home. Egil was sorry about this, for the king's men were impatient to be off and unwilling to wait.

7 1

Egil made ready for the journey, and his three comrades with him. They had horses and sleds just like the king's men. There were great snows at the time and all the routes were altered. They started off once they were ready and drove up inland, and, as they were heading east towards Eid, it happened one night that there was such a heavy snowfall that they could hardly see the way. They got along slowly the next day, for they were sinking deep the minute they left the path. In the course of the day they stopped and fed their horses. Nearby was a wooded ridge. They said to Egil: "The ways part here now, but at the foot of the ridge here lives a farmer by the name of Arnald, a friend of ours. We comrades will make our way there for lodging, but you must carry on up to the ridge, and once you reach it there will soon be a big farm in front of you, where you are sure of a night's lodge. A very rich man lives there, known as Ármód Beard. Then we will join forces early in the morning and reach Eidaskóg tomorrow evening. There is a good farmer living there whose name is Thorfinn."

With that they parted company. Egil and his men carried on up to the ridge, but this has to be reported of the king's men, that the moment they and Egil were out of each other's sight they took the skis they had with them, put them on, and then took the road back as hard as ever they could. They kept going night and day, turning for the Uplands and from there north past Dofrafjall, and made no stay before they fell in with King Hákon and told him of their journey and the way it had gone.

Egil and his comrades crossed the ridge that evening. The quickest thing to say of it there was that they at once got off the path. Time and again the horses fell into drifts, so that they had to be dragged out. There were rocky climbs and some thick underwoods, and at these underwoods and climbs it was very hard going. Then they were greatly delayed with the horses, and for men progress was heavy indeed. They grew very exhausted, but got themselves off the ridge even so, saw a big farm facing them, and made toward it. When they

entered the farmyard they could see men standing outside, Ármód
and his servants. They exchanged greetings and asked each other
the news, and once Ármód understood that they were king's messengers he offered them quarters there. They accepted. Ármód's
housecarles took charge of their horses and harness, but the farmer
invited Egil to enter the hall, and so they did. Ármód set Egil in the
high-seat on the lower bench, and his comrades outwards from him.
They had much to say of how painfully they had fared that evening,
and the household thought it a great wonder that they had got
through, declaring that it was not safe going for anyone there, even
though it should be free from snow.

Then: "Does it not seem to you the best cheer," said Ármód, "that
a table should be set for you and supper provided, and then you go
to sleep? That is the best way to get yourselves rested."

"We should be only too glad of it," said Egil.

Ármód now had a table set for them, and big bowls full of skýr
were afterwards set out. Ármód made out he thought it a great pity
that he had no ale to give them. Egil and his men were very thirsty
from exhaustion: they took up the bowls and sipped hard of the
skýr, and Egil by far the most even so. No other food was produced
there. There were a lot of servants present. The housewife sat on the
cross-dais, with women there beside her. The farmer's daughter, some
ten or eleven years old, was wandering about the floor. The housewife
called to her and whispered in her ear, whereupon the girl walked out
in front of the table where Egil was sitting. She chanted:

> (44) "For this sent my mother
> Me with thee to confer,
> And, Egil, word bear ye
> That you should be chary.
> Adds this, drinkhorn goddess:
> Staid make your stomach;
> For guest that guesses right
> Shall feed on food more nice."

Ármód struck the child, telling her to be quiet. "You are for ever
babbling what is least proper!" The girl walked away, but Egil flung
down the skýr bowl, which was by that time nearly empty. The bowls

were now taken away from them. Then the household went to their seats, tables were erected throughout the hall and food set out. Next, meat-dishes came in and were placed before Egil as before other men.

Next ale was fetched in, and it was the strongest good beer. Soon they were at the drinking, each man for himself (one man only should drain the horn). Especial care was taken where Egil sat with his companions that they should be drinking their hardest.[1] To begin with, Egil drank bottoms up for quite a while, then once his comrades grew helplessly drunk he drank on their behalf anything they could not themselves manage. It continued this way till the tables were removed. By then all who were inside had grown very drunk; and every cup that Ármód drank—"I drink to you, Egil!" he cried; while his housecarles drank to Egil's housecarles, using the same pledge. A man was appointed to carry cup after cup to Egil and his men, and kept encouraging them to drink fast. Egil warned his comrades to lay off for the present, whilst he drank for them anything they might get rid of no other way.

But Egil found this would not do. He got to his feet and walked across the floor to where Ármód was sitting, took hold of him by the shoulders with his hands and bent him backwards against the posts. Next Egil puked up from inside him a great spew, and it gushed into Ármód's face, into his eyes and nostrils and into his mouth, and so ran down over his chest, till Ármód was pretty well smothered. And when he was able to breathe out, then up gushed *his* spew. All of Ármód's housecarles who were by swore that Egil must be branded the beastliest behaved of mankind, and the worst-conducted ruffian alive, if he would not go outside when he wanted to spew, and not make a show of himself in the drinking-hall.

"No need to blame me," said Egil. "I am only doing as the master does. He is spewing with all his might, no less than I."

Next Egil returned to his own place and sat down, telling them to bring him drink. Then with a roar he chanted:

> (45) "Witness to what mess you fed me
> I gladly avow with my vomit;
> Witness of weight I deposit
> To all my hall-crossings.

Many a guest pays guesting
At night with coin less naughty;
We seldom meet, yet meet 'tis
Ale lees in Ármód's beard lie."

Ármód lurched up and got himself outside, but Egil demanded that they give him drink. Then the housewife spoke with the man who had been serving them the whole evening, that he should let it flow so that there was no lack for as long as they wanted to drink. With that he took and filled a great horn and carried it to Egil. Egil emptied the horn at a swallow, then chanted:

(46)   "Quaff we off (through sea king
       Ekkil's beast-bestrider[2]
       Ale-oceans hales to poet,
       Verse-speaker) every beaker.
       No tot I'll leave, no spot,
       Though Ármód's in mood to have borne
       Cornmash-tarn in horn
       Till dawns the morrow's morn."

Egil drank on for a while and quaffed every horn that came his way, but there was little merriment in hall by now, for all that some men were drinking. Later Egil and his comrades got to their feet. They took their weapons, which they had hung up, from the walls, and got themselves out to the barn where their horses were. And there they lay down in the straw and slept the night.

72

Egil rose up in the morning as soon as it was day. The comrades put themselves in readiness, and as soon as they were ready went back to the farm to hunt for Ármód. And when they reached this bower where Ármód slept with his wife and daughter, Egil thrust open the door and walked up to Ármód's bed. He drew his sword, and with the other hand caught at Ármód's beard and lugged him forward to the bedpost, but Ármód's wife and daughter started up, begging Egil that he should not kill Ármód. Egil said he would do this for their sakes. "For it is your due. But he deserved that I should kill him." Then Egil chanted:

(47) "By this token this illspoken
Gold-armsnake-holder
(A not too frightening fighter)
Owes life to wife and daughter.
And yet you'll think for drink
What shame, all things the same,
You took potluck with a poet.
Well, on our way we'll lumber!"

Next Egil cut off his beard to the chin. Next he crooked his finger into his eye, so that it spilled out on to the cheek. After that Egil went off to his comrades. They continued on their way and reached Thorfinn's farm by breakfast time. He lived alongside Eidaskóg. Egil and his men asked to breakfast and feed their horses, and farmer Thorfinn said it should be attended to. Egil and his men entered the hall. Egil asked whether Thorfinn had seen anything of his companions. "We had spoken of this as our meeting place."

Thorfinn had this to say: "Six men together traveled past here a little before day, and they were heavily armed."

Then Thorfinn's housecarle added: "I was driving after firewood last night, and on my way I came across six men who were housecarles of Ármód's. This was well before day. Now I don't know whether these would be all one and the same six men as those you mentioned just now?"

But Thorfinn said that the men he had met with had gone past after the housecarle had come home with his load of wood.

As Egil and his men were sitting and eating, Egil saw that there was a sick woman lying on the cross-dais. He asked Thorfinn who this woman might be who was so heavily afflicted. He said her name was Helga, and that she was his daughter. "She has been failing in strength a long while." This was a great and wasting sickness. She got no sleep by night and was as though out of her mind.

"Has anything been tried for her affliction?" asked Egil.

"Runes have been graven," replied Thorfinn, "and it is a farmer's son a short way off who did that; but ever since it has been far worse than before. But can you do anything, Egil, for such afflictions?"

"Maybe," said Egil, "it will not grow worse should I lend a hand."

So when Egil was full he went to where the woman was lying and talked with her. He said to lift her from bed and lay clean clothes under her, and this was done. Next he ransacked the bed she had been resting in, and found whalebone there, with runes on it. These Egil read and afterwards shaved the runes and scraped them down into the fire. He burned all the whalebone and had carried out into the wind the clothes she had made use of before. Then Egil chanted:

> (48) "No leech should unleash runes
> Save rightly he can read them;
> Of men it happens to many
> A mirky stave benights him.
> Well, spied I on scraped whalebone
> Ten secret runstaves graven;
> Those to leeklinden maiden
> Brought wasting all too lasting."

Egil graved runes and laid them under the pillow of the bed where she was resting. It seemed to her as though she were awaking from sleep, and she said she was now well again; though even so she was far from strong. Her father and mother were joyful past measure, and Thorfinn begged Egil to accept of him all the futherance he felt he needed.

73

Egil told his comrades that he would like to get on with his journey and delay no longer. Thorfinn had a son whose name was Helgi, a gallant young fellow. Father and son offered Egil their company through the forest, saying they felt certain that Ármód Beard had set six men in the forest ahead of them, and that it was even more likely that there would be further ambushes in the forest if the first one slipped. They were four in all, Thorfinn and those men of his who offered themselves for the journey. Then Egil chanted a verse:

(49) "Know if I fare with four
There fare no six dare mix
In fight against my might
With Ódin's red shield-shearers.[1]
But gang I my gait with eight,
Not weight of twelve can abate
Where drawn swords drone together
Proud heart of swartbrowed Egil."

Thorfinn and his men were insistent that they should accompany Egil to the forest, so they were now a party of eight. When they arrived where the ambush was lying in wait they could see men there. But those of Ármód's housecarles who lay in wait observed how eight men were traveling there and thought it risky to make an attack. They then stole away into the forest. But when Egil and his men came to where they had lain in ambush they could see that the prospect ahead was by no means a peaceful one. Egil told Thorfinn and his men to turn back, but they offered to continue still further. Egil would have none of this; he told them to return, and they did so and turned back, but Egil and his men proceeded on their way, and were now four in all. As the day wore on Egil and his comrades came to know there were six men in the forest, and they felt sure it was Ármód's housecarles who would be there. The ambushers leapt up and attacked them, and they attacked in return, and this came of their encounter that Egil felled two men, and those who survived ran off into the forest.

After that Egil and his men pushed on their way, and nothing worth telling of happened before they emerged from Eidaskóg and took quarters alongside the forest with the farmer whose name was Álf but who was known as Álf the Rich. He was an old man and blest with riches, but strange and self-willed, so that he might not get servants to stay with him, except for just a few. Egil found a good welcome there, and Álf talked to him freely. Egil inquired closely after the news, and Álf informed him of whatever he asked after. Chiefly they talked of the earl, and of the king of Norway's messengers who had earlier made journeys out east there to fetch home the tribute. In what he had to say Álf was no friend to the earl.

7 4

Egil and his comrades made ready for their journey early in the morning, and at parting Egil gave Álf a fur cloak. Álf accepted the gift
thankfully—"I can make myself a fur cape out of this"—and he invited Egil to call on him when he was on his way back.

They parted friends, and Egil proceeded on his journey and came
in the afternoon to Earl Arnvid's court and had an excellent welcome
there. Seats were found for those comrades next to the second high-
seat. And when Egil and his men had been there overnight, they delivered their errand to the earl, with the king's message out of Norway, stating how he desired to receive from Vermaland all the tribute
which till then had been left outstanding, ever since Arnvid was put
in charge there. The earl said that he had paid up all the tribute and
delivered it to the king's messengers. "But I have no idea what they
have done with it since, whether they delivered it to the king or have
themselves fled the country with it. But because you are carrying sure
tokens that the king has sent you, I shall pay all the tribute which
rightly belongs to him and deliver it into your hands. But from that
point on I am not to be held answerable for anything you do with it."

Egil and his men remained there for a while, and before Egil left
the earl paid them the tribute. Some of it was in silver, some in gray
wares; and once Egil and his men were ready they set off on their return journey. At their parting Egil had this to tell the earl: "We will
now convey this tribute we have received to the king, but you must be
aware, Earl, that this is far less wealth than the king reckons belongs
to him here, and even then there is no account taken, so it will seem
to him, how you have to recompense him with wergelds for those
messengers of his whom you are deemed to have had killed."

The earl denied that this was true, and on those terms they parted.
But the minute Egil had taken his departure the earl called two
brothers before him, both of whom bore the name Ulf. This is what
he had to tell them: "That big Egil who was here for a while, I think
it will be a sorry day for us when he reaches the king. We can tell how
he will display this affair of ours before him, when he threw such a

thing as killing the king's men in our teeth. You two must now get after them and kill them all, and not let them carry this slander before the king. It seems to me the best plan that you set an ambush for them in Eidaskóg. Take with you so many men that it is certain none of them shall get away, yet you yourselves lose not a man for them."

The brothers now made ready for their undertaking and had thirty men. They went to the forest where they knew every path in the place. They then spied out Egil's movements. In the forest there were two roads. By the first one must proceed over a certain ridge, and there was a steep climb there and a narrow path to travel. This was the shorter way. But by the other one must proceed out round the ridge, and there were big swamps there with felled trees across them, and there too there was a narrow path to travel. So fifteen lay in wait at either place.

75

Egil kept going till he reached Álf's, where he spent the night with good cheer. The next morning he was up before day making ready for his journey. As they were sitting over breakfast, farmer Álf came to them.

"You make ready early, Egil," he said, "but my advice would be different: don't rush your journey. Look out for yourselves rather, for I believe there will be men lying in wait for you in the forest. I have no one I can get to accompany you, so that you would be the stronger for it; but I should like to invite you to stay here with me till I can assure you that it will be safe to cross the forest."

"This will be nothing but an old woman's tale," said Egil. "I shall be on my way, as I planned before."

Egil and his men made ready for their journey, but Álf spoke against it, urging him to return if he found that the pathway was trodden; no one, he said, had crossed the forest from the east since Egil himself went eastwards—"Unless those have crossed it who I suspect are wanting to fall in with you."

"How many do you think they will be, if things are as you say? We are not just for the taking, even if there is some disparity of numbers."

"I had gone out to the forest," he replied," and my housecarles with me; we came across the tracks of men, and the trail led on into the forest, and there must have been a great many of them altogether. But if you do not believe what I tell you, then go and take a look at the trail, but turn back if it looks to you the way I say."

Egil continued on his way. When they reached the pathway which led to the forest they could see the track of both men and horses there. Egil's comrades said they ought to turn back. "We will keep going," Egil told them. "I see nothing strange in it, though men have made their way through Eidaskóg, for it is the common highway."

With that they pressed ahead, and the footprints continued, and then there were a lot of tracks, and when they came to where the ways parted the trail parted too and was of similar size in each place.

"It looks to me now," said Egil then, "that maybe Álf has told the truth after all. We will now put ourselves in the same readiness as if we were expecting a brush with them."

Egil and his men next threw off their cloaks and all loose garments. These they put in the sleds. In his sled Egil kept a very long line of bast, for it is the practice of men who drive long distances to have loose ropes with them, in case there is need to make tackle. Egil took a big stone slab and placed it before his chest and belly; he next hitched the rope about it, looping it round and round, and fixed it so right up to his shoulders.[1] After that they continued on their way.

Eidaskóg is after this fashion, that the timber stays big right to the settlements on either side, but in the middle of the forest there is extensive scrubwood and undergrowth, and some quite treeless places. Egil and his men turned the shorter way which lay over the ridge. They all had shields and helmets and weapons for cutting and thrusting. Egil proceeded at their head. And when they made their way on to the ridge, it was forested down under but treeless up on the cliff. When they had come up into the rocky part of the climb, seven men ran out of the forest and up on to the rock-climb after them, and shot at them. Egil and his men turned on them, and they were standing in line abreast across the path. Then other men came down against them to the bluff, and from there threw stones at them, which was more dangerous to them by far.

"You must now withdraw to the rock-climb and take what cover you can," ordered Egil, "while I look for a way up on to the rock."

They did so. And when Egil came up off the cliff, there were eight men facing him who made for him as one and attacked him. But there is nothing to tell of their exchanges: it ended so that he killed them all. Next he went to the edge of the rock and rolled stones down, and there was no standing against that. Three Vermalanders lay there behind, and four got away into the forest—and they too were wounded and bruised. Egil and his men now took their horses and pressed ahead till they came over the ridge. But those other Vermalanders who had got away brought news to their comrades who were by the fen. They set off then by the lower road, and so ahead of Egil and his men on their path.

"We must now proceed against them cannily," Ulf informed his comrades, "and so arrange matters that they cannot get away. This is the way the land lies," he said, "their way leads on round the ridge, but the fen stretches right up to it, and there is a crag higher up. The roadway lies in between and is no broader than the breadth of a footpath. Some shall go on round the bluff and give them a welcome if they want to go ahead, but some shall hide here in the forest and later fall upon them from the rear as they come past. And mind this, that not a single man escapes!"

They did as Ulf ordered. Ulf went on round the rock, and ten men with him. Egil and his men were pressing on their way and knew nothing of this plan till they reached the narrow path, where men made an assault upon them from the rear and at once bore weapons against them. Egil and his men faced about to meet them and defended themselves. Now too there came running at them those men who had been in front of the bluff, and when Egil saw this he swung round to meet them. There was a brief exchange of blows between them; some of them Egil killed there in the pathway, but some dropped back to where there was leveler ground. Egil chased after them, and Ulf fell dead there, and before the finish Egil killed eleven men singlehanded. Next he hurried to where his comrades were defending the path against eight men, and by this time there were men wounded on either side. When Egil arrived, the Vermalanders fled at once, and the forest lay there handy. Five got away, all of them sorely wounded, but three perished. Egil had many wounds, but none of them serious. They now held on their way. He bandaged his comrades' wounds, and none of them was deadly. They then sat in the sleds and drove for what was left of the day.

But the Vermalanders who got away took their horses and managed to get east from the forest to the settlements, where their wounds were bound up. They found themselves conveyance till they came before the earl and told him of their disaster. They reported that the two Úlfs had fallen and that twenty-five men were dead. "Five only escaped with their lives, and even they were all wounded and bruised."

The earl asked what might be the news of Egil and his comrades.

"We did not know exactly how much they were hurt," was the reply, "but they attacked us boldly enough. When we were eight and they four, it was then that we fled. Five got away to the forest and three perished, but for all we could see, Egil and his men were still as good as new."

The earl held that their journey had turned out as badly as could be. "I would have been content that we suffered great loss of men if only you had killed those Norwegians! But now when they come from the forest and tell this news to Norway's king, we can expect a hard time of it from him."

76

Egil pressed on till he came west from the forest. They made their way to Thorfinn's by evening and received a splendid welcome there. Egil's wounds and his men's were now bound up, and they stayed there some nights. Helga the farmer's daughter was on her feet by this time and healed of her sickness; she and all of them thanked Egil for this. They rested themselves there and their sled-horses.

Now the man who had graven runes for Helga was living only a short way off. It now came to light that he had asked to marry her, but Thorfinn was unwilling to give her. Then the farmer's son wanted to seduce her, but for this she was unwilling. Finally he thought to grave love-runes for her, but didn't know how, and he had graved for her what she got her affliction from.

When Egil was ready to leave, Thorfinn and his son saw him on his way. They were ten or twelve together. They traveled with them all that day as a safeguard against Ármód and his housecarles. But once this news was heard, how Egil and his men had fought against overwhelming force in the forest and won the day, there seemed to Ármód no hope that he could lift shield against Egil. So Ármód stayed at home with all his men. Egil and Thorfinn exchanged gifts at parting, and pledged friendship between them.

Next Egil and his men continued on their way, and it is not recorded that anything worth telling of took place on their journey before they reached Thorstein's. And now their wounds were mended. Egil and his men remained there till the spring, but Thorstein provided messengers to King Hákon to bring him the tribute Egil had gone to Vermaland to fetch. When they appeared before the king, they told him what had happened on Egil's journey, and made over the tribute to him. The king now felt certain that what he had suspected earlier would be true, and that Earl Arnvid must have slaughtered those two embassies of his which he had sent east. The king said that Thorstein should now have leave to live in the land and be at peace for him. The messengers next made their way home, and when they returned to Thorstein they told him how pleased the king was with this exploit, and that Thorstein should now live there in peace and friendship with the king.

That summer King Hákon proceeded east to Vík, and from there made a journey east to Vermaland in great force. Earl Arnvid fled away, but the king exacted heavy payment from those farmers he thought had offended him, as was reported by those who had sought for the tribute. He set another earl in charge there and took hostages of him and the farmers. On this expedition King Hákon traveled wide throughout western Gautland and subdued it, as is recounted in his saga and may be found in the poems which have been composed about him. And then it is recorded that he went to Denmark and raided far and wide. He cleared twelve ships of the Danes with his two, and thereafter he gave the name of king to Tryggvi Óláfsson, his brother's son, with dominion east over the Vík.

Egil put his merchant-ship in readiness that summer and picked
her crew, but the longship he had brought from Denmark in the
autumn he presented to Thorstein at their parting. Thorstein gave
Egil fine gifts, and they pledged deep friendship between them. Egil
sent messengers to his kinsman Thórd in Aurland and laid on him
his charge to dispose of the estates belonging to Egil in Sogn and
Hördaland, requesting him to sell if there should be a buyer for them.
And when Egil was ready for his voyage, and had a following wind,
they sailed out past Vík and so on their way north off Norway and
thereafter out to sea. They had a breeze after their own heart, came
from the sea into Borgarfjörd, and Egil held on with his ship along
the firth to a harbor a short distance from his own farm; he had his
wares carried home and his ship drawn up on shore. Egil went home to
his own dwelling, and men rejoiced to see him. And there Egil spent
the winter.

77

When this made news, that Egil was back in Iceland from that expedition of his, by then the countryside was fully settled. All the original
settlers, indeed, were dead, but their sons or sons' sons were alive and
living there in the neighborhood.

Ketil Gufa came to Iceland when the land was substantially settled. For the first winter he was at Gufuskálir in Rosmhvalanes. He
had come from west over the sea, from Ireland, and had many Irish
thralls with him. All territory in Rosmhvalanes was settled by that
time, so Ketil decided to remove from there in to Nes, and spent the
second winter at Gufunes but found no settled home there. Next he
went on into Borgarfjörd, to spend the third winter at the place which
has since been called Gufuskálir, and Gufuá the river which runs
down there, where he kept his ship that winter.

Thórd Lambason was then living at Lambastadir. He was married
and had a son named Lambi, who was now a grown man, big and
strong for his age. The following summer, when men rode to the
Thing, Lambi too rode to the Thing. But Ketil Gufa had travelled
west to Breidafjörd, to look for a home there. His thralls now ran off.
They came on by night to Thórd's at Lambastadir, set fire to the

houses and burned Thórd and all his household indoors there, but broke open his storehouse and carried out the valuables and wares. Next they drove in horses and loaded them and afterwards made their way out to Álftanes.

That morning, about the hour of sunrise, Lambi returned home and had seen the fire by night. They were only a few men together. He at once rode to hunt down the thralls, and men rode from the neighboring farms to join him. When the thralls discovered the pursuit they made off, abandoning their plunder. Some rushed out to the Mýrar, but some out along the sea till the firth was facing them. Lambi and his men chased after them and killed there the one whose name was Kóri (the place on that account has since been known as Kóranes), but Skorri and Thormód and Svart plunged in and swam from land. Next Lambi and his men looked around for boats and rowed to hunt them down, and Skorri they found on Skorraey and killed him there. They then rowed out to Thormódssker, where they killed Thormód (and from him the skerry gets its name). They laid hands on yet more thralls where the placenames are assigned ever since.

Later Lambi lived at Lambastadir and was a fine farmer. He was of great bodily strength, but in no way a turbulent man. Ketil Gufa went out to Breidafjörd next and made his home in Thorskafjörd. From him Gufudal and Gufufjörd received their names. He married Ýr, the daughter of Geirmund Helskin: Váli was their son.

There was a man named Grím who was Sverting's son. He lived at Mosfell under the Heath, and was rich and well descended. His sister on the distaff side was that Rannveig whom Thórodd Godi of Ölfús married. Their son was Skafti the Lawspeaker. Grím too became Lawspeaker later on. He asked for Thórdis, Thórólf's daughter, who was niece and stepdaughter to Egil. Egil loved Thórdis no less than his own children. She was a most handsome woman. And because Egil knew that Grím was a man altogether notable, and the match a good one, it was agreed to. Thórdis was given in marriage to Grím, and Egil paid out her father's inheritance. She went to keep house with Grím, and they lived at Mosfell for a long time.

78

Living at Hjardarholt in Laxárdal, west in the Breidafjörd Dales, was a man named Óláf, the son of Höskuld Dala-Kollsson, the son too of Melkorka, daughter of Mýrkjartan king of the Irish. Óláf had immense wealth, and in looks was the handsomest man then in Iceland. He was a lordly man. Óláf asked for the hand of Egil's daughter Thorgerd. Thorgerd was a tall and good-looking woman, clever and rather proud, but in general equable of mood. Egil knew all about Óláf and felt sure the match was a fine one, and for that reason Thorgerd was married to Óláf and went to live with him at Hjardarholt. Their children were Kjartan, Thorberg, Halldór, Steindór, Thuríd, Thorbjörg, and that Bergthóra whom Thórhall Godi Oddason married. Ásgeir Knattarson married Thorbjörg first, and Vermund Thorgrímsson later. Gudmund Sölmundarson married Thuríd. Their sons were Hall and Víga-Bardi. Özur Eyvindarson, brother of Thórodd from Ölfús, married Egil's daughter Bera.

Egil's son Bödvar was now in his prime. He was a most promising man, handsome, big and strong, just as Egil had been, or Thórólf at his age. Egil loved him dearly, and Bödvar was devoted to Egil. It happened one summer that there was a ship in Hvítá, and there was a great marketing there. Egil had bought a lot of timber there and was having it fetched home by ship. Housecarles made the journey; they used an eight-oared ship belonging to Egil, and it happened on the one trip that Bödvar asked to go with them, and they let him. So he went up to Vellir with the housecarles (they were six all told in the eight-oared ship). When they were to proceed downriver, just then high water was late in the day, and since they had to wait for it they were late setting off that evening. A fierce south-wester sprang up, and the ebb-race streamed against it. This made a very rough sea in the firth, as is often the case there; and it ended so that the ship went down under them, and they all perished. Next day the bodies were cast ashore. Bödvar's body came in at Einarsnes, but some reached the south shore of the firth, and the ship drifted there too. It was found in by Reykjahamar.

That same day Egil heard the news, and he immediately rode to look for the bodies. He found Bödvar's body washed ashore. He took it up and set it on his knees and rode with it out to Digranes, to Skallagrím's howe. He had the howe opened, and laid Bödvar down there beside Skallagrím. The howe was then closed, and this was not finished before the hour of sunset. After that Egil rode back to Borg, and when he reached home he went straight to the lock-bed where he used to sleep, lay down and shot the bolt. No one dared try to talk with him.

This was the way Egil was dressed, they say, when they laid Bödvar down: his hose were tied close about the leg, and he was wearing a red fustian kirtle, tight-fitting in its upper part and laced at the sides. But men report that he so swelled that the kirtle split off him, and the hose too.

Next day Egil did not unfasten the lock-bed, and he took neither meat nor drink. He lay there that day and the night following. No one dared speak to him. But the third morning, as soon as it grew light, Ásgerd had a man set on horseback (he rode his hardest west to Hjardarholt) and had Thorgerd informed of all that had happened. It was about mid-afternoon when he arrived there. He reported this too, how Ásgerd had sent her word to come south to Borg as soon as possible. Thorgerd had her horse saddled at once, and two men kept her company. They rode through the evening and night till they reached Borg. Thorgerd went into the hall immediately. Ásgerd greeted her and asked whether they had eaten supper.

"No supper have I had," Thorgerd answered loudly, "and none will I, till I am with Freyja.[1] I know of no better plan for me than my father. I don't want to live after my father and brother." She went to the lock-closet, and, "Father," she called, "open the door. I want us both to go the same road."

Egil shot back the bolt, and Thorgerd went up into the bed-closet and had the door fastened behind her. She lay down in a second bed which was there.

"You do well, daughter," said Egil, "when you want to keep your father company. Great love you have shown me. What hope is there that I will want to live after this sorrow?"

Next they were silent for a while. Then, "What is it now, daughter?" Egil asked. "Are you chewing something?"

"I am chewing seaweed," she replied, "for I believe it will then go worse with me than before. Otherwise I fear I shall live too long."

"Is it bad for a man?" asked Egil.

"Very bad," she assured him. "You would like some to eat?"

"What difference will it make?" he said.

Some time later she called out, asking them to give her something to drink. She was now given water to drink. "So it goes if one eats seaweed," said Egil then. "One grows thirstier all the time."

"You would like to drink, Father?" she asked.

He took hold and swallowed deeply. It was in a horn. "We have been tricked!" cried Thorgerd then. "This is milk!" At these words Egil bit a notch in the horn, as big as his teeth could fasten on, and afterwards dashed the horn down.

"What plan shall we take now, we two?" asked Thorgerd then. "For this design is at an end. I should like now, father, that we prolong our lives so that you might compose a funeral-ode after Bödvar, and I will grave it on the roller, and after that let us die, if we think fit. I fear your son Thorstein will make heavy work of it composing an ode after Bödvar—and it is wrong that he should not be properly waked. For I cannot think you and I will be seated at the drinking when he is waked."

Egil held it unlikely he would be able to compose, even though he should make the attempt. "Still, I could try," he said.

Egil had had a son who was named Gunnar, and he too had died a short while before. And this is the beginning of the poem:[2]

> Heavy I find it
> To heave my tongue,
> Or swing aloft
> A songscale's balance.
> Small prospect now
> Of poet-god's plunder;
> No lightdrawn load
> From heart's deep lair.

Not easy to force
From seat of thought
(For grief holds sway
With hand too heavy),
That joyous finding
Of Frigg's own kinsfolk,
Of yore borne off
From Jötunheim—[3]

Which lived before
Free from blemish
On dwarf Nökkver's
Ship of verse.[4]
Giant's neckwound-[5]
Seastream's wailing
Down below Náinn's
Boathouse doors.[6]

For line of mine
Stands at an end,
By storm heeled over
Like forest maples.
Not blithe the man
Who bears the limbs
Of a kinsman's corse
From his homestead down.

Yet must I now
My mother's corse
And father's fall
Seek first to tell of.
That move I forth
From mouth, words' temple,
Proud timber of speech
All word-beleaféd.

Grim was the breach
Broke by the sea
In the closed fence
Of my father's line.
Bare now I know
And open stands
That gap in my sons
Sea won on me.

Deeply has Rán
Wrought for my ill;
Naked I'm laid
Of loving friends.
Sea has cut bonds,
Severed my line,
Kinrope's strand
Struck from my heart.

Know, if my wrongs
I could right with the sword,
Soon for the Alesmith[7]
All would be over.
The stormwind's brother,
Might I bear weapons,
I would go match him
And Ægir's moonmate.

But never a whit
Had I, so I found,
Of strength to this end
Against son's slayer.
For all men's eyes
May easily see
An agéd fellow's
Helpless faring.

Me has ocean
Sadly plundered.
Cruel the fall
Of kinsfolk to tell of,
Ever since he,
Shield of my line,
On heaven's glad path
Turned lifeless away.

This too I know,
How in my son
Was no ill timber
Grown of a man,
Had that targetree
But come to his prime,
So that he reached
For Hostgod's hand.

Much made he ever
Of what father spoke,
Though all men else
Held the other way.
He upheld me
In ordering my house,
Of strength of mine
Main prop and stay.

Oft comes to me
My brother's loss
On memory's wind
Of the Moon's Bear.[8]
I think of him
When warfare waxes,
Look round for him,
And think on this:

Who else boldthoughted,
What other thane,
Shall stand by me
In trouble?
I need this oft
'Gainst froward men;
Wary my flight
Now friends grow few.

Full hard to find
A friend I trust in
Midst all the folk
Of Elgr's gallows.[9]
A scoundrel ever
Confounds his kin,
Bartering for rings
His brother's body.

I find that oft
Once wealth is offered*

.   .   .   .
.   .   .   .
.   .   .   .
.   .   .   .
.   .   .   .
.   .   .   .

'Tis also said
That none may get
Amends for a son,
Save a man's self breed
A further scion
May seem to others
One born to fill
His brother's place.

* The words here are missing.

I take no mirth
In all mankind,
Though each of them
Should prove him true.
My lad is come
To Ódin's homestead,
My wife's own son
To seek his kin.

For me I find
With mind severe
How mashtarn's Master[10]
Stands against me.
I cannot rear
My grim old head,
Thoughtwain of mine
More upright hold,

Since my son
A sickness-flame
So savagely
Rapt from my home:
A son I knew
Shunned all reproach,
And held him blameless
Of all blemish.

This mind I too:
He lifted high,
Did Gauts' good friend,[11]
To the gods' home
My line's ashbranch
Which grew from me,
That kindred timber
From wife's side sprung.

Well stood I
With spear's Master;[11]
I made me true
To trust to him.
Till Friend of wains,[11]
Wargain's Awarder,
His friendship's ties
Cut free of me.

I revere not then
Vílir's brother,[11]
Guardian of gods,
Because I'm glad to.
Yet Mímir's friend[11]
Has found for me
All wrongs' amendment,
If truer I reckon.

He gave me my art,
Did Fenrir's Foe,[11]
Battle's Frequenter,
—Free of blemish;
And that same mind
Wherewith I made me
Open foes
Of secret haters.

Goes hard with me now!
The near sister
Of Ódin's wolf-foe[12].
Stands on the ness.[13]
Yet will I gladly
With a good heart,
Strong, unrepining,
Abide Hel's onset.

Egil began to perk up as the composition of his poem went forward, and when the poem was finished he recited it to Ásgerd and Thorgerd and to the people of his household. Next he rose from his bed and took his place in the high-seat. He called this poem his *Sons' Wreck*. Later Egil had his sons waked after the old fashion. And when Thorgerd returned home, Egil saw her on her way with gifts.

Egil lived at Borg a long while and became an old man; but it is not reported that he had lawsuits with men here in Iceland. Nor is anything recorded of holmgangs of his or manslaughters, once he settled down here at home. Men relate that Egil did not go abroad from Iceland after these happenings which have now been recounted; and what contributed most to this was that Egil could not be in Norway because of the grievances which, as was told earlier, the kings[14] reckoned they had against him. He kept a splendid household, for there was no lack of means for this. He had the right disposition for it too.

King Hákon, Athelstan's foster son, held sway over Norway for a long time, but in the latter part of his life the sons of Eirík came to Norway and fought for dominion in Norway against King Hákon. They fought battles one with the other, and Hákon had ever the victory. Their last battle they fought in Hördaland, on Stord at Fitjar. King Hákon got victory there, and his death wound with it; and thereafter the sons of Eirík held the kingdom of Norway. Arinbjörn Hersir was with Harald Eiríksson, and became his chief adviser and had immense rents of him. He was in command of his army and of the land's defence. Arinbjörn was a great soldier and victory-blest. He had the Firthafylki to rent.

Egil Skallagrímsson heard this news, how a change of kings had come about in Norway, and this too, how Arinbjörn had now come to Norway to his own home and was there in high esteem. Egil then composed a poem on Arinbjörn,[15] and this is the beginning of it:

> I am prompt of speech
> To praise princes,
> But stiff of tongue
> Towards the stingy.

Wordhoard open
For warlord's deeds,
But silent fallen
At folks' deceit.

With libels fraught
Against lie-bearers,
But laud on lips
For my loving friends.
Sought have I many
Seats of the mighty
With my unsullied
Poet's soul.

I had of old
Of Yngling's scion
Right royal monarch's
Wrath drawn down;
Pulled daring's helm
Over dark hair,
Planned for hersir's
Home a visit,

Where allpowerful
Under awe-helmet
The people's leader
Reigned in the land;
Ruled this king
With ruthless will
There within York
His wet domains.

'Twas no soft moonlight
Safe to observe
Nor terrorfree
From Eirík's eyes,

When the snakebright
Brows' moonradiance[16]
Of King's eyes gleamed
With glances grim.

Yet bolsterprice
Presumed I to bear
Of poet-god's mead[17]
To monarch.
So that Ygg's cup[18]
Came spilling o'er
Into the mouths
Of each man's ears.

Nor shapefair
It showed to men,
My poem's prize
In prince's house.
When, wolfgray,
For Ygg's songvessel
My hat's knob
From him I won.

That I took.
There followed two
Blacksun jewels
Of my sunken brows,
And this my mouth
Which moved for me
My Headransom
Before monarch's knee.

There my teeth's tale
With tongue I won,
And my ears' tents
With hearing dowered:

That good gift
Of the gallant king
Than brighthued gold
Was rated better.

There stood one
Staunch beside me,
Better than many
A foe to money;
True friend of mine
I'm free to trust in,
Glorious grown
In every counsel.

Arinbjörn!
Alone he bore me,
Of all men foremost,
From the king's hate;
Folklord's friend
Who never failed me
In that martial
Monarch's garth.

And   .   .*
.   let the prop,
Muchforwarder
Of my deeds,
As   .   .   .
.   of Hálfdan
It might denote
His line's deep notch.

Friendship's thief
I shall be called,
And a sad liar
In skaldship's bowl,

* The words here are missing.

For fame unfit,
And named faithbreaker,
Save for this help
I handsel pay.

Now that is seen,
Where I shall set
(A steep path
For poet's feet)
Before mankind
In sight of many
Fame of haughty
Hersir's scion.

Easy to plane
With my mouth's blade
Glory's timber
For Thórir's kinsman,[19]
My own friend,
For chosen lie
Strains three or twain
Upon my tongue.

Recount I first
What most men reck of,
And to all folk's ears
Has found a way:
How generousminded
Men have thought him,
Hearthfire-Bear,[19]
The birches' Dread.

This by mortals
A marvel's held,
How the world's folk
With wealth he dowers;

But this Rock-Bear[19]
The gods have blest,
Freyr and Njörd,
With riches' fee.

For at the homestead
Of Hróald's kinsman[19]
Wealth unstinted
To men's arms streams.
One sees friends riding
By every road
Over the windbowl's
Wide earthbottom.

He a drawrope
Has gotten him
As warriorprince
To ears' precincts;
Godbeloved
Among living men,
Véthorm's friend,
The weak's defender.

That he performs
Which others fail of,
Almost all men,
Though they have money;
Spaced far I hold
Freegivers' halls,
Nor simply shafted
All men's spears.

Went no man e'er
At Arinbjörn's
Forth from his bed's
Long shipchamber,

Scorn-escorted
By scandal's words,
With spear's handhome
Still empty.

He's cruel to wealth
Who dwells in the Firths;
Dread enemy
Of Draupnir's kin;[20]
And a stern foe
To bracelets stands;
Fatal to rings,
And treasure's bane.

He a life's field
Has found for him,
Amply sown with
Peace-despoilings.*

. . . . .
. . . . .
. . . . .
. . . . .

Not good it were
If goldwaster
Should cast away
On seamew's course,
So roughridden
By Rökkvi's steeds,[21]
Those many gains
He granted me.

Woke I betimes,
Bore words together
For Tongue, speechservant,
His morning-task.

* The words here are missing.

Praisecairn I piled [22]
Which long shall stand,
Nor soon be scattered
In skaldship's meadow.

There was a man named Einar, who was the son of Helgi Óttarson,
son of Björn the Easterner who settled in Breidafjörd. Einar was
brother to Ósvif the Wise. While still a youth Einar was big and
strong and a most accomplished man. He took to poem-making while
he was young, and was a man eager to learn. It happened one summer at the Althing that Einar went to Egil Skallagrímsson's booth:
they fell into conversation and soon it entered into their talk together
that they debated of poetry. Each found the discussion a great pleasure,
and Einar used afterwards often to go and talk with Egil. A strong
friendship grew up between them. Einar had not long returned home
from his travels. Egil had a lot of questions to ask him about the news
from the east and about his friends—and about those he believed to be
no friends of his too. He also had many questions to ask about the
great men. In turn Einar asked Egil for news of what had happened
on his journeyings and his great adventures, and this talk pleased Egil
and bore good fruit. Einar asked Egil on what occasions he had given
the best account of himself, and asked him to tell him about this.
Egil chanted:

(50)   "One time I ate up eight,
          And twice I sliced eleven;
          Fed bellyful to balewolf,
          Their bane I'd been alone!
          Hot blows we swapped and hateful
          With swords that made shield shudder;
          From bold hand, Embla's ashbowl,[23]
          I rolled the flashing swordflame."

Egil and Einar pledged friendship between them at parting. Einar
was abroad a long time with highborn men. He was a free-handed
man and most of the time short of money, but a lordly man and a
good comrade. He was a member of Earl Hákon Sigurdarson's
bodyguard.

At this time there was great enmity and strife in Norway between Earl Hákon and the sons of Eirík, and they fled turnabout from the land. King Harald Eiríksson fell south in Denmark, at Háls in Limafjörd, and he was betrayed. He fought there against Harold Knútsson, who was nicknamed Gold-Harald, and the Earl Hákon. And there with King Harald fell Arinbjörn Hersir, who was told of earlier. And when Egil heard tell of Arinbjörn's fall, he chanted:

(51) "Minish they now who diminished
Dawnfire of meadfoaming horn;
Wane now the heroes, time-vanquished,
War's flaunters, the henchmen of Ingvi.
Who now showers limbeck's snowsilver
I garnered past earth's sea-isled girdle?
Or fills high hawkfell of my hand
With skald's reward for skilled word?" [24]

The poet Einar Helgason was nicknamed Jinglescale. He composed a drápa on Earl Hákon which is called *Goldlack,* and for a long time it happened that the earl would not listen to the poem, because he was angry with Einar. So Einar chanted:

(52) "Skaldmead of Ódin[25] made I,
Sleepless whilst others slumbered,
For men's lord, land's commander,
—Now I regret my rashness!
This knowledge now may gnaw me,
That to this wealth-dispenser,
(Eager I came to greet him)
No poet shows more paltry."

And again he chanted:

(53) "Find we that earl does not mind
Glutting the wolf with glaive-leavings;
Line we with shieldwall fine
Vessel's thwarts of Sigvaldi.[26]

> There's one, that woundsnake-shaker,
> Scoffs not at hand I proffer
> To earl met fair. My shield I'll bear
> To sea-king Endil's ski-ship."

The earl was not prepared for Einar to go away, and he now gave ear to the poem, and later he gave Einar a shield, which was a treasure indeed. It was pictured with old tales, but all between the pictures there were crosspieces of gold overlaid, and it was set with stones. Einar went back to Iceland to stay with Ósvif his brother; and that autumn he rode from the west and came to Borg and was a guest there. Egil was not at home just then—he had gone off into the north of the district—but was expected back. Three nights Einar waited for him, but it was not the custom to stay longer than three nights on a visit. Einar then made ready to be off, and when he was ready he went to Egil's bed and hung up that precious shield there, and told the household that he was giving the shield to Egil. Next Einar rode away, and that same day Egil arrived home. As he came in to his bed he saw the shield and asked who was the owner of so precious a thing. He was told how Einar Jinglescale had come visiting there and had given him the shield.

"To Hel with him and his gift!" cried Egil then. "Does he plan for me to lie awake over this and make poems on his shield? Catch my horse! I am going to ride after him and kill him."

He was told that Einar had ridden off early that morning. "By now he will have reached Dalir in the west."

In time Egil composed a drápa, and here is the opening of it:

> (54)   Time now to shape laud's shining
> For sheen of shipfence shield;
> Word sent by treasure-spender,
> Sped home, to my hand's now come.
> No rein awry I'll strain
> On seasteed of Gylfi's domain,[27]
> The skilled dwarf's ship of skaldship.
> Give ear now to my words!

Egil and Einar maintained their friendship as long as the two of them lived. But this is the story of what happened to the shield in the

end, that Egil took it with him on that bridal-journey which he made
north to Vídimýr with Thorkel Gunnvaldsson and Trefil and Helgi,
the sons of Red Björn. The shield was spoiled then—it was thrown
into a whey-tub; but later Egil had the decorations stripped off, and
there were twelve ounces of gold in the crosspieces.

79

When he grew up, Egil's son Thorstein was the handsomest in appearance of all men, white-haired and clear of countenance. But big
and strong as he was, he was not the man his father was. Thorstein
was wise and level-headed, easy-going, the least ruffled of men. Egil
had little love for him, nor had Thorstein any overwhelming affection
for Egil; but Ásgerd and Thorstein were devoted to each other.

Egil had now begun to age greatly. It happened one summer that
Thorstein rode to the Althing[1] while Egil stayed at home. Before
Thorstein left home he and Ásgerd laid their heads together and took
out of Egil's chest the silk gown which Arinbjörn had given him, and
Thorstein took it to the Thing. When he wore it at the Thing it
trailed behind him and became dirty underneath when they were in
the procession to the Hill of Laws, but once he came home Ásgerd
laid away the gown where it had been before. A good while later,
when Egil opened up his chest, he found that the gown was spoiled,
and raised with Ásgerd the question of how this had come about. She
told him the truth. Then Egil chanted:

> (55) "An heir I have to inherit
> Indeed, but have I the need?
> Quick as I am he has tricked me,
> Tricked me, I say, aye and nicked me.
> This rider might well have been bider
> (Bestrider of oceanbeast he),
> Till masters of sea-skis muster,
> My bones to bury with stones."

Thorstein married Jófríd, daughter of Gunnar Hlífarsson. Her
mother was Helga, Óláf Feilan's daughter and sister to Thórd Bellow.

Jófríd's first husband had been Thórodd Tungu-Oddsson.

Not long after this Ásgerd died. Thereafter Egil gave up his home
and handed over to Thorstein, while Egil moved south to Mosfell to
his kinsman Grím's, for he loved Thórdís his stepdaughter above all
people who then drew breath on earth.

It happened one summer that a ship came out to Iceland, to Leiru-
vág. Her master's name was Thormód. He was a Norwegian and a
member of Thorstein Thóruson's household. He brought with him a
shield which Thorstein had sent to Egil Skallagrímsson—it was a notable treasure. Thormód presented the shield to Egil, and he accepted
it with thanks. In the course of the winter Egil composed a drápa on
the gift of the shield which he called *Targe-pæan*, and here is the
opening of it:

> (56) "Let then the king's thane listen[2]
>   To fall of my words which flow
>   (But seal your men to silence)
>   From stallfire's longhaired friend.
>   Oft shall be heard in Hörda
>   High praise for ernbeak-garner,
>
>   .   .   .   .
>
>   .   . O raven's steerer!" *

Thorstein Egilsson lived at Borg. He had two natural sons, Hrifla
and Hrafn, but once he was married Jófríd and he had ten children.
Helga the Fair was daughter of theirs, over whom Skald-Hrafn and
Gunnlaug Wormtongue fought. The eldest of their sons was Grím,
the second Skúli, the third Thorgeir, the fourth Kollsvein, the fifth
Hjörleif, the sixth Halli, the seventh Egil, the eighth Thórd. Thóra
was the name of that daughter of theirs whom Thormód Kleppjarnsson
married. From Thorstein's children has come a great progeny and a
power of fine men. They call that the Mýramen's kin, all that has
come from Skallagrím.

* The words here are missing.

80

Önund Sjóni was living at Ánabrekka when Egil lived at Borg. Önund Sjóni married Thorgerd, Björn the Fat's daughter from Snæfellsstrand. Their children were Steinar and Dalla, whom Ögmund Galtason married—their sons Thorgils and Kormák. When Önund grew old and weaksighted he gave up housekeeping, and his son Steinar then took over. Father and son had abundance of wealth. Steinar was a very big man, and of great bodily strength, ugly, bow-backed, long-legged and short of trunk. Steinar was very turbulent and headstrong, stiff-necked and brave, and most choleric. When Thorstein Egilsson took over at Borg there at once grew up a coolness between him and Steinar. South of Háfslœk lies a mire which is called Stakksmýr. Water covers it in winter, but in the spring when the ice breaks up there is grazing there for cattle so good that that and stacked homefield hay were reckoned equal. Háfslœk determined the boundaries there of old, but of a spring Steinar's cattle frequently went on Stakksmýr when they were driven towards Háfslœk, and Thorstein's housecarles complained about it. But Steinar paid no attention, and it happened that first summer that nothing took place worth telling of.

The second spring Steinar continued with the grazing, so Thorstein had a talk with him, and yet talked calmly. He told Steinar to keep grazing his beasts as had been the practice of old. Steinar maintained that the stock should go just where it wanted. He talked of it all rather unyieldingly, and he and Thorstein exchanged some strong words. Later Thorstein had the cattle driven back out to the mires beyond Háfslœk, but when Steinar knew of this he set his thrall Grani to stay with the cattle on Stakksmýr, and there he stayed the whole day through. This was the latter part of summer. All the meadows south of Háfslœk were then grazed up.

Now it happened one day that Thorstein had gone up to the rock to look round.[1] He saw where Steinar's cattle were straying. He walked out into the mires (it was getting late in the day), and saw how the cattle had come a long way out into the strip between the rock-ridges. Thorstein ran out over the mires, and when Grani saw this he drove

the cattle unmercifully till they reached the milking-shed. Thorstein
chased after him and he and Grani encountered in the wall-entry,
where Thorstein killed him. The place is since known as Granahlid: it
is in the wall of the home-meadow. Thorstein pushed the wall down
on Grani, and in that fashion covered his dead body. He afterwards
returned to Borg, but the women who went to the milking-shed discovered Grani where he was lying, and so returned to the house and
told Steinar what had happened. Steinar buried him up in the ridges,
but later got another thrall to stay with the cattle—though this one is
not named. Thorstein acted as though he was indifferent as to the
grazing for what was left of the summer.

It so happened that Steinar went to Snæfellsstrand in the early
part of winter and spent some time there. Steinar saw a thrall there
whose name was Thránd: of all men he was the biggest and strongest.
Steinar made an offer for the thrall, and bid a high price for him, but
the thrall's owner rated him at three marks of silver, rating him as dear
again as a common thrall, and that was their deal. He brought Thránd
home with him.

When they reached home Steinar had a talk with Thránd. "The
way things have turned out, I want you to do a job for me—only it
happens that all the jobs have been handed out already. So for the
present I shall be setting you a task which will be but small trouble
to you: you are to tend my cattle. It is of great concern to me that they
are well maintained as to pasture, and I want you to take no one's
opinion save your own as to where the pasture is best in the mires. I
am no judge of a man if you lack might and mind to hold your own
against any housecarle of Thorstein's."

Steinar handed Thránd a big axe, almost an ell across the cutting-
edge, and it was hair-sharp.

"As for you, Thránd," Steinar told him, "it looks this way to me, as
though it will not be apparent that you greatly esteem Thorstein's
priesthood if the pair of you meet face to face."

"I know no obligation to Thorstein," Thránd replied, "and I think
I understand what task you have laid on me. You must think your
outlay is small in respect of me. But I reckon I have a good chance,
come what may, if Thorstein and I are to have this out between us."

From now on Thránd started minding the cattle. He had a good idea, though he had not been long about it, where Steinar had had his cattle pastured, and Thránd tended the cattle on Stakksmýr. Once Thorstein came to know of this he sent a housecarle of his to go and see Thránd, and said to explain to him the boundaries between him and Steinar. When the housecarle came across Thránd he told him his errand and said for him to pasture the cattle some other way, explaining that Thorstein Egilsson owned that land the cattle had then come into.

"It is no concern of mine which of them owns the land," replied Thránd. "I shall keep the cattle where I think the pasture best."

With that they parted. The housecarle went home and told Thorstein the thrall's answer. Thorstein let it lie quiet, but Thránd took to watching the cattle night and day.

8 1

Thorstein rose one morning with the sun and walked up to the rock. He could see where Steinar's cattle were. Next Thorstein walked out on to the mires till he reached the cattle. There is a wooded crag standing by Háfslœk, and up on this crag Thránd was asleep and had taken off his shoes. Thorstein walked up on to the crag and had an axe, by no means a big one, in his hand and no further weapon. Thorstein poked Thránd with the axe-shaft and told him to wake up. He jumped up quick and hard, catching up his axe with both hands, and swinging it on high. He asked what Thorstein wanted.

"I want to tell you that I own this land, and that you have the grazing the far side of the brook. It is not surprising though you do not know the boundaries here."

"To me," said Thránd, "it makes no odds who owns the land. I shall let the cattle go where they think best."

"It is more likely," said Thorstein, "that I will now be wanting to rule my own land, and not Steinar's thralls."

"Thorstein," said Thránd, "you are a much less clever man than I thought if you want to find your night's rest under my axe, and even stake your honor on it. I think we can count on it that I will have twice your strength, nor am I short of resolution. Besides, I am better armed than you."

"That is a risk I will take," Thorstein assured him, "if you do nothing about the grazing. I have hopes that our luck will prove as different as our reasons for quarreling are unequal."

"You shall see now, Thorstein," said Thránd, "whether I am put out in any way by your threats."

With those words Thránd sat down and tied his shoe, but Thorstein swung his axe up hard and cut at Thránd's neck, so that his head fell on to his chest. Next Thorstein heaped him with stones and covered his corpse, and then walked home to Borg.

That day Steinar's cattle were late coming home, and once this seemed past hoping for, Steinar caught and saddled his horse. He had all his weapons about him. He rode south to Borg, and when he arrived there found men to talk to. He asked where might Thorstein be, and was informed that he was sitting indoors. Then Steinar asked that Thorstein should come outside; he said he had business with him. When Thorstein heard this he caught up his weapons and walked out into the doorway. He asked Steinar what might his business be?

"Have you killed Thránd, my thrall?" asked Steinar.

"That's how it is, to be sure," replied Thorstein. "You needn't be suspecting anyone else of it."

"Then I see you must be telling yourself you defend your land with a hard hand, just because you have killed a brace of my thralls. But to my eyes that looks no such mighty deed. I shall now offer you rather more scope if you are planning to defend your land in this high fashion. There will be no trusting now to other men to drive the cattle. And you shall know this much, that the cattle will be on your land both night and day."

"It so happens," replied Thorstein, "that last summer I killed that thrall of yours whom you got to graze the cattle on my land; but I afterwards let you have the grazing just as you liked, right until winter. I have now killed another of your thralls for you, against whom I had the same case as against the first. From now on you shall have the grazing for the summer, just as you like; but next summer, if you graze my land and get men to drive your cattle this way, then I shall again kill for you each and every man who accompanies them—aye, even though you accompany them yourself. And I will do as much every summer as long as you hold to your chosen course over the grazing."

With that Steinar rode off home to Brekka. A short while later he rode up to Stafaholt, where Einar was living at this time. He was a man with a priesthood. Steinar asked him for help, offering money in return. "My help will avail you little," said Einar, "unless more men of reputation back the suit." So Steinar rode up into Reykjardal to find Tungu-Odd, and asked him for help and offered him money in return Odd took the money and promised to lend a hand to assist Steinar in bringing the law home to Thorstein. Steinar afterwards rode home. In the spring Odd and Einar accompanied Steinar a-summoning, and they had a strong body of men. Steinar summoned Thorstein for the thralls' slaying, and pronounced three years' banishment the punishment for each slaying, because that was then the law when a man's thralls were killed and thrall-geld was not offered before the third sun. And two suits for banishment should be reckoned equal to one suit for life-outlawry.[1]

Thorstein brought no summons against him for offences in return, but a short while later dispatched men south to Nes. They came to Mosfell to Grím's and recounted this news there. Egil pretended he was not much interested, but all the same inquired closely in private about the exchanges between Thorstein and Steinar, and also about the men who had backed Steinar in this suit. Later the messengers returned home, and Thorstein felt well satisfied with their journey.

Thorstein Egilsson furnished himself with a strong body of men for the spring Thing; he arrived there a night ahead of other men and roofed his booths, and so did those thingmen of his who had booths there. And when they had attended to this, Thorstein had his thing-men set to and they built big booth walls there. Next he had a booth roofed, bigger by far than those other booths that were there. In that booth there were no men.

Steinar rode to the Thing and had furnished himself with a big force of men. Tungu-Odd had charge of their company there, and was very well off for men. Einar from Stafholt was well off for men too. They roofed their booths. The Thing was a crowded one, and men set out their lawsuits. For his part Thorstein offered no atonement, answering those men who sought for such that he proposed to let all go for judgment; he said he thought poorly of the suits Steinar was proceeding with for the killing of the thralls, and maintained that Steinar's thralls had wrought ample offences for it. Steinar acted big over his lawsuits. His cases looked to him sound in law, and his strength sufficient to drive the law home. For that reason he was aggressive in his suits.

That same day men proceeded to the Thingbank, where they spoke to their suits, but the court was to go into procession in the evening for the law-cases. Thorstein was present there with his troop. He had the biggest say in Thing-procedure, for that was how it had been while Egil held the priesthood and its authority. Each party was armed to the teeth. From the Thing they noticed how a troop of men was riding from below along Gljúfrá, and there were shields sparkling there too. And when they rode up to the Thing, there was riding at their head a man in a blue hooded cloak, with a gilded helm on his head and a gold-decked shield at his side, and in his hand a barbed spear, its socket inlaid with gold, and wearing a sword in his belt. This was Egil Skallagrímsson, arriving there with eighty men, all well armed as though they were ready for battle. That troop was a very choice one. Egil had brought with him up from the south the best farmers' sons from the Nesses, and those he thought the best fighters. Egil rode with his troop to the booth Thorstein had roofed earlier but which had stayed empty up to now, where they dismounted. When Thorstein learned of his father's arrival he went to meet him with his whole company, and welcomed him warmly. Egil and his men had their baggage carried into the booth and the horses driven to pasture, and when that had been attended to Egil and Thorstein proceeded to the Thingbank with their entire following, and sat where they were accustomed to.

And now Egil got to his feet and spoke up loudly. "Is Önund Sjóni here on the Thingbank?"

Önund admitted that he was there. "Glad am I grown, Egil, that you have come! This will entirely amend what stands here between men's suits."

"Is it your idea that Steinar your son brings lawsuits against Thorstein my son, and has assembled a gang of men to make him an outlaw?"

"It is not my doing," claimed Önund, "that they are not atoned. I have spent many a speech in the matter, urging Steinar to be atoned with Thorstein, for to me your son has been at every point a man to be spared dishonor; and what causes that is the old and loving friendship which you and I have shared, Egil, ever since we were raised up here next door to each other."

"It will soon grow clear, " replied Egil, "whether you say this in earnest or deceit—though I think the second the less likely. I remember the day when to each of us it would seem unthinkable that we should bring lawsuits one against the other, or not restrain our sons so that they do not act with such folly as I hear is now the case. To me it seems wise, while the two of us are alive and so closely involved in their squabbles, that we take this suit upon ourselves and compose it, and not let Tungu-Odd and Einar goad our sons against each other like horses in a fight. From now on let them have some other source of profit than resorting to the like of this."

Önund stood up. "You say right, Egil," he declared. "It is little credit to us to be at that Thing where our sons are in conflict. And never shall such shame befall us that we were so paltry as not to atone them. Now, Steinar, it is my will that you hand over this suit to me, and let me do with it just as I please."

"I don't know about that," replied Steinar, "whether I so want to throw away my lawsuits, for I have already sought backing from great men. I want my lawsuits to have only such an ending as satisfies Odd and Einar."

Odd and Steinar next talked things over between them. Odd had this to say: "I will be as good as my word to you, Steinar, in the help I promised to give you, whether for law or for such an end to your suits as you are willing to accept. But it will be your responsibility how your suits turn out if Egil is to be their judge."

"I need not entrust this to Odd's tongue-roots," was Önund's retort to that. "At his hands I have received neither good nor ill, but Egil has done me many a good turn. I rely much more on him than on anyone else, and I am going to have my way in this. It will be as well for you not to have us all on your hands! Also, I have had the say for the two of us so far, and so it shall continue."

"You are headstrong in this suit, father—and I think we are going to regret it, often."

Steinar now handed the suit over to Önund, and it was for him to compound or pursue it, even as the law recognized. And as soon as Önund had the say in these suits he went to see those kinsmen, Thorstein and Egil.

"Now, Egil," said Önund then, "I want you alone to shape and shear in these lawsuits, just as you like, for I trust you best to sort these suits of mine and everyone else's."

Next Önund and Thorstein took each other by the hand and named their witnesses, and this with the naming, that Egil Skallagrímsson alone should pronounce sentence in these lawsuits, just as he liked, all unchallenged there at the Thing. This was the end of these lawsuits, and men returned afterwards to their booths. Thorstein had three oxen led to Egil's booth and had them slaughtered for his food at the Thing.

When Tungu-Odd and Steinar returned to their booth, "Now, Steinar," said Odd, "you and your father have ruled for the end of your lawsuit. I now reckon myself free of you, Steinar, in that matter of backing which I promised you, whichever way Egil's arbitration may affect you—for the agreement between us was that I should help you to bring your suits to success or to such an end as contented you."

Steinar admitted that Odd had helped him well and manfully, and that their friendship should now be far stronger than before. "I will announce that you are free of me in the matter to which you were bound."

The court went into procession in the evening, and it is not recorded that anything happened there worth telling of.

82

The following day Egil Skallagrímsson went to the Thingbank, and Thorstein and their entire troop with him. Önund came there too with

Steinar. Tungu-Odd had come as well, and Einar and his men. When men had spoken to their lawsuits there, Egil got to his feet.

"Are that father and son, Steinar and Önund, here at hand," he asked, "so that they can distinguish my words?"

Önund said that they were.

"Then I will open my arbitration between Steinar and Thorstein. I take up the case at the point when Grím my father arrived here in Iceland and took all the territories here throughout the Mýrar and far and wide throughout the district, and chose himself a place to live at Borg and determined its extent, but beyond its limits gave his friends such choice of land as they have inhabited ever since. He gave Áni a home at Ánabrekka, where Önund and Steinar have been living until now. We all know, Steinar, where the boundaries lie between Borg and Ánabrekka, and how Háfslœk determines it there. Now it was not in ignorance what you did, Steinar, grazing Thorstein's land and bringing his property into your own charge, and presuming that he should be so far degenerate from his line that he would consent to prove your prey—for you, Steinar, and you too, Önund, must know that Áni received land of Grím my father. But Thorstein killed two thralls for you. Now it is clear to everybody that they have fallen through their own acts, and that they were not men to be paid for; nay, further, even though they were free men, they were still not men to be paid for. And because it was your intention, Steinar, that you would rob my son Thorstein of his land, which he took with my consent and I took by inheritance after my father, for that you shall forfeit your own land at Ánabrekka and get no payment for it. It shall follow too that you shall have neither home nor lodging here in the district south of Langá, and be off from Ánabrekka before the removal-days are past, but fall unhallowed before any man who will grant aid to Thorstein immediately after the removal-days, should you not go away or hold to any part of what I have now laid down for you." And when Egil sat down Thorstein named witnesses to his award.

"Egil," said Önund Sjóni then, "it will be the talk of the place how the award you have made and pronounced is on the crooked side. Now it can be said of me that I have laid myself out wholeheartedly to avert these troubles, but from here on I shall be sparing in nothing I can do to injure Thorstein."

"On the contrary," said Egil; "I believe the prospects of the pair of you, aye father and son, will always be the worse the longer our quarrels last. I thought, Önund, you would know that I have held my own against men as good as you and your son. While as for Odd and Einar, who have so concerned themselves over this suit, they have got from it what credit they deserve."

83

Egil's sister's son Thorgeir Blund was present at the Thing, and had been most helpful to Thorstein in these lawsuits. He asked father and son to give him some land out there in the Mýrar. Before this he had been living south of Hvítá, below Blundsvatn. Egil was all for this and urged Thorstein that he should let him come there. They established Thorgeir at Ánabrekka, while Steinar shifted his dwelling-place out over Langá and settled down at Leirulœk. But Egil rode home south to Nes, and father and son parted in kindness.

With Thorstein there was a man by the name of Íri, the fleetest-footed of men and the keenest-sighted. He was from overseas and a freedman of Thorstein's, but even so he had charge of the sheep-tending, and above all else of gathering the barren sheep up to the high ground of a spring and in autumn down to the folding. And now, after the removal-days, Thorstein had the barren sheep assembled which had been left behind in the spring and was planning to have them driven on to the mountain. Íri now had his hands full with the sheep-driving, but Thorstein and his housecarles rode up to the mountain, and they were eight together. Thorstein was having a wall built across Grísartunga, between Langavatn and Gljúfrá, and he had a lot of men working at this that spring. When Thorstein had looked over his housecarles' work he rode home, and as he came opposite the Thingstead Íri came running to meet them and said that he wanted to speak with Thorstein in private. Thorstein suggested that his companions should ride on while they were talking.

Íri told Thorstein how he had gone up to Einkunnir that day and seen to the sheep. "And I saw," he said, "in the forest up above the winter road how twelve spears were shining, and some shields."

Thorstein spoke out loud, so that his companions clearly heard him. "Why should he be so set on seeing me that I cannot ride on home? Yet it will seem hard to Ölvald that I refuse him a chat if he is ill." Íri then ran as hard as he could up to the fell. "It will lengthen our road, I fear, now," Thorstein told his companions; "if we are to ride south to Ölvaldsstadir first. Ölvald has sent me a message that I should call and see him. Even so, he will consider it no great return for the ox he gave me last autumn that I call and see him, if he regards the matter as important."

Thorstein and his men rode south after this across the mires below Stangarholt, and so south to Gufuá, and down along the river by the bridlepath. And when he came down from Vatn they could see a lot of cattle south of the river and a man near by. This was Ölvald's housecarle. Thorstein asked how was everything there, and he replied that things were very well indeed, and that Ölvald was in the forest cutting wood.

"Then you can tell him," continued Thorstein, "that if he has urgent business with me he may come to Borg, but I will now be riding home."

And so he did. It was learned later even so that Steinar Sjónason had that same day lain in ambush up by Einkunnir with eleven men. Thorstein acted as though he had heard nothing about it, and the matter was afterwards let rest.

84

There was a man, Thorgeir by name, who was a kinsman and great friend of Thorstein's. He lived these days at Álftanes. Thorgeir used to hold an autumn feast every autumn. Thorgeir went to see Thorstein Egilsson and invited him to his house. Thorstein promised to go, and Thorgeir returned home.

On the day appointed Thorstein made ready for the journey, and there were then four weeks to winter. Along with Thorstein went his Norwegian guest and two housecarles. Grím was the name of a son of Thorstein's who was now ten years old, and he too went along, and they were five all told, and rode out to the waterfall and across Langá there, and on out afterwards as the road lay to Aurridaá. But on the far side of the river Steinar was at work, and Önund and housecarles of theirs, and no sooner did they recognize Thorstein than they ran for their weapons, and then in pursuit of Thorstein and his party. And once Thorstein saw Steinar in pursuit they rode out then from Langaholt. There is a hillock there, a high one but not wide. Thorstein and his men climbed down from their horses and got up on to the hillock. Thorstein ordered the boy Grím to get into the forest and keep out of harm's way. As soon as Steinar and his men reached the hillock they attacked Thorstein's company, and a fight took place there. Steinar had six grown men all told, and a ten year old son of Steinar's was the seventh of their company. Men who were on the meádow-strips of other farms saw this clash and ran up to part them. By the time they were parted, both of Thorstein's housecarles were dead. In addition, one of Steinar's housecarles had fallen, and some were wounded.

As soon as they had been parted Thorstein looked where he had put Grím, and they found him. Grím was badly wounded, and Steinar's son lay beside him, dead.

As Thorstein jumped on his horse, Steinar called out to him with these words: "You are running then, Thorstein the White?" [1]

"You will run further," said Thorstein, "before the week is out."

Thorstein and the Norwegian then rode out over the mires, carrying the boy Grím with them. When they reached the mound which stands there the boy died, and they buried him there in the mound which is called Grímsholt; but the place where they fought is called Orrostuhváll.

Thorstein rode to Álftanes that evening, just as he had planned; he spent three nights there at the feast, and then made ready for his journey home. Men offered to go with him, but he would not have it, and they rode just the two of them together. This same day, when Steinar knew it was to be expected that Thorstein would ride home, he rode out along the sea; and when he reached the sand dunes below Lamba-stadir he lay in wait there on the dune. He was wearing the sword Skrýmir, the best of all weapons; and there he stood on the dune, with his sword drawn, and eyes for nothing save the one direction, for he had just spied Thorstein riding back along the sands.

Now Lambi was living at Lambastadir and saw what Steinar was up to. He walked from home down to the bank, and when he got to Steinar grabbed him under the arms from behind. Steinar tried to break free of him, but Lambi kept his grip, and down they went off the dune on to the flat. Thorstein and his companion were now riding on the lower road. Steinar had been riding his stallion, which now went racing in along the sea. Thorstein and his companion saw it and were puzzled, for they had known nothing of Steinar's movements. Meantime Steinar was edging his way back up on to the bank, for he did not see how Thorstein had ridden on past; but just as they reached its front edge Lambi shoved him down off the dune. Steinar was not on his guard against this. He went headlong down on to the sand, while Lambi raced for home. Once Steinar got to his feet he tore after Lambi, but as Lambi reached his doorway he sprang inside slamming the door behind him. Steinar cut after him, so that the sword stuck fast in the barge-boards. That was their parting, and Steinar returned home.

But when Thorstein arrived home, the following day he sent his housecarle out to Leirulœk to tell Steinar that he must shift his dwelling-place across Borgarhraun, for otherwise he would bring it to bear against Steinar that he had the greater power. "And then there will be no question of getting away."

Steinar made plans to go out to Snæfellsstrand, and established a home at the place called Ellidi, and with that the exchanges between him and Thorstein Egilsson came to an end.

Thorgeir Blund was living at Ánabrekka. He was a bad neighbor to Thorstein in every possible way. It happened once when Egil and Thorstein met together that they talked a good deal about their kinsman Thorgeir Blund, and all their talk came to the one thing. Then Egil chanted:

> (57) "Freed I first by pleading
> Land from Steinar's hand;
> Thought that work I'd wrought

Seemed to Geir's scion seemly.
My sister's son deceived me,
Yet first he promised fair;
He could not fail find bale,
This Blund. Such makes me wonder!"

Thorgeir Blund left Ánabrekka and went south to Flókadal, for it
seemed to Thorstein that that was no way of getting on with him, even
though he was prepared to meet him more than half way. Thorstein
was no fox of a man, but fair-minded and not an encroacher on other
men's rights; but he held his own if others edged in on him, and it
proved hard work for most to take him on in a quarrel.

At this time Odd was the leading man in Borgarfjörd to the south
of Hvítá. He was temple-priest and controlled the temple to which all
men paid temple-toll this side of Skardsheid.

85

Egil Skallagrímsson became an old man, and in his age he grew infirm, and was enfeebled in both hearing and sight. He grew stiff-
legged too. Egil was now at Mosfell with Grím and Thórdís. It
happened one day that Egil was walking outside by the wall and
stumbled and fell. Some women saw this and laughed at it, saying:
"It is all over with you now, Egil, when you fall of your own accord."

"The women took us more seriously," said farmer Grím, "when we
were younger!"

Then Egil chanted:

>   (58)   "Neck halter's steed falters,[1]
>   I fall dread on bald head;
>   Lovelimb's left limp, and
>   Last, hearing fails fast."

Egil grew quite blind. It happened one day when the weather was
cold in winter that Egil went to the fire to warm himself. The house-
keeper prated of how strange it was that a man such as Egil had been

should loll about under their feet, so that they could not get on with
their work.

"Be easy," said Egil, "though I toast myself by the fire, and let us
give and take a little here."

"Stand up," she ordered. "Be off with you to your place, and let us
get on with our work."

Egil stood up and went to his place and chanted:

> (59) "Blind towards brands' blaze turn I,
> Patch-goddess ask for pity;
> So ail I where my eyelids
> Alight on eyesight's meadow.
> Mine! whom land-glorious lord
> Rewarded with giant's goldhoard;
> A king long since took liking,
> Though angered, to song I sang."[2]

It happened one time again when Egil went to the fire to warm
himself, that a man asked him whether his feet were cold, and warned
him not to stretch them too near the fire.

"So be it," said Egil, "but my feet are not easy for me to steer now
that I do not see. And how dismal a thing is blindness!"

Then Egil chanted:

> (60) "Long seems it to me
> I lie all alone,
> An old, old fellow
> Flushed from king's cover.
> Widowed heels twain
> Are mine, all too cold;
> And those same relicts,[3]
> They relish the fire!"

It happened in the early days of Hákon the Mighty, when Egil
Skallagrímsson was in his eighties (and he was still an active man in
every respect save lack of sight), it happened that summer when men
were getting ready for the Thing that Egil asked Grím to ride to the

Thing with him. Grím was reluctant to agree, and when he and
Thórdís were talking together, Grím told her what Egil was asking.

"I want you to find out what lies behind this request of his."

So Thórdís went to have a talk with Egil her kinsman: talking to
her was now Egil's greatest pleasure.

When she found him, "Is it true, kinsman," she asked, "that you
are wanting to ride to the Thing? I should like you to tell me what
lies behind this notion of yours."

"I must tell you," he agreed, "what I have had in mind. I mean to
take with me to the Thing those two chests King Athelstan gave me,
each of which is full of English silver. I mean to have those chests
carried to the Hill of Laws when it is thickest with men. Next I mean
to sow that silver all over the place—and no one will be so surprised
as I if all there share it evenly between them.[4] I plan there should be
kicking then and clouting, or it might even turn out at last that the
whole Assembly are at one another's throats."

"A fine plan I think that," said Thórdís, "and one to be remembered
as long as the land is lived in!"

Later Thórdís went to speak with Grím and told him Egil's plan.
"It shall never happen that he commits so great an outrage!" And
when Egil came to discuss going to the Thing with Grím, Grím quite
talked him out of it, and Egil stayed home over the Thing. But he did
not like it, and wore quite a scowl.

At Mosfell they had a hill-pasture shieling, and Thórdís stayed at
this shieling over the Thing. It happened one evening when men were
preparing for bed at Mosfell that Egil called to him two thralls belonging to Grím. He told them to get him a horse.

"I want to go to the baths."

And when Egil was ready he went out and took his chests of silver
with him. He climbed on to his horse, went down after that along the
home-meadow past the slope which stands there, which was the last
they saw of him.

But in the morning when men rose, they could see Egil blundering
about on the mound east of the farm and trailing the horse behind
him. They went for him and fetched him home; but neither thralls
nor chests ever came back, and many are the guesses as to where Egil

had hidden his money. East of the garth at Mosfell a gully runs down from the mountain, and it has been a thing to remark how in sudden thaws there is a great waterfall there, and after the waters have run away English pennies have been found in the gully. Some guess that Egil will have hidden his money there. Below the home-meadow at Mosfell there are fens, big and notably deep; many feel certain that Egil will have thrown his money into these. South of the river there are hot springs, and a short way off big holes in the earth, and some guess that Egil would have hidden his money there, for howe-fire is often seen that way. Egil admitted that he had killed Grím's thralls, and this too, that he had hidden his money, but where he had hidden it he told to nobody.

The following autumn Egil took an illness which brought him to his death. When he had died Grím had Egil shifted into fine clothes, and afterwards had him moved down to Tjaldanes, and had a howe built there, and Egil was laid inside it with his weapons and clothes.

86

Grím of Mosfell was baptized when Christianity became the law in Iceland.[1] He had a church built there, and men maintain that Thórdís had Egil moved to this church, and there is this by way of proof, that when a church was built at Mosfell later, and the church dismantled at Hrísbrú which Grím had built, the churchyard there was then dug up. Under the altar site were found human bones which were bigger by far than other men's bones. From old men's tales people feel sure that these must have been Egil's bones.

Skafti Thórarinsson[2] was priest there at the time—a good sensible man. He picked up Egil's skull and put it in the churchyard. The skull was astonishingly big, yet another thing seemed even more past belief: how heavy it was. The skull was all wave-ridged on the outside like a harp-shell. Then Skafti wanted to find out about the skull's thickness. He took a hand-axe, a very big one, and swung it with one hand as hard as he could, and smote with the back hammer on the skull, proposing to smash it, and where it landed the place whitened, but it was neither dented nor cracked, and from such a thing one may mark how that skull would not be easily damaged by the blows of small fellows while skin and flesh were still on it. Egil's bones were laid in the outer verge of the churchyard at Mosfell.

8 7

Thorstein Egilsson accepted baptism when Christianity came to Iceland and had a church built at Borg. He was a man firm of faith and of good ways. He lived to be an old man, then died of an illness, and was buried at Borg at the church he had built.

From Thorstein has come a great progeny, a power of fine men, and many a poet. That is the Mýramen's kin, and so with all who have their descent from Skallagrím. It long held good in that line that the men were strong and great fighting-men and, some of them, wise and far-sighted. There was great variance in their looks, for in that line have been bred the men who have been handsomest in Iceland, as were Thorstein Egilsson and Kjartan Óláfsson (Thorstein's sister's son) and Hall Gudmundsson, and Helga the Fair too, Thorstein's daughter, over whom Gunnlaug Wormtongue and Skald-Hrafn fought. But most Mýramen were the ugliest of men.

Thorstein's son Thorgeir was the strongest of the brothers, but Skúli was the biggest. He lived at Borg after his father Thorstein's day. Skúli was for a long time out on viking cruises. He was forecastleman to Earl Eirík on Ironbeak, when King Óláf Tryggvason fell. Skúli had fought in seven battles while out viking, and was held a foremost champion and a brave. Later he returned to Iceland and settled at Borg and dwelt there till his old age. A great many men are descended from him. And there this story ends.[1]

NOTES

Chapter 1

1. *He was a berserk.* The berserk (*berserkr*) was a warrior who experienced a battle-madness, during which he felt no pain and had a great increase of strength. The whole subject of *berserksgangr* is wrapped up with superstition. The names *berserkr* (bear-sark), *úlfheðinn* (wolf-coat), show that in popular belief there was an element of "skin-changing," "shape-changing," in what seems to be a well-attested phenomenon. The author of *Vatnsdœla Saga*, who was something of a rationalizer, describes the berserks who fought for Harald at Hafrsfjörd as Wolf-coats (*Úlfheðnar*)—"they wore wolf-pelts (*vargstakka*) instead of mail shirts"; but our own saga goes nearer the mark in what it tells us of Kveldúlf (Evening-Wolf), who grew sullen and drowsy of an evening, and whose soul certainly ranged in animal shape while his body slept. That he was a true berserk and experienced fury and subsequent exhaustion is attested by Chapter 27.

The fictitious berserks who infest many sagas (like Ljót the Pale and Atli the Short in our own Chapters 64-65) are somewhat tiresome creatures; with their howling, shield-biting, and all the rest of it, they were on a level with our bucket-biting all-in wrestlers of today, and one has nothing but admiration for the hero who, when *his* berserk stood champing, kicked upwards and split his jaws (*Grettis Saga* 40). Egil was still tougher in his handling of Atli: we can only hope he enjoyed the taste.

2. *Landed man.* The *lendrmaðr*, like the *hersir*, held his land of the king, and was responsible for the law and defense of his district. They came next in rank after earls, and according to Snorri Sturluson correspond to the *greifar* of Germany and the barons of England. Next came the *hölðr* or franklin (in Chapter 41 we learn how Björn did not become the king's officer or member of his household, and for that reason was known as *Björn hölðr*), the holder of an estate held not of the king but by right of patrimony. Then came the *bóndi*, householder, farmer; the *leysingi* or freedman; and at the bottom of the barrel the *þræll*, the slave or thrall.

Chapter 3

1. *Harald Shock-head.* In Snorri's *Heimskringla* may be read the story of how the young Harald sent messengers of his to Gyda, daughter of King Eirík of Hördaland, to ask her to become his lady. But she refused to throw herself away on so petty a king.—"And it seems strange to me that there is no king who

will make himself master of Norway, so that he alone has the ruling of it, as King Gorm has done in Denmark or Eirík at Upsala." The messengers poohpoohed all this, but not so Harald when he heard their words. "She has brought to my mind things I now think it strange I never thought of before." And he added: "I make this vow—and the god who made me and rules over all, let him be my witness—that never shall my hair be combed or cut till all Norway pays me scat, dues, and allegiance, or else I perish!" In later days, after the battle of Hafrsfjörd and his expedition to Shetland and Orkney, when he had subdued the whole country, "King Harald took a bath and had his hair combed; and thereupon Earl Rögnvald cut off his hair, which had stayed uncut and uncombed these ten years. Till now he had been called Harald Shock-head (*lúfa*), but now Earl Rögnvald gave him a nickname, calling him Harald Fairhair (*hárfagri*); and everyone who saw him vowed that was the properest name for him, for he had hair both thick and lovely."

Chapter 4

1. *Odal rights.* Odal rights (*óðal, plur. óðul*) in land were rights pertaining to land held not of a superior but in absolute ownership (*allodium*), and were at first inalienable from the family. Harald either seized this land from his foes or set some kind of (redemptory?) tax on it.

2. *It was now that Iceland was discovered.* The Norwegians were not the first men to reach Iceland. It is possible, even likely, that Pytheas of Massilia came so far north in the fourth century B.C., and that the land he called Thule was Iceland. Recently it has been argued that the discovery of three Roman copper coins of A.D. 270-305 in the east of Iceland is reasonable evidence that Roman ships, possibly from Britain, were driven there early in the fourth century A.D. (Kristján Eldjárn, *Gengið á Reka*, 1948; and so Jón Jóhannesson, *Íslendinga Saga I, þjóðveldisöld*, 1956). In any case, with the Irish scholar-monk Dicuil in 825 we reach certainty. Thirty years before he recorded their brief story in his *Liber de Mensura Orbis Terræ* (i.e., in 795) some Irish clerics spent a summer in an island-country which can only be Iceland. And finally there is the evidence of the twelfth-century Icelandic historian Ari Fródi, in his *Íslendingabók* or *Libellus Islandorum*, that, "There were then (when the first Norse settlers reached Iceland) Christian men here, whom the Norwegians call *papar* or priests, but they afterwards went away, because they would not live here with heathen men, and left behind them Irish books, bells, and croziers, from which it might be perceived that they were Irishmen."

Sturla's version of *Landnámabók,* The Book of the Landtakings or Settlements, gives the credit of the Norse discovery to Naddod the Viking, but according to *Hauksbók* and certain other works Gardar Svávarsson was the man, and this is undoubtedly correct. Gardar circumnavigated the island and spent a winter at Húsavík north in Skjálfandi; he then returned home and highly praised the land, which he named Gardarsholm. He lost a boat with one of his crew, Náttfari by name, on board, together with a thrall and bondwoman. These three stayed on in Iceland.

Naddod the Viking named the country Snæland or Snowland, because of a great snowfall as he sailed away. He too praised the land highly.

Next a famous viking, Flóki Vilgerdarson, set sail from Rogaland in Norway to seek Snæland, taking with him three ravens to show him the way. First he sailed to the Faeroes, then again put to sea with his ravens. "And when he loosed the first he flew back to the prow; the second flew up into the air, then back to the ship; the third flew straight ahead from the prow to the quarter where they found the land. Their landfall was at Horn in the east, and they sailed along the south of the land. And when they sailed west round Reykjanes and the firth began to open up so that they could see the mountain Snæfellsnes, said Faxi: 'This must be a big country we have found, there are such great rivers here.' . . . Flóki and his men sailed west across Breidafjörd and took land in settlement at the place called Vatnsfjörd. The entire firth was full of fish (*veiðiskapr:* fish, seals and whales), and what with fishing they neglected to make hay, and all their livestock died over the winter. The spring was very cold. Flóki walked north to a mountain and saw a certain firth full of sea-ice; and because of that they called the land Iceland."

These voyages took place somewhere between 855 and 870. *Íslendingabók* says nothing of any of them, for according to Ari Fróði: "Ingólf was the name of a Norwegian who is truly reported to have journeyed first from there to Iceland, when Harald Fairhair was sixteen years old, and a second time a few years later. He settled south in Reykjavík. The place where he first came to land is called Ingólfshöfdi, east of Minthakseyr; and Ingólfsfjall, west of Ölfusá, the place he took into his possession thereafter." This is that Ingólf Arnarson whose example helped decide Kveldúlf and Skallagrím to sail for Iceland after the death of their kinsman Thórólf (p. 74). *Landnámabók* celebrates Ingólf as "the most famous of all Settlers, for he came here to a desert land and was the first to settle the country." This was in 874. Ingólf and Hjörleif his foster brother had fallen foul of Earl Atli the Slender and killed two of his sons. This cost them their estates, and they thought to find new ones in Flóki's new country. On their first voyage out they spent the winter in Álftafjörd in the east. On the second Ingólf's movements were those recounted in *Íslendingabók*. Hjörleif set up house at Hjörleifshöfdi, where he was murdered by his Irish thralls; they carried off the women and stock to some islands in the southwest. However, Ingólf learned of his foster brother's death, hunted them down and killed them all· in the islands, which so won their name, Vestmannaeyjar, the Isles of the Men from the West, the Isles of the Irishmen.

The Period of Settlement was at an end by the year 930. All of Iceland which was habitable (probably never more than a sixth of the country) was by that time occupied. The population may have been 40,000, but any such guess is uncertain. The leavening of Celtic blood was considerable.

Chapter 7

1. *Skúta.* A small warship of some 15 oars aside.

Chapter 8

1. *Snekkja.* A medium-sized warship, usually of twenty oars aside, light and fast. The longship often exceeded thirty. Such ships as these were not used for ocean travel. They had a sail, but customarily went under oars.

Chapter 13.

1. *Gray wares.* These were squirrel skins.

Chapter 14

1. *Finnmark.* "But in his (i.e., Óttar the Hálogalander's) own country is the best whale-hunting; they are eight and forty ells long, these, and the biggest fifty ells long. He said that in company with five other crews he killed sixty of these in two days. He was a very wealthy man in those possessions in which their wealth consists, that is, in wild animals. He had still when he visited the king six hundred tame unsold beasts. These beasts they call reindeer; six of them were decoy reindeer. These are very costly among the Lapps (*Finnum*), for with them they capture the wild reindeer. He was among the foremost men in the land; even so, he had not more than twenty head of cattle and twenty sheep and twenty pigs, and the little that he ploughed he ploughed with horses. But their wealth consists for the most part in the tribute which the Lapps pay them. The tribute consists in animals' skins and birds' feathers, in whalebone and the ships' cables which are made of whale's (i.e. walrus) hide or of seal's. Each pays according to his rank. The highest in rank must pay fifteen martens' skins, and five of reindeer, and one bearskin, and ten measures of feathers, a kirtle of bearskin or otterskin, and two ship's cables; each must be sixty ells long, the one to be made of whale's hide, the other of seal's. . . .

"The land of the Norwegians, he said, was very long and very narrow. All of it that can be grazed or ploughed lies alongside the sea, and that moreover is in some parts very rocky. And wild mountains (*moras*) lie to the east, above and parallel to the cultivated land. On these mountains dwell Lapps. . . . Then on the other side of the mountains, parallel to the south part of the country, is Sweden . . . and parallel to the north part of the land Kvenland (Cwenaland). Sometimes the Kvens make war on the Norwegians over the mountains, sometimes the Norwegians on them. There are very big freshwater lakes throughout the mountains, and the Kvens carry their boats overland to the lakes and from there make war on the Norwegians. They have very small boats, and very light." (King Alfred's translation of Orosius's *History of the World,* here translated from Sweet-Onions, *Anglo-Saxon Reader,* tenth edition.)

Clearly the Kvens (*Kainulaiset*) and the more distant Kirjáls or Karelians, with the men of North Norway as their rivals, fought each other for the Lapp-tribute.

Chapter 17

1. *White wares.* These were white wadmal-cloth and sheepskins.

Chapter 22

1. *Set fire to the hall.* The terrible expedient of setting fire to the house over a man's head, and either driving him out into the open or burning him alive, was, if a man could bring himself to do it, a legitimate method of waging warfare or conducting a private feud. Harald Fairhair was nothing if not a realist. He meant to destroy his enemy Thórólf and at the same time not throw away his own men's lives. The practice was carried to Iceland. The burning of Bergthórshváll in the year 1010 is the central incident of *Njála*, the greatest of sagas; the burning of Flúgumýrr in 1253 is one of the unforgettable events of its century.

It was customary, as here at Sandnes, to allow the women and children, the aged and the low-born, to come out to safety. *Brenna, brenna inni*, was aimed at the fighting-men only. The only exception out in Iceland was at the burning of Blund-Ketil in Örnólfsdal by the mean and vicious Hen-Thórir. "They hauled a pile of timber to the house and set fire to it, and Blund-Ketil and his people did not awake till the house was in flames above them. Blund-Ketil asked who was lighting so hot a fire, and Thórir told him. He asked whether there was any chance of terms, but Thórir replied: 'There is no other choice but to burn.' Nor did they leave till every living soul was burnt to death inside the house" (*Hœnsa-Thóris Saga*).

Chapter 24

1. *Verse 1.* I have heard now that Thórólf has fallen in an isle to the north. The Norns are cruel! Ódin (Thunder) chose the warrior (sword-edge-stirrer) too early. Oppressive age [Thór's wrestling partner, Elli (Old Age), who brought Thór to one knee during their struggle in the hall of Útgardaloki] has stopped me going to battle (Thing-meeting of metal *or* weapon-goddess *or* valkyrie). Revenge will not come soon, though my heart incites me.

Chapter 27

1. *They put him in a coffin, then shot it overboard.* Many chieftains on their way to a new home in Iceland threw their house-pillars overboard at sight of land and left it to the gods to appoint where pillars and owners should start life afresh. So Kveldúlf now.

Chapter 28

1. *Placenames.* Among the placenames of Skallagrím's settlement are: Knarrarnes, Merchantship Ness; Mýrar, the Mires; Borg, Rock, Rock-Bastion,

Hvanneyr, Angelica Bank; Andakíl, Duck Kyle; Álftanes, Swan Ness; Langá, Long River; Hvítá, White River; Nordrá, North River; Gljúfrá, Gorge River; Thverá, Thwart River.

2. *A most peculiar color.* Hvítá means White River. But it is hard to believe that none of these Norwegians had seen glacier-streams before.

Chapter 31

1. *Verse 4.* The bed of the snake (the ling's glittering thong) *and* the land of the snake: gold.

Chapter 36

1. *Karfi.* This was a light, even a transportable, smallish warship of six to twenty oars aside.

Chapter 40

1. *They jumped into a boat.* Thórólf and his company were sleeping on board and jumped into the larger of the two ship's boats.

Chapter 44

1. *Troll-foe.* Enemy of trollwives: brave man.
2. *Ear-root.* Tree of the ear-root: horn.
3. *Verse 10.* I grow drunk, besides ale has now turned Ölvir pale. I let beer (foam of the aurochs' halberd *or* horn) froth over my lips. You are unaware what is happening, warrior (bidder of the spearcloud's, shield's, rain; i.e., rouser of battle). It is raining poetry (rain of the High One's, Ódin's, thanes).

Chapter 45

1. *Listi's guardian.* The guardian of Listi or Listerland: king of Norway.

Chapter 48

1. *Woundgrouse.* Raven, the proverbial follower of battle and feaster on the slain.

Chapter 55

1. *Egil Skallagrímsson.* Our author's sense of occasion in delaying his description of Egil till this dramatic moment has been much praised. The curious may see confronting p. 100 of Jón Helgason's *Handritaspjall* a late

seventeenth century portrait of Egil, reproduced in color from AM 426 fol. (*ca.* 1680), which does full justice to the famous eyebrows but otherwise presents a remarkably innocuous picture of him. At Kalmanstunga, near the eastern or inland extremity of Hvítársíða, in July 1952, the translator who had expressed some doubt whether the brows could be moved in such sensational fashion received from a descendant of Egil a convincing demonstration that they can.

2. *Verse 19.* The warrior or king (Höd of the corslet) lets a ring (clashing snare of the handgrip) hang about my arm or hand (the hawktrod falcon's swaying-tree or gallows). I lifted the ring (cord of the staff of shield-exhauster or sword) on the sword (gallows of the spearwind or battle). The warrior (feeder of the corpse-birds or ravens) earns praise.

3. *Drápa.* A drápa was a poetic panegyric in set form. A poem in length, content, and finish worthy of a king or prince. *Höfuðlausn* (p. 160) is such a poem.

4. *Verse 21.* Now has the royal stirrer of battle, main shoot of monarchs, felled three kings (Óláf, Hring and Adils: the poem in the Anglo-Saxon Chronicle says that five young kings fell on the field of battle). The land falls to Ella's kinsman (but Athelstan was not a descendant of Ælla, the usurping king of Northumbria killed in 867 by the sons of Ragnar Lodbrók, nor would he be pleased to be called such). Athelstan achieved other deeds too. All get the worse of it from the kin-famed monarch—I swear this, generous man (breaker or distributor of billow-flame or gold).

Chapter 56

1. *Verse 23.* I have tried to convey the concealed reference to Ásgerd (if indeed I understand it) by "Berg-Onar's girdle." In the original *berg-Óneris fold* may mean "giant's country" or mountain, which may point to the word *ás*. Second, *faldr*, headcloth, may point to the word *gerða*, headband or girdle. We should then have the clue *ás-gerða* to *Ásgerðr*. No translator will feel surprise that Arinbjörn did not spot it.

The lady (goddess of hawks' cliff or arm) must expect constraint on my part. Earlier, when young, I dared look up (lift the cross-crags of the forehead, eyebrows). Now I must hide my nose (brows' mid-pillar) in my cloak once Ásgerd comes to mind.

2. *Narfason's nurture.* The nurture (beverage) of Narfi's scions (giants) was verse.

3. *Stronghold of seaflame (gold).* Woman.

4. *My cloakclasp Norn.* Norn of cloakclasps (brooches): woman.

5. *Quivering shaft.* Shaft (thorn) of the goddess or valkyrie of wound-salmon (swords): spear.

6. *Verse 28 and Verse 29.* There is good reason to believe that these two verses are an exact transliteration of those graved in runes along the *niðstöng* or scorn-pole itself (see p. 151). The older runic alphabet (*fuþark*) consisted of 24 runes; the later alphabet of 16. The numbers 3, 9, and 12 were significant, magic numbers. When runes were graved by way of a spell

or curse, their power was increased by their being used in the most potent numbers or multiples of those numbers. Magnus Ólsen made the experiment of writing out various of Egil's verses in the speech forms and runes of Egil's day, and discovered that verses 28 and 29 are each composed of two halves, and these in turn composed of 72 runes each (that is to say 3 x 24 or 8 x 9), the most potent number conceivable, or at least practicable, in court meter. That Egil was not only a consummate craftsman but also rune-skilled, we know further from verses 9 and 48 and their contexts. (See the Fornrit edition, pp. xviii-xix, cvii, and the plate facing p. 163.)

Chapter 57

1. *The scorn-pole. Vatnsdœla Saga* 23-24 records a brisk challenging to holmgang " in a week's time, at the stackyard which stands on the island below my house at Borg." This was Borg í Víðidal, not the Borg of our saga, Borg á Mýrum. "And if anyone come not, then shall ill fame be raised against him with this form of words: that he shall be every man's dastard, and never be in the fellowship of decent men, and bear the wrath of the gods and the name of a truce-breaker." Thorstein and Jökul, the two brothers from Vatnsdal, set off in witch-brew weather to find their challengers, Finnbogi and Berg, at the appointed place, but they did not appear. "The brothers waited till midafternoon, and when the time came Jökul and Faxi-Brand (a warlock-helper of theirs) went to Finnbogi's sheep-house which was alongside the yard there, took a post and carried it up to the yard. There were horses there too, which had gone to find shelter from the storm. Jökul carved a man's head on the end of the post, and cut runes on it with that whole form of words spoken of earlier. Next Jökul killed a mare, opened her down the breastbone and put her on the post, and had her turned to face Borg."

In Norway Egil used a hazel for his scorn-pole, a tree of notable qualities, used to hedge or fence the Thing, and to mark out the field of battle and holmgang. It did not grow in Iceland, so Jökul would have to make do with whatever tree he could find. The mare in part signified a mare's heart not a man's in the person libeled; it seems sometimes to have had an obscene significance; while again this horrid object might be expected to frighten away the *landvættir,* the guardian-spirits of the place. That these were on the sensitive side is attested by the following passage from *Hauksbók.* "This was the beginning of the heathen laws, that men should not keep a ship at sea with a figure-head; but if they had such, then they must take off the head before they came in sight of land, and not sail to land with gaping heads and yawning jaws, so that the *landvættir* be affrighted therewith."

The terms *nið, níðingr, níðingsverk,* are very strong indeed. They convey a charge of the foulest infamy: to maltreat a woman, a child, a cripple, to betray a comrade, to flee from or refuse a challenge to battle. To erect a scorn-pole (*níðstöng*) was a mortal insult.

2. *Verse 32.* The angry wind (troll of trees *or* mast) smites with tempest's chisel a file's rasp (i.e., of wave-ridges) out on the level sea (prow-bullock's *or*

ship's road) before the prow. The cold storm (wolf of willows) rasps with its (the file's?) merciless gusts the ship (swan of sea king Gestil) about the prow, out before the forestem.

Chapter 58

1. *The death of Skallagrím.* Skallagrím died in the sleeping-hall (*skáli*). A raised floor or dais (*set*) ran most of the length of the side walls, and here the household slept. There was often a separate bed-closet at the inner end of the *set* for the chief persons of the household. This was the *lokrekkja* or lock-bed, with its own door, to which Egil retired after the drowning of Bödvar (p. 203). Sometimes, as here at Borg, there was a narrow passage (*skot*) running between the outer walls of the room and its inner wainscotting. In time of need it gave the house-owner a chance to escape his attackers, it could serve as a hiding-place in less mortal crises, and was sometimes used for secret visits.

2. *Broken open in readiness.* There is a passage in *Eyrbyggja Saga* 33 strikingly parallel to this of *Egil's Saga*, when Arnkel tackles his dead father (a most wicked old man) from behind, straightens him out and pays his body it rites, first, however, having enclosed the dead man's head in a cloth—a recognized precaution when dealing with warlocks. He too had the housewall broken down, brought his father out that way, and carried him a good way off for burial. "It would seem that in those times it was customary to teach him who was supposed to be likely to walk again a way to the house which did not lead to the door of it, but to the obstructing wall" (Eiríkr Magnússon's note to the passage).

Chapter 59

1. *Ívi's sea-steed.* The steed of sea king Ívi: a ship.
2. *Flaunter* or *brandisher of wound-fire* (sword): warrior.
3. *Some shape-shifter.* The shape-shifter, we assume, was Gunnhild.

Chapter 60

1. *Höfudlausn.* Headransom.
2. *Breastfoam of Vidrir.* Sea of Vidrir, but the meaning here intended is poetry.
3. *Ódin's toast.* Mead (lit.) but as with the above the figurative meaning is poetry.
4. *Sharp loads* (lit., saddle) *of the whetstone:* swords.
5. *Ódin's oak.* Ódin's oak-timber: warriors.
6. *Battlecranes* and *woundmews.* Names for ravens.
7. *Gjalp's steed.* The wolf.
8. *Woundbees.* Arrows.

9. *Armfire, hawkstrand's goldshower* (lit., stone) and *Frodi's flour*. Kennings for gold.

Chapter 61

1. *Helmcrag*. Head.
2. *Verse 35*. The untrue warrior (spell-strengthener of the raven's sea = blood) let Egil live (take joy in his dark-browed eyes). My kinsman's (Arinbjörn's) courage was a great help to me. Now as before I am master of my high-descended head (inheritance-seat *or* destined seat of the sea king Áli's headpiece) in the warrior's (*regnaðar reginn, rógnaðra reginn*, Hj. Falk's emendation, for *regnaðar* is so far inexplicable: god of warsnakes *or* swords) presence.

Chapter 64

1. *Verse 36*. I found the ugly king's (land-craver's) anger irksome. The cuckoo settles not to rest if he knows that the eagle (clamor's carrion-bird) lunges over him. Then (there), as more often I found the benefit of Arinbjörn (*arnstalls sjötulbjörn*, bear of the eagle's ledge-stall or rock, *arinn;* the reference is thus to Arin-björn, the Hearth-Bear). He is not all-lacking who boasts of such helpers on his travels.
2. *Fridgeir's sister*. It happened to the translator to return to this portion of *Egil's Saga* fresh from the reading of the Welsh versions of the romances of Owain, Peredur and Geraint, as they are preserved in the Mabinogion MSS. Surely, he felt, Fridgeir's sister is an old acquaintance, this fair and well-dight maiden, so sparing of words, so lavish with her tears. Certainly there is a borrowing in the Fridgeir-Egil-Ljót exchanges from the *Fornaldarsögur;* one is further tempted to believe that the sagaman has also borrowed here from southern knightly romance. Egil will seem a new kind of knight-errant, and Blindheim a new kind of castle; the protective coloring throughout is admirable; and the borrowing has been blended with a part of the saga where it will do least violence to the memories and imaginations of the Mýramen; but the pattern, the disposal of persons and events, seems to me unmistakably that of the romances. To what extent we believe this must, of course, determine the degree of uneasiness with which we regard the accompanying verses.
3. *Holmgang*. In Norway and Iceland the holmgang (*hólmganga*: island-going, because the combat traditionally, though not invariably, took place on an island) was the formal encounter in single combat of two adversaries. Until the year 1006 in Iceland, and probably till 1012 in Norway, it was recognized as a legal procedure, and many sagas preserve accounts, more or less detailed but often far from clear, of how this lawful combat should take place. The fullest of these is in *Kormáks Saga* 10, which says: "It was the law of holmgang that the cloak or hide (on which the fighters stood) must be five ells square, with loops in the corners, where there shall be set down pegs with heads on one end: these are called *tjösnur* (*tjasna, tjarsna,*

phallus?). He who attended to this must walk to the *tjösnur* in such fashion that he could see the sky between his legs, holding the lobes of his ears, with that formulary which is afterwards employed in the sacrifice known as *tjösnublót.* There must be three demarcation lines all round the cloak of a foot-breadth, and verging on these lines shall be four cords (*strengir,* Möðruval-labók) or poles (*stengr,* other MSS). These are called *höslur;* and that is a hazeled field which is so arrayed. A man shall have three shields, but when they are gone he must step on to the cloak, though he may have left it before, and from there on defend himself with his weapons. He that is challenged shall strike (the first blow). If either be wounded, so that blood comes on the cloak, there shall be no further fighting. Should a man step outside the hazels with one foot he 'goes a-heel' (i.e., flinches before his adversary); should he step so with both feet he 'runs.' His second shall hold the shield for each of them. He shall pay holm-ransom who is the more wounded, three marks of silver as holm-ransom."

Egil's Saga, Svarfdœla Saga, Gísla Saga, and *Gunnlaugs Saga Ormstungu* offer additional information. The abolition of holmgang in Iceland in 1006 followed upon the institution of the Fifth Court a year or two earlier, which gave sentence in every lawsuit. Holmgang, it is worth noting, had never been a form of ordeal in Iceland.

4. *Quivering rod or spit of corslets:* sword or spear.
5. *Shieldmoon.* Moon of shield: sword.
6. *Spearflame's spurter.* Spurter of the spear's fire (sword): warrior.
7. *Seaflame-breaker.* Breaker of seaflame (gold): man.

Chapter 71

1. *Drink their hardest.* We must understand that Ármód is planning to murder his guests, and that having failed to do it the cheap way, switches from the dead-tired to the dead-drunk for Egil and his comrades. But in drinking stoup for stoup with Egil he has taken, in native metaphor, a bear by the snout, a wolf by the tail. The episode is remarkably consonant with that on Atley in Chapter 44.

2. *Ekkil's beast-bestrider.* Rider of sea king Ekkil's steed *or* ship: seaman, man.

Chapter 73

1. *Ódin's red shield-shearers.* (To exchange blows) with Ódin's red shield-shearers (lit., with Wargod's red cutting knives of defence) is to do battle.

Chapter 75

1. *Egil's armor of stone.* So Ingólf Thorsteinsson in *Vatnsdœla Saga* 41: he used flat stones to protect his chest and back. Less lucky than Egil,

he died of his wounds; he bade his relatives "bury him in another hill than that his kinsmen were buried in, saying it would be a solace to the Vatnsdal maids if he were so near the roadway." A stone breastplate in *Vápnfirðinga Saga* 2 helped Brodd-Helgi kill the outlaw Svart.

Chapter 78

1. *With Freyja.* To have supper at Freyja's is to sup in the next world, after death. The whole scene is a wonderful one, and by analogy with the Prose Edda might be styled "The Beguiling of Egil." No wonder that when Thorgerd returned home, Egil saw her on her way with gifts (p. 211). She had saved his life, his face, and his greatest poem. And he knew it.

2. *Sonatorrek.* The title means something like "Irreparable Loss of Sons."

3. *That joyous finding.* Joyous discovery of Frigg's kinsfolk: Suttung's mead (i. e., poetry), which Ódin carried off from Jötunheim.

4. *Nökkver's ship.* Poetry.

5. *Giant's neckwound.* The blood of the giant Ymir's neck wound: the sea.

6. *Náinn's boathouse.* Boathouse of the dwarf Náinn: cliff (Egil is thinking of the sea beating in on Digranes, where Bödvar lies in Skallagrím's howe).

7. *The Alesmith.* This is Ægir, god of the sea and brewer to the gods. He is also brother of the wave's reddener (the Wind). Ægir's moon *or* mate is Rán, goddess of the sea. But, alas, Egil knows himself helpless; he cannot take vengeance on these despoilers.

8. *The wind of the Moon's Bear or giant.* Mind *or* thought.

9. *The folk of Elgr's gallows.* Presumably Ódin's gallows, the world-ash Yggdrasil: all living things *or* people.

10. *Mashtarn's Master.* Ægir.

11. *Gaut's friend, spears' master, friend of wains, Vilir's brother, Mímir's friend, foe of the wolf* (Fenris). Terms for Ódin.

12. *Sister of Ódin's wolf-foe.* Hel, the sister of Fenris.

13. *On the ness.* On Digranes (the modern Borgarnes), where Egil had howed his father and his sons.

14. *The kings.* Egil stood in good case with no ruler or potential ruler of Norway, Hákon or the sons of Eirík.

15. *Arinbjarnarkvida.* The first twelve stanzas of the poem are concerned with Egil's visit to King Eirík at York and Arinbjörn's saving his life there.

16. *Brow's moon.* Eye.

17. *Bolsterprice of poet-god's mead.* Lit., bed-price of salmon's (=snake's) mate *or* equal *or* likeness: the reward given by the maid Gunnlöd to Ódin, who entered Suttung's stronghold in the likeness of a snake: poetry.

18. *Ygg's (Ódin's) cup.* Poetry.

19. *Thórir's kinsman, Hearthfire-bear, Rock-bear, Hroald's kinsman.* Arinbjörn (see note to Verse 36, p. 250).

20. *Enemy of (the gold ring) Draupnir's kin.* Enemy of rings, generous man.

21. *Rökkvi's steeds.* The sea king Rökkvi's steeds or stud: fleet of ships.

22. *Praisecairn I piled, etc: Exegi monumentum ære perennius regalique situ pyramidum altius.* It detracts not at all from Egil's heartfelt yet stately eulogy that he was fully aware of its value. One adjective comes first and last and always to mind when one thinks of Arinbjörn. He was a noble man. A man, too, of high birth and great possessions, wise and generous, loyal and brave; qualities which Egil has here celebrated as handsomely as they deserve. In many ways he was Egil's opposite, in some his complement, and steady as the pole star—understanding the deep contrarieties of Egil's nature, many a time interposing his broad shoulders between the poet and his foes, and tender of the god-given power of words in this savage, greedy, childish, self-centred, and yet ferociously affectionate friend of his. His nobility is revealed best by his faithfulness to the causes he made his own. One of these was the fortunes of Egil, for whom he was willing to lay down his own life. The other was the fortunes of Eirík and, after him, his sons. This brought him to exile once in England, with Eirík; to exile a second time in Denmark, with his sons; and to his death alongside King Harald Graycloak, his foster son, at the battle of the Neck, in Limafjörd.

23. *Embla's ashbowl.* (Embla was the first woman): the hand.

24. *Verse 51.* The warriors (brightness *or* famed ones of sea king Ingvi's Thing-meeting *or* battle) grow few now who diminished (i.e., distributed) gold (day *or* light of the meadhorn). Where shall I look for generous men who beyond earth's isle-studded girdle (i.e., the sea) let silver (snow of the crucible) shower into my hand (hawk's high fell) in return for my words?

25. *Óðin's drink or mead.* Poetry or poem.

26. *Sigvaldi.* Sigvaldi was leader of the Jómsborg vikings, and Einar suggests he would prove a more generous patron than Earl Hákon. No long time after this the Jómsvikings were overwhelmed by Hákon at the seafight in Hjörungavag, when Sigvaldi turned to flight, leaving half his fleet to a bloody defeat.

27. *The steed of sea king Gylfi's domain. The ship of the earth-grown (dwarf):* poetry.

Chapter 79

1. *Althing.* It is difficult to understand the organization of the Icelandic court of law or the National Assembly for law (*Alþingi*) without some reference to the status and functions of the *goði* and his office the *goðorð*, most inadequately translated "priest" and "priesthood."

During the period of settlement (870-930) Iceland took shape as an aggregation of numerous local units of varying size and population, like the settlements of Skallagrím and Ketil Hœng, at the head of which were the wealthy landed men and vikings who, having sailed from Norway and the Western Isles, took land by right of priority and settled down to an aristocratic and patriarchal existence which was to correspond, they hoped, to the manner of life they had led at home. Some of these early settlers brought their temples piecemeal with them, others set up temples where they built their new homes. The ownership of a temple was an obvious source of power, for it was a piece of personal property absolutely at the disposal of its master, who opened it to would-be worshippers and feasters only on his own terms. "All men had to pay toll to the temple, and were bound to all expeditions of the temple priest as thingmen now are to their chieftains. But the priest (goði) must maintain the temple at his own cost." Clearly to build a temple and maintain its sacrifices was too expensive for all save the most wealthy. To the end of the Commonwealth the goðorð was *veldi en ekki fé*, "power but not wealth." But the wealthy settlers were inevitably the great chieftains, and this gave the goðorð its peculiar characteristic—its blending of secular and religious leadership. Above all the goði's influence throve on his ability as a landowner to award land in the district, whether to freedmen, kinsmen, dependants or newcomers, only in return for a definite promise of submission and assistance. This process is excellently illustrated by chapters 28-29 of *Egil's Saga*.

The relation of the goði or "priest-chieftain" to his thingman or dependant was defined early in the settlement period. Within his own district he was sovereign and the law, and all disputes must be referred to him for settlement. He was expected to look after his thingman's interests, or the latter might leave him, and put himself under the protection of some other chieftain. In the last resort the goði's power and authority were personal, so naturally certain goðar became stronger than others. The goðorð was transferable, and could be sold, loaned, given away, or even wrested from its owner. Much of the intensification of feud in the thirteenth century arose from the acquisition of as many as half-a-dozen chieftainships by one family, which raised family disputes almost to the horrid dignity of civil wars.

The Thing (þing) was a meeting for law. The local units of which the goðar were leaders had each its own Thing from very early times, but a need was soon apparent for Things at which disputes between the thingmen of different districts might be settled. We hear of local experiments at Thórnes and Kjalarnes, in which the chief men of the area cooperated. The next step was a Thing for the whole country. In the year 927 Úlfljót of Lón was sent to Norway to study the law and constitution of the Gulathing, and in 930 his recommendations were embodied in the Althing, which was to meet each June on the great sunken plain of Thingvellir. The local Things were to continue working in their limited spheres.

The Althing was a national assembly and rallying point for the whole Icelandic people. However, it kept all power in the hands of the goðar. It was composed, we believe, of two committees, the Althingisdómr and the Lögretta, each probably composed of thirty-six goðar, and each with its separate function. The Althingisdómr was the court to which all lawsuits were referred, while the Lögretta was entrusted with the power of making new laws. These were announced to the people by the Lawspeaker, who must also recite the whole law of the land before the assembly during his three year term of office. To the Lawspeaker, also, were referred all queries about points of law.

The working of the Althing was at no time satisfactory. It had no power to enforce its decisions, and at the local Things the course of justice was still more uncertain. The rule that suits for manslaughter must be prosecuted at the Thing which stood nearest the scene of action meant that oftentimes the litigant must proceed against his adversary in a hostile district. It was a case of this kind, arising out of the burning to death of Blund-Ketil, which led to a reorganization in the year 963.

The country was now divided into four Quarters, the Southlanders', Westfirthers', Northlanders' and Eastfirthers' Quarters. Each Quarter was subdivided into three judicial districts, the fellow-thingmen of which must seek justice at their own court. In the Northlanders' Quarter there should be four such subdistricts. Each Quarter was to have its own special court, the Quarter Thing, and each of its subdistricts its *várþing* or Spring Thing, which took the place of the court formerly held by the *goðar*. The number of *goðar* was fixed at thirty-nine. The Spring Things proved highly efficient, in contrast to the *leið* or Autumn meeting, of which we hear very little, and the Quarter Things of which, surprisingly, we hear nothing at all. It was at the Spring Thing by Grísartunga that Steinar hoped to outlaw Thorstein of Borg.

The Althing was greatly changed by the new reforms. The Lögretta remained, but instead of the Althingisdómr there were now four Quarter Courts, corresponding to the four Quarters of the country, and handling the cases of that Quarter. In 1005 a Fifth Court was set up as a Court of Appeal, and the number of *goðar* increased to forty-eight. This was the last change before the end of the Commonwealth in 1262-64.

The Althing was not only an assembly for law. It was the annual meeting-place for the whole country. Men went there to renew their friendships, do business, marry off their sons and daughters, display their best clothes, (or like Thorstein, their father's), buy and sell, and generally find out what was going on in the world. To be at the Althing was to be at the hub of the wheel, the heart of the body social, legal, and politic.

2. *Verse 56*. May the king's thane (Thorstein Thóruson) hearken to my poem (the waterfall of the long-haired friend of the altar's fire=Ódin). Let your retinue be mindful of silence. Praise of my poem (grain of the eagle's beak) shall be heard throughout Hördaland . . . seafarer (*hrafnstyrandi?*).

Chapter 80

1. *The rock*. This is the noble rock-bastion behind the present farm and church at Borg, with its immense view over Borgarfjörður and the sea: the cone of Baula and the creamy ice-sheet of Eiríksjökull in the east; southwards, across the white river, a wall of mountains, Hafnarfjall and Skarðsheiði; westwards the Mýrar, Borgarnes on its rocky headland, and the ocean horizon; north, fold upon fold of mountains, and the vision closed north-west by the incomparable beauty of Snæfellsnes.

Chapter 81

1. *Legal procedure.* There were three methods of conducting a feud in medieval Iceland: by law (*lög*), by agreement or arbitration (*sætt, görð*), or by private action, which in a case for manslaughter meant *hefnd*, revenge. Andreas Heusler (*Strafrecht der Isländersagas*, Leipzig, 1911, p. 17) presents the following figures for cases of feud in the sagas: Total cases 520; private vengeance 297; pure agreement 104; legal cases becoming agreement 60; legal cases 50; legal cases wrecked by private action 9. The lawsuit between Egil and Bergönund at the Gulathing in Chapter 56 of our saga is a Norwegian example of a legal case wrecked by private action; the lawsuit at the Varthing up by Grísartunga in Chapters 81-82 an Icelandic example of a legal case becoming agreement. Such agreement could be directly between the principals, between the arbitrators they appointed or accepted, or by a grant of selfdoom (*sjálfdœmi*), the right to make his own award, to one of the parties or his representative—in this case to the defendant's father, Egil.

The conduct of the Icelandic lawsuit was almost entirely in the litigants' hands. The community provided a court, witnesses if they were summoned by pursuant or defendant, and a verdict; but the preparation of prosecution and defence, the pleading in court, and the implementing of verdict and sentence, were left to the contestants.

There were at least three, and sometimes four, steps which had to be taken before a suit for manslaughter could receive a legal hearing. The first was the notification of his deed by the slayer (*víglýsing*). This freed him from a charge of murder (*mörð*) and the opprobrium and penalties attendant on it. No opprobrium at all attached to a killing (*víg*) consonant with the ethos of the age. Thus, Thorstein would certainly have announced his killing of Grani and Thránd to the near neighbors, though the saga does not specifically tell us that he did. His action in protecting the corpses, as public sentiment required him to do (we may compare Egil's advice to the shepherd-lads at Fenhring regarding the dead bodies there, p. 150), shows him to have been a stickler for propriety. The second step was the pursuant's. Straightway after the slaying he rode to the scene of action and there gave notice (*lýsa*) against the slayer and set on foot his lawsuit. It was also for him to summon the Inquest of Neighbors who were to bear witness on his behalf at the court hearing. Then, third, the pursuant completed his pre-court procedure when on the appointed days of spring he rode to his opponent's home to summon (*stefna*) him to the Thing at which he proposed to prosecute him. Fourth, in certain flagrant cases the defendant could "unhallow" (*óhelga*) his victim, by showing that he had by his own actions put himself outside the law's protection—rather like a plea of justifiable homicide. Thorstein appears to have done this in respect of Grani and Thránd.

The litigants would all this while be enlisting whatever help they could—and by whatever means. Then men rode to the Thing, where they either pleaded their own case or formally entrusted it to a representative. Prosecution and defense were heard, and then the judges decided either for the defendant, in which case the lawsuit fell through, or for the pursuant, which meant a sentence of full outlawry against the defendant, for that was the only penalty known to the Icelandic courts in the tenth century—a very good reason for not pushing a lawsuit to its bitter end. With this pronouncement the court had discharged its responsibility for law: it was for the pursuant to make the sentence operative.

Sentences of lesser outlawry, whether they led to banishment abroad, usually for three years, or to banishment from a given district in Iceland, as befell Steinar by the terms of Egil's award, were not legal sentences. They were always imposed by the arbitrators.

Chapter 84

1. *Thorstein the White.* A sneering pun: the White distorted to the white-faced or white-livered.

Chapter 85

1. *Neck-halter's steed.* Steed of the neck-halter *or* collar: neck.
2. *Verse 59.* Blind, I move to sit by the fire. I ask the woman (goddess of gores *or* patches) to be gentle with me, I have such affliction in my eyes (fields where eyelids strike *or* encounter)—I, whom a monarch (Athelstan) honored with gold (speech of the giant Geirhamðir). A wrathful king (Eirík) took pleasure of old in my words.
3. *Widowed heels . . . those same relics.* This is an elaborate pun: *ekkja* means "widow"; *hæll* means "widow"; it also means "heel."
4. *I mean to sow that silver.* Egil hoped to see one more good fight before he died.

Chapter 86

1. *When Christianity became the law in Iceland.* This happened in the year 1000.
2. *Skafti Thórarinsson.* He was born towards the close of the eleventh century and was still alive in 1143. He was connected with the Mýramen, and of the sixth generation after Egil.

Chapter 87

1. *And there this story ends.* The Möðruvallabók text ends with, "Skúli had fought in seven battles while out viking." The concluding words are from Ketilsbók, AM 453 4to.